Let Them Live

Kai Curry-Lindahl

LET THEM LIVE

*A Worldwide Survey
of Animals Threatened
with Extinction*

William Morrow & Company, Inc.
NEW YORK   1972

Printed in the United States of America.
Library of Congress Catalog Card Number 79–188750

To Peter Scott
who has done so much to save
the world's threatened animals.

Foreword

Never in the realm of nature have so many been exterminated by so few in so short a time.

This is the grim truth about the relations of one single species —the human one—with hundreds of animal species during the last centuries. More than three hundred species and subspecies of animals have owing to man vanished from the earth during historic time, and 257—probably as many as 306—during the last three centuries. However, today at least 982 mammals, birds, reptiles, amphibians, and fishes are endangered by extinction. An additional number of invertebrates and plants are threatened by the same fate.

With very few exceptions the reason for the present dramatic state of affairs is man. Through unnecessary, unwise, and uneconomic destruction and overexploitation of living natural resources, man wipes out one species after another.

The rate of extermination is increasing; at present it is on the order of at least one species or subspecies per year. These are frightful losses. Such needless destruction continues as long as man through ignorance and indifference seems to believe that he is independent of natural laws and of natural environments. Man's technical progress has dangerously enabled him to forget that he is himself a biological being. This seems paradoxical, because at present man is favoured by his intelligence, which gives him a privileged position on our planet. Nevertheless, man drastically affects in increasing scale the possibilities of environments to support life. He destroys ecosystems, reduces the renewable natural resources, eradicates kinds of wildlife, and brings his own populations to levels leading to a catastrophe.

All this disorder and thoughtless destruction can be avoided by careful, long-range ecological planning. Conservation is applied ecology and may also be regarded as bioeconomy. In other words, *conservation* can be defined as sound preservation, management, and optimum utilization on a sustained-yield basis of the planet's renewable natural resources. The decision is ours. It is up to man alone to choose the course to follow, to decide what is to survive or what is to die among the animal species that share the life on this earth with us. The chance to choose will not last long.

This book is concerned with the vanishing wildlife around us. Why should we care about disappearing animals? Some people claim that such a concern is of no importance for mankind. This is not surprising, because man represents a tremendous variation of thinking, behaviour, and interests. However, there is increasing evidence that an accelerating number of human beings turn to nature and wildlife for spiritual, psychological, physical, and cultural benefits. In addition, there are a growing number of people who derive satisfaction by just knowing that wild animals still exist in free nature in their country or in the world, even if these people are unable to go and see for themselves.

Civilization is not just great cities, industrial developments, miles of highways, enormous airfields, and numerous other technological conveniences. If by building our civilization and culture we destroy the last remains of wildlife, we can no longer speak of any civilization at all.

It is strange that cultural treasures like the Egyptian temples at Aswan, the Acropolis in Athens, the splendours of ancient Rome or Renaissance Florence are by everybody regarded as indispensable objects of civilization, which must be preserved at all costs, while relatively few people are concerned with the preservation of endangered plant and animal species, which not only represent the results of many millions of centuries of evolution but also constitute an environmental heritage of the past, a world which once surrounded our forerunners. Moreover, there is an ethical aspect. Why should man deny that animals as species have the right to live and coexist with ourselves? We are also responsible to the coming generations to leave as an inheritance an unspoiled world with intact living beauty and richness.

However, there are many reasons other than aesthetical and ethical ones to preserve and manage wildlife. There are material reasons. Many wild animals are a source of proteins. Many wild mammals produce continuously more human food per acre without environmental deterioration than domestic animals do at a price of irreversible destruction of vegetation and soil. On all continents wildlife is becoming an increasingly important recreational asset and tourist attraction. In many habitats wild animals maintain the health of the living landscape and the productivity of the ecosystem.

Moreover, man can never foresee the future economic value of a species. There are also many scientific reasons to keep samples of habitats with their species intact for present and future research. Such investigations can yield data which in the world of tomorrow may be of inestimable value and importance.

There are also educational arguments to preserve wildlife.

Finally, man's own survival depends on his willingness and ability to co-operate with the living environment. His attitude must change from a constant warring against nature to a permanent collaboration and peace with nature. This includes the fauna, from which man can learn a lot.

Nevertheless, animal life around us disappears rapidly owing to our own destruction of habitats. We contaminate the air; we pollute streams, lakes, and oceans; we drain swamps and wetlands, lowering the water table; we rape prairies and forests; we spray pesticides over all waters and lands; we kill animals excessively for immediate profit (e.g., whales, hoofed animals, spotted cats, or marine turtles) or on false assumptions that they are noxious (e.g., predatory mammals and birds or grazing ungulates) or for fashionable "sport" (e.g., polar bears or, as in Texas and Wyoming, golden eagles and bald eagles shot from airplanes).

Man alone, though often in combination with his livestock, is destroying the natural environments of the world. No wild animals do that in habitats unaltered by man. But as many habitats are changed, it is man's responsibility to manage them properly in order to maintain a rich and varied wildlife. This is a part of the quality of the environment for man himself. Man is the custodian of wildlife on this globe of ours. As such he must equip himself with an ecologically based management policy and step out from the era of ecological illiteracy. Such a step will also help him to avoid snaring himself in the technological traps he is setting all over the world. It may even save him from the most dangerous trap of all: human overpopulation. Man's rapid increase in numbers is in itself a most decisive detrimental change of environment.

Sooner or later, man will in a general way discover that his own overpopulation is disadvantageous to him as an individual. However, urgent and drastic action must be taken immediately. This is a task for enlightened political and religious leaders.

Along with man's treatment of living environments goes the fate of remaining wild animals.

The struggle to preserve wildlife and endangered animals has gone on for decades. First, a few foresighted men in North America and Europe fought for a better understanding of the wild animals' role in living landscapes and for the necessity of preserving threatened species. Later, the pioneering efforts of these dedicated men led to the establishment of national and international conservation organizations. In the international field the first important conservation organization was the International Council for Bird Preservation (ICBP), founded in 1922. Ornithologists have in almost every country been the vanguard for conservation. However, it was not until after World War II that a broader concept of conservation became manifest through the creation of the International Union for Conservation of Nature and Natural Resources (IUCN) in 1948 under the sponsorship of UNESCO. ICBP founded the International Wildfowl Research Bureau (IWRB), another important body, and IUCN took the initiative to form in 1961 the World Wildlife Fund (WWF), a fund-raising organization.

Of the United Nations organizations UNESCO, since the conservation-minded Sir Julian Huxley was its first director-general, has been directly interested in conservation. During the 1960's, the Food and Agricultural Organization of the UN (FAO) has through impulses from IUCN taken up conservation on its program. Other important international conservation organizations are the Smithsonian Institution and the Conservation Foundation, both in Washington, D.C., and the Fauna Preservation Society in London. The Zoologische Gesellschaft in Frankfurt, West Germany, has raised important funds for conservation, particularly for Africa.

All these organizations are working vigorously for the conservation of animal life. Particularly IUCN, through its Survival Service Commission (SSC), is dealing specifically with animals threatened by extinction. The functions of the SSC are primarily to collect and disseminate data on endangered plant and animal species throughout the world and to initiate action to prevent the extinction of these species. In carrying out this task the SSC investigates the status and ecology of rare species and gives advice to governments and organizations. Such advice is often continued with direct action financed by the WWF. The SSC has long maintained a list of threatened mammals and birds. In 1966 these lists were published in the form of loose sheets divided into two volumes, *The Red Data Book*. This information on mammals and birds will be progressively completed by other lists and volumes on reptiles, amphibians, fishes, and plants. At a later stage invertebrates will also be covered.

The present author has since 1954 been associated with the SSC (since 1963 as vice-chairman). The work of the SSC is to a great extent inspired by the leadership of one of the world's foremost conservationists, Peter Scott, who since 1963 has been chairman of the Commission. The activities of the SSC have increased tremendously during recent years and so has the size of the Commission. There are now over eighty members of the SSC and in addition twenty specialist groups with a total membership of over 275. This conservation expansion has produced positive results in many parts of the world. Nevertheless, we are still in the initial phase of work, facing enormous problems, and are involved in a battle with time in order to save animal species before it is too late.

In 1964 it was first proposed that I write this book on the world's threatened animal species. My countersuggestion was that Peter Scott, as chairman of the SSC, should do the job. Scott himself suggested that we should write the book together, but as time went on his many commitments prevented him from sharing the authorship. So it fell on me alone to write the text. However, Peter Scott has kindly read the manuscript and has given advice, for which privilege I am most grateful to him. Moreover, our collaboration within the SSC and more widely within the IUCN and the WWF has been very stimulating to me as author of this book.

The text of this book was completed and delivered in 1966. Its publication has been delayed owing to technical circumstances (the planned artwork took a very long time to produce and did not turn out satisfactorily, so it was finally abandoned). However, the data have been continuously kept up to date and reflect the situation as of April 1, 1972.

Let Them Live deals with vertebrates that have become extinct during historic time or are actively threatened by extinction or are so rare or specialized that even minor restrictions or alterations of their habitats may result in their extermination. There are also declining species which still occur in numbers adequate for survival, but if their present depletion continues, their numbers will go down to dangerously low levels. Such vertebrates are included in the book.

Not only species but also subspecies are treated. The latter category are often represented by geographically isolated races and are in an evolutionary sense species in *formation*.

The regional chapters follow a continental pattern, but within each continent the approach is ecological (coasts, deserts, savannas, etc.). By this continental, ecological, but not strictly zoogeographical arrangement I have tried to connect environmental factors like man-made changes in various habitats to the disastrous effects which have often struck the animals living in these habitats. Usually there are a number of factors behind the decrease of each species besides man's direct predation and habitat alterations.

The marine areas (e.g., islands, archipelagoes, and oceans) are, however, dealt with on a geographical basis alone.

The order of continents begins with Africa, where man appeared earlier than elsewhere. This has led in some cases to a more thorough description of African habitats than of similar habitats in Asia, South America, and so on, simply because the text on Africa comes first.

Europe and Asia are treated as a complex, Eurasia.

As nearly fourteen hundred species and subspecies of animals are dealt with in this book, it has been impossible to give an extensive treatment to each form. Such an approach would have required several volumes. Many species are, however, dealt with at length, while others receive short comments.

Species or subspecies that occur on several continents are, in general, treated where their main distribution range is located, although they may be mentioned under two continents. Where the range of an animal form is similarly divided on two or more continents, it is, in general, dealt with in connection with the continent that appears first in the text.

Species or subspecies occurring in various habitats or regions within a continent or marine area are mentioned only in connection with their characteristic habitat or main range. In general, geographical subspecies occurring on the same continent but frequenting different habitats receive separate textual treatments.

Many species or subspecies have locally become extinct or are regionally threatened by extinction although they are common in other parts of the world, for example, the wolf, the red deer, the golden eagle, and several fish. Such animals may be briefly mentioned but are, in general, not dealt with, because they are as a species or subspecies not at present endangered by total extinction. It would have led too far to describe in this book all local exterminations or locally endangered populations of species.

Likewise, it has been impossible to go into details concerning species that have locally been almost exterminated owing to exploitation but later have reappeared thanks to conservation measures, as, for instance, the egrets in Florida and Central Europe, the beaver in Scandinavia, and the saiga in the U.S.S.R.

Hence, this book deals with all species and subspecies of mammals, birds, reptiles, amphibians, and fishes of the world that at present, as far as we know, are threatened by total extinction as well as with those which have become extinct during historic time.

It has been impossible, because of lack of space, to include references to literary sources on which the presented data are based. The Bibliography lists only some major works that have been used in the preparation of this book.

Numerous expeditions and conservation missions to all continents have given me invaluable experiences which have been an important help when trying to understand the ecology of various regions. Therefore, I am grateful to a number of international organizations, many governments, and numerous national institutions, which have designated me to undertake missions on their behalf or have invited me to visit their countries or have financially contributed to several expeditions. It would go too far to mention all here, but I am anxious to express acknowledgments to the following: United Nations Development Programme, UNESCO, FAO, International Union for Conservation of Nature and Natural Resources (IUCN); the governments of Australia, Cameroon, Ceylon, Chad, Dahomey, Denmark, Ghana, Hungary, India, Indonesia, Italy, Japan, Kenya, Madagascar, Mauritius, New Zealand, Poland, Romania, Sweden, Tanzania, Thailand, Togo, Uganda, Upper Volta, U.S.A., U.S.S.R., Zaire, and Zambia; and

institutions such as the Academy of Science of U.S.S.R.; National
Audubon Society, U.S.A.; American Museum of Natural History,
U.S.A.; Bahamas National Trust, Bahamas; Commonwealth Scientific and Industrial Research Organization (C.S.I.R.O.), Australia; Engkvist Foundation, Sweden; Institut des Parcs Nationaux
du Congo, Belgium and Zaire; Institut pour la Recherche Scien-
tifique en Afrique Centrale (I.R.S.A.C.), Belgium and Zaire;
Musée Royal de l'Afrique Centrale, Belgium; Natal Parks Game
and Fish Preservation Board, South Africa; National Parks Board
of Trustees, South Africa; Nature Conservancy, Great Britain;
Nordic Museum and Skansen, Sweden; Royal Swedish Academy
of Science, Sweden; Smithsonian Institution, U.S.A.; Swedish
Natural History Research Council, Sweden; Tanzania National
Parks, Tanzania; Uganda National Parks, Uganda; United States
National Park Service, U.S.A.; United States Fish and Wildlife
Service, U.S.A.; University of California, U.S.A.; and University
of Nairobi, Kenya.

A number of specialists have kindly read the whole manuscript
or regional chapters and have given constructive suggestions. I
have already above expressed my gratitude to Peter Scott, Great
Britain. Other biologists who have been helpful are Dr. Maria
Buchinger, Argentina and the U. S.; Professor J. C. de Carvalho,
Brazil; Dr. Italo Costantino, Argentina; Alec Forbes-Watson,
Kenya; Professor William Fuller, Canada; Dr. Paul S. Martin,
U. S.; Dr. A. Zahavi, Israel; and Dr. Herbert S. Zim, U. S. I am
most thankful to all these scholars.

Within the SSC I have had the favour of a stimulating collaboration with all colleagues. Although the manuscript of this book
was completed before the publication of the Commission's *The
Red Data Book* on mammals and birds, I had considerable help
writing this book by consulting the lists of endangered mammals
and birds prepared for the SSC by Noel Simon and Colonel Jack
Vincent of the IUCN and ICBP staffs. They have not helped me
directly, but it would be ungrateful of me not to include a special
word of appreciation and indebtedness to them for their effective
work. Also, the list compiled by the Committee on Rare and
Endangered Wildlife Species of the Bureau of Sport Fisheries and
Wildlife, U. S. Department of the Interior, has been most useful
to me. At the end of 1968, some additional data on rare and
endangered reptiles, amphibians, and fishes became available
through compilations from the SSC by René E. Honegger and Dr.

Robert Rush Miller. These data are now also published in *The Red Data Book*.

Finally, it is a pleasure to acknowledge the assistance given to this book by Dr. Milton Rugoff, U. S., who suggested that I should write it and who has polished the manuscript in terms of language.

If this book on vanishing animals threatened by extinction can contribute to a better understanding of the values they represent and also to increased global efforts to preserve them effectively, its primary purpose will have been fulfilled.

KAI CURRY-LINDAHL

Contents

Contents

Let Them Live

CHAPTER ONE

From Harmony to Violence–
Human Relations with the Environment
Past and Present

BEFORE MAN

Although it may seem as if human beings have inhabited the
earth for countless ages, man has in fact existed for only a very
brief part of the earth's four or five billion years. For about half of
this incredibly long period, the earth was a lifeless planet, though
the scene of remarkable natural dramas. The crust of the earth
hardened and became cool, and enormous banks of clouds surrounded the sphere, condensed, and gave birth to the oceans. Repeated volcanic eruptions and earthquakes carved the surface of
the land, erosion during millions of years wore down the mountains, and the primeval landscape took shape.

Perhaps three billion years ago, the earliest life appeared on
earth. The first manifestations were probably algae, which probably
originated in the seas but soon colonized cliffs along the shores.
All primeval creatures and plants, and all those now on earth,
arose from these humble sources.

Looking back, we may well get the impression that changes in
the environment were drastic and violent. Some were abrupt, but
most changes took place over long periods, allowing for a harmonious relationship between the various forms of life and the
inorganic world. Living organisms simply adapted continuously
to new conditions. There are, however, at least two spectacular
examples of the extinction of animals that are still unexplained.
About 230 million years ago, in the Permian period, a drastic reduction in the forms of marine life took place. At the end of the
Mesozoic era, about 65 million years ago, a large number of reptile species disappeared. The exact reasons for these great changes
are puzzling, but they were obviously caused by environmental

factors in which man played no part, for man did not yet exist. The widespread, seemingly violent decline of dinosaurs, pterosaurs, ichthyosaurs, plesiosaurs, and mosasaurs after a reptilian dominance of about 100 million years has been interpreted as the consequence of a sudden catastrophe. But the change may not have been so sudden as it appears. Probably it was brought on by such factors as changes in climate and plant life and the emergence of mammals that presumably played an important role as predators on reptiles and their eggs. Whatever the cause of the extinction of these reptiles, nature has never again produced such large terrestrial animals.

Evolution and Natural Selection

Fossil records tell the story not only of the evolution of plants and animals but also of the earth itself and the climates prevailing in the geological past. All these changes had an important influence on the five essential elements in nature: air, water, soil, vegetation, and fauna.

The mechanics of evolution are well-known today. As a marvellous continual process of adaptation, specialization, and speciation, evolution explains the astonishing conquest of the world that life in the form of plants and animals has achieved since the first algae struggled in the sea. Out of the algae have evolved about 350,000 plant species and about one million animal species. They have colonized oceans, lakes, and rivers, plains, forests, and mountains, including all climatic zones. They are an integral part of the living environment and every single species occupies its ecological niche as a piece in Nature's mosaic and a guarantee of future life on the earth.

Of the vertebrates, with which this book is chiefly concerned, the fishes have existed for about 430 million years, while mammals are only about 190 million years old. Man is very recent indeed: As far as we know, he took his first bipedal steps about two million years ago, in Africa. If we consider the mammals, the most recent class of animals, it is impossible not to admire them for what they have achieved in the course of their development. They have colonized and adapted themselves to practically all regions and elements in our world. They live in water, under and on the surface of the earth, in trees, and in the air; they are found in the arctic and in the tropics, in the depths of the oceans and high up the mountains. And when we consider what the end product of the mammals, man, has achieved in his biological evolution, some self-admiration is justified.

The evolution and adaptation of species still is a necessity for plants and animals if they are to continue their conquest of the oceans and continents as well as to ensure their existence in the habitats they already occupy. Physically and in behaviour, organisms must be constantly prepared to cope with environmental changes; it is only the adaptability and capacity for evolution of the various life forms that can save them from extinction. Man's rapid reshaping of the world's surface in our time through technological (largely chemical) means produces environmental changes which may often be too rapid for the adaptability of organisms, and the result is tremendous new pressure on wildlife.

Evolution by natural selection works slowly. The process has often been misunderstood. Charles Darwin defined natural selection clearly, but later writers have unfortunately emphasized the catch phrase "survival of the fittest." By this phrase Darwin meant that various individuals in a population are different from one another in many ways and that these variations have a decisive bearing on the evolutionary potential of the species and the individual's chances for survival. As Darwin put it, an individual that varies "slightly in any manner profitable to itself under the complex and sometimes varying conditions of life, will have a better chance of surviving, and thus be naturally selected." This means that the environment does not create new forms to fit specific habitats, but it operates by determining which forms and mutations should survive to produce the next generation. Such modern evolutionists as Sir Julian Huxley and Ernst Mayr stress success in reproduction rather than survival as the dominant factor in natural selection. In any way, natural selection is the only mechanism that produces orientation in the evolutionary process. And it does it in close co-operation with a changing environment which in evolution has a directional function rather than a creative one. This role of the environment in natural selection is emphasized by the fact that speciation proceeds most rapidly under tropical conditions. During warm periods of the earth extensive tropical landmasses allowed a much more rapid rate of speciation than at present, when the tropical belt is narrower and relatively mild temperatures prevail.

Evolution by any definition is an uneven process. One important factor in evolution is mutation. There is an enormously wide range of genetic combinations and recombinations following mutations, but successful mutations do not occur regularly. The increase of genetic diversity is not continuous, nor is the capacity to store genetic variability.

In habitats that are changed in an unnatural way from one day to another, which in our time happens all too often, the loss of accumulated genetic diversity may be fatal for a species. Its genetic equipment is often insufficient to respond to drastically changed conditions of life. When he is altering the face of the world, man cannot afford to forget the significance of this slow process of evolution by natural selection in various life organisms, including man.

Changes on the Earth Before Man

Before man appeared on the earth there were great changes in the landscape formed entirely by natural forces. Three major environmental forces can be distinguished that greatly changed the surface of the globe from time to time. Volcanic and tectonic forces, by the uplifting and mountain building already mentioned, sculpted the basic geologic structure. These forces have not yet stabilized. One of the last great topographic changes, the formation of the Virunga volcanoes in tropical Africa, probably took place only about twenty thousand years ago. This new chain of giant volcanoes reshaped the land on a vast scale and had great repercussions: It changed the hydrography of the continent's two largest river systems, those of the Nile and the Zaire (formerly called the Congo); it created entirely new conditions for vegetation and animals. This is just one example from a geologically recent period of the importance of tectonic or volcanic changes.

A second factor, at least as important as a creator of topography, is the great changes in climate that have marked the history of the earth. Climate affects the landscape, because it produces erosion as well as deposits. Climate also governs living conditions for plants and animals. But the biotic factors—the living plants and animals—modify the climate as well as the soil; in fact, biological factors are the third major environmental force on the earth.

Ever since the world was first colonized by plants and animals there has been intimate interaction between geologic, climatic, and biotic factors. This ensemble is responsible for stability in nature, despite the modifications in various areas and habitats that go on constantly.

During the last 430 million years, that is, since the first vertebrate animals evolved, there have been several very great tectonic and climatic changes on the earth. Greenland shows evidence of one: In the Devonian age, when the first fishes had emerged, that large island, judging from its fossil remains, had a warm, moist climate. Antarctica, too, was once a lush region with forests and a diverse flora. Large parts of North America and Europe were tropical at about the time of the great changes in animal life mentioned earlier; presumably, extreme climate changes were connected with these extinctions. The upper Tertiary period, about 25 million years ago, saw continental uplifts that produced a drier climate, and this in turn converted lowland forest to grasslands; many mammals that had been browsers, eaters of twigs and branches, changed to grazers. All the major environmental changes of the past have contributed to an increasing diversity of species.

How Species Come and Go

Animal species have come and gone chiefly as a result of evolution by natural selection, which in turn is directed by the environment. It is sometimes claimed that before man the rate of appearance of new species and subspecies in mammals and birds was greater than the rate of extinction, while in reptiles and amphibians it was less after their culmination in the Cretaceous period. In reality, there seems to have always been a rather high rate of extinction in mammals and also birds before man emerged as a predator. As the only group of vertebrates that have always been completely adapted to life in water, fishes have apparently been less influenced by environmental changes than terrestrial vertebrates. But even in this group new forms have appeared and old ones disappeared. The early ostracoderms, which included both marine and freshwater species characterized by a covering armour of bony plates or scales, and the plate-skinned placoderms are, for instance, extinct groups of fishes. They were already gone about 345 million years ago. At the end of the Paleozoic era, about 230 million years ago, many main fishes disappeared. In Mesozoic times, many early forms of bony fishes were replaced by more advanced teleosts. Hence the evolution of fishes has steadily produced more and more species, while, judging from fossils, only a relatively small number, compared to about twenty-five thousand currently surviving species, have been eliminated. But there must certainly be more undiscovered fossils of fish than known ones, so this balance is only theoretical.

There are at present about 4,200 species of mammals and 8,600 species of birds. Of reptiles there are about six thousand species and of amphibians about 2,900 species. Although mammals today dominate life on the earth (through man), they have been declining in numbers since the Miocene, about twenty-five million years ago, when they reached their peak. In fact, 44 percent of the mammalian orders have since then become extinct. Of families, 54 percent are extinct and of genera 67 percent. Hence, this decline has gone on for several millions of years, but the last two centuries have seen a tremendous increase in the rate of mammalian extinctions.

It has been calculated by Pierce Brodkorb (in 1963) that about one million species of birds have existed at one time or another since birds appeared about 140 million years ago. Another estimate by James Fisher and Roger Tory Peterson (in 1964) gives a figure of less than half a million. But calculations in this field are really speculation, for innumerable fossils are certainly still to be discovered, particularly in Africa, Asia, and Australia.

Of the 9,517 species of birds hitherto described, 854 are known only as fossils; 173 species and subspecies have become extinct during historic time; 162 species and subspecies have been directly or indirectly exterminated by man since 1600, and 157 since 1700. This means that in the last three centuries an average of more than fifty-two species and subspecies of birds have disappeared per century and the rate of extinction is increasing. The situation with mammals is about the same. During the last two thousand years over a hundred mammalian species and subspecies, since 1700 at least sixty-nine and since 1800 at least forty-four species, have become extinct. A frightful number of other species are now threatened with the same fate: 401 mammals, 388 birds, ninety-five fish, and so on.

The natural forces that previously eliminated animal species have now been exceeded by artificial factors on a vast scale.

THE COMING OF MAN

The remains of the first men on earth may have disappeared forever. Their fossilized bones, buried under countless ages of sediment, may have turned into dust. On the other hand, they may some day be brought to light. During the last fifteen years alone, research based on human bones found at Olduvai in Tanzania has pushed the age of the first known humans more than twice as far back in time as previously estimated—at a conservative calculation, 1,750,000 years. Recently, tools have been found at Lake Rudolf in Kenya which have been accurately dated to 2,600,000 years. That is 800,000 years older than those of Olduvai. New finds may well increase this period, but this will make little difference in any consideration of early man's place in nature. Man evolved, like all other animals, slowly, almost imperceptibly. He was a natural part of the animal community and, like other animals, a little cog in the mighty ecological machinery. It is only during a very brief, recent phase of his long sojourn on earth that man has really become an environmental factor of great importance. In this role he differs from all other animals in a way that is far from flattering.

Long before man became the dominant species on earth, the mammals had superseded the reptiles in most habitats. The extraordinary adaptability and elasticity of the mammals as a group have, of course, contributed to their success on land, in air, and in water. But only one species, man, has developed the abilities that make him dominant on our interesting planet. What would happen if man were to be exterminated? Those mammals whose only enemy is *Homo sapiens* would suddenly be freed from human predation, and at first they would increase in numbers, and competition between them would become keener. But it is not likely that any species would soon be powerful enough to occupy such a pre-eminent position on earth as man has held for the past few thousand years.

In about two-and-a-half million years—a brief span in the context of earth's history—man has evolved from a primitive hominid to the creature he is today; he has moved very rapidly away from his ancestors among the animals and his evolution has followed paths quite different from those of other animals. In the first place,

man's intelligence has developed incredibly, and this has made
him lord of the earth in a very brief time. The milestones in that
rapid development were the use of tools, mastery over fire, and
ability to express thoughts in words. In short, the unparalleled
organ we know as the brain of man may be said to be the prime
reason for man's remarkable progress as a species.

But this evolution of the human brain has also a negative side
for man himself. The dilemma he now faces owing to his destruction of his environment and the increase in his numbers is a result
of the way he has used great intelligence. But curiously enough,
he seems unable to realize that he is destroying the foundations of
his own existence. No such suicidally destructive behaviour can be
found in any other species of animal.

Appreciation of biological evolution is necessary if we are to
understand the whole meaning of man's situation in relation to his
environment. Our unique adaptability and receptivity as human
beings is so great that we hardly realize how quickly we adjust to
our surroundings, which we ourselves are changing so rapidly.
This has made human evolution a cultural evolution.

Some nonbiologists occasionally consider man an unimportant
onlooker, passively watching the events in nature, while others
consider him the prime mover in these events, without partners
and without opponents. These theories ignore the fact that the object of their concern, man, is a product of a biological treadmill
that has been grinding away ever since the dawn of life on our
planet, and they underestimate the inherited driving force which
often conditions our actions.

Man as a Member of Animal Communities

Being vegetarians, early hominids did not differ from present-
day apes in their utilization of the environment. Even when evolving from a vegetarian stage to an omnivorous one, the effect
human hominids had on nature was not of vital importance. Their
competition with other species was neither directly nor indirectly
serious. Today the pygmies of the Congo equatorial rain forest
are still, in principle, food gatherers living much as their ancestors
did a million years ago; they utilize everything in the forest that
is edible. Likewise, the Bushmen of the Kalahari have depended
for thousands of years entirely on the arid bushveld for their
existence. Yet they have no impact on it, perhaps in some cases

with the exception for their lighting of grass fires. Both pygmies and Bushmen are outstanding examples of the fact that if man does not produce food but only collects it, he does not overexploit the living natural resources. In the long-term sense, the interrelationship is perfect. Ecologically the pygmies are members of the forest fauna and part of a habitat in balance. They are dependent on the carrying capacity of the environment, which in its turn exerts control over the size of their population. The pygmies harvest animal species in the same way as other predators, and as far as we know, no animal species has ever been exterminated by the pygmies, even though they have been hunters and food collectors since a dim past. The pygmies of today and their environment are a model of the ecological interaction that existed between early man and the living landscape for almost two million years.

The food-gathering techniques used by man had a decisive influence on his biological and cultural evolution. Stage by stage, man's impact on his environment increased, but it took a very long time before his activities caused disasters. It is instructive to follow this development, because it shows us how dangerous it is for a species to try to escape from natural laws.

Everybody today agrees that the earliest hominids originated in Central Africa about two to three million years ago. It can be reasonably supposed that they were vegetarians. The massive molars of the about two-million-years-old *Australopithecus* (he has also been called *Paranthropus* and *Zinjanthropus*) *boisei* indicate a mainly vegetarian diet. There are also good reasons to believe that early vegetarian hominids or pre-hominids were forest-dwellers. For some reason these creatures shifted from forests to the savannas, but they left behind them in the forests such closely related species as gorillas and chimpanzees. Perhaps the ancestors of the pygmies also remained; if not, the pygmies must have returned to the forests at an early stage, because they are in an evolutionary sense so admirably adapted to this habitat.

We can speculate that the "forest-men" gradually made more frequent excursions to the open edges of savannas next to the forest. In this way they added to the food-gathering habits of their apelike ancestors and became adapted for life in an entirely new environment. They discovered a great number of new items of food, which favoured their food economy and brought them far out on the open savannas. Probably the forest-men had already been partly insectivorous and carnivorous during the last stages of their forest life; it seems likely that the abundance of carrion left by various predators on the savanna was decisive in their making this remarkable step from the dark, damp forest out to the relatively dry and open savannas.

On the other hand, there were many carrion-feeding species to compete with on the savannas. First, the killers themselves, the large felines, did not abandon their prey voluntarily. Secondly, hyenas and jackals were waiting for their share. The British anthropologist Kenneth P. Oakley (in 1962) has suggested that the early South African hominids were scavengers who collected meat. Oakley has advanced the theory that these carrion-feeders were the first toolmakers, since it would be natural for them to tear off and carry away parts of hoofed animals that had been partially eaten by carnivorous mammals. Sharpened pebbles, which were frequently used, enabled them to do this. This way of living led to active hunting of small and young animals.

This is exactly what chimpanzees do today. Although they are chiefly vegetarians and not at all scavengers, they hunt and eat meat. In fact, they are efficient hunters, organizing themselves in hunting groups, and can kill large mammals such as monkeys and young bushbucks, but they never touch carrion. They share the food of the kill and distribute it to members of the clan. They use stone, wood, grass, and leaves as tools.

Early man was presumably not more restricted than modern chimpanzees as a tool-user. (Incidentally, tool-using of an indisputable character occurs also in some other mammals and even in birds and invertebrates.) Probably the use of wood tools and stone tools had a dominant influence on human evolution for more than two-and-a-half million years. However, there is a significant distinction in evolution between using tools and making tools. It would seem probable that the mainly (or entirely?) vegetarian *"Paranthropus"* used tools. There is evidence that small-brained man *(Australopithecus)* made simple stone tools, and that two million years later much more complex tools had evolved and were used by large-brained man *(Homo erectus)*. In this context it is interesting to note that the genera *Australopithecus* and *Homo* may have been contemporaneous in Africa during the early Pleistocene and were evolving along parallel lines but at different speeds. Although they may even have shared habitats, there is no evidence of any direct relationships between australopithecine populations and those of *Homo*.

We know that the earliest known hunters in East Africa, about two million years ago, lived largely on catfish, tortoises, rodents, and shrews which could be caught by hand. Stones could be used to kill smaller animals; bones from carcasses could become weapons for defense and attack. Wooden clubs may also have been a part of early man's arsenal. These tools helped man to evolve from a rather clumsy carrion-feeder to a skillful and active hunter who could plan his predation on other animals or on his own species. Sharpened sticks became spears. It seems certain that the hunters of the mid-Chellean period in Africa, about 400,000 years ago, used bolas as hunting weapons, especially in bringing down huge antelopes. Presumably, there were also other means of human predation at this early stage, but we are still ignorant of the details.

It can be presumed that large ground-dwelling birds like the ostrich and the bustards had already at this stage become exposed to early man's predation.

Through all these food-gathering stages man's influence on the environment was nil and his competition with other animals was negligible. He still exploited the living natural resources as did other animals. The food-gathering stage of man lasted for an immense period of time in comparison to the following period of human existence. In fact, during the Paleolithic, which lasted for about 99 percent of human history, man was chiefly a gatherer and hunter. The increase of hunting ability coupled with other expressions of cultural evolution led to a slow expansion of human populations to temperate and subarctic zones about 140,000 to twelve thousand years ago.

Fire as a Tool

The first important step toward the conquest of environment was taken when man discovered how to use fire. That fire produces heat and roasts meat might have been discovered accidentally; the advantages were obvious. We know that fire has been used by man for at least 350,000 years. Before man knew how to make fire himself, he presumably maintained constantly burning embers —as the forest pygmies still do today.

We may also assume that burning grasslands and forests was a method of hunting. As long as men were few in number, their artificial burning probably did not interrupt the stability of their habitats any more than do fires caused by such natural causes as lightning and volcanic eruptions. Unfortunately, we do not know much about the density of human populations during the early Pleistocene. The long-term ill effects of burning could, at least locally and temporarily, be considerable even at a rather early stage.

In any case fire became more and more important as man's tool. In many regions of the earth it greatly modified the vegetation cover and affected the fauna. The landscape became impoverished, and the biocommunities were devastated. This was the beginning of man's misuse of his own environment, but it was still on a rather modest scale. Fire is not always a destroyer. It can be an aid when wisely employed and strictly controlled. However, frequent burning over a long period has an injurious effect on living organisms, including man.

The Pleistocene Drama

The Quaternary period, that is, the last million years, including the Pleistocene and the relatively recent Holocene epochs, is an age of instability, marked by frequent climatic changes. Continental ice sheets spread over vast areas of the Northern Hemisphere. Plant and animal movements took place in the same region. The majority of the large mammals that existed during most of the Pleistocene were extinct by the end of the period.

One wonders what the reason was for the disappearance of such large herbivorous mammals as the mastodonts (various species of mammoths and elephants), species of rhinoceroses, elk, deer, bison, camels, horses, tapirs, glyptodonts, ground sloths, and bear-sized beavers, as well as such carnivores as the saber-toothed cats, the giant jaguar, several bears, the cave hyena, giant wolves, and others. It almost seems as if a cataclysm had suddenly wiped out whole families and genera of well-established mammalian species, among them the most spectacular terrestrial mammals that have ever existed.

Many explanations of this mass disaster have been offered, but none is generally accepted. The key to this enigma is doubtless in the ecological background of this Pleistocene extinction.

Presumably, many factors were involved. The climatic changes resulting from at least four great glacial advances and retreats in North America, Asia, and Europe certainly had a great effect. About one-third of the earth's surface had an arctic climate during the ice ages. Plant and animal species were forced to withdraw to warmer climates or adapt to extremely severe life conditions. In both cases the competition among species increased greatly.

Since the mammals had survived several glacial and interglacial periods, climatic changes during each glaciation can hardly be held responsible for the extinction of most of the large species of late Pleistocene mammal life in the Northern Hemisphere. Was it the cumulative effect of repeated glaciations that thinned out the late Pleistocene assemblage of mammals? Or was the arrival of prehistoric man in northern latitudes the explanation?

The extinction of the large mammals about ten or twenty thousand years ago was particularly drastic in North America. It has been estimated that about 95 percent of the North American megafauna, including twenty-four genera and considerably more species, became extinct at the end of the last glaciation. Several of these animals vanished soon after the time that man is thought to have arrived in North America over a land bridge from Asia. It has been suggested that man was responsible for the extinction of mammals in the New World during the Pleistocene. In the view of the American palynologist Dr. Paul S. Martin, the shock of man's sudden arrival as a big-game hunter of the Eurasian Paleolithic, sweeping in on a fauna totally unfamiliar with his habits (unlike the fauna of Eurasia), magnified man's effect and made possible the dramatic extinction in the Americas. But on the other hand, it would surely have been an arduous task for a newcomer like early man to exterminate so many large and powerful animals all over North America in environments where they had long been settled.

It should be added that during the same periods large mammals also vanished in Eurasia, Australia, and Africa, where man had been long established; and in South America, but timing is uncertain in the latter area. At the end of the Pleistocene five genera and nine species of larger mammals became extinct in northern Eurasia. Many of these animals are well-known from the cave paintings: woolly mammoth (*Mammuthus primigenius*), woolly rhinoceros (*Coelodonta antiquitatis*), giant deer (*Megaloceros giganteus*), steppe bison (*Bison prisca*), musk-ox (*Ovibos moschatus*) (which survived in North America and has been reintroduced in Europe), cave bear (*Ursus spelaeus*), cave lion (*Panthera spelaea*), and cave hyena (*Crocuta spelaea*). In northern Africa a buffalo (*Homoioceras antiquus*) became extinct during the same period.

Recent research indicates, moreover, that the extinction of mammals in tropical Africa was much more extensive than has previously been presumed, even though not so concentrated in time as in North America. The rich deposits of Olduvai have, for example, yielded many vanished giants such as *Dinotherium,* a genus of elephants having tusks growing downward from the lower jaw; *Pelorovis,* an enormous sheep; the saber-toothed tiger; an extremely large swamp antelope; a giant pig; a huge porcupine; and so on. In brief, there were at Olduvai, according to Dr. Louis S. B. Leakey (in 1962 and 1964), no fewer than fifty-eight different large ungulates, twenty species of pigs, and a much richer total fauna than is present today. A large proportion of this mammalian multitude in Africa died out, as did the giant lemurs of Madagascar (though much later than on the mainland).

It is not easy to tell apart past sources of significant environmental disturbance. In the late Pleistocene we are dealing chiefly with climatic and cultural changes affecting ecosystems and species in various ways. To what degree these sources of disturbance were responsible for the dramatic Pleistocene extinctions of mammals remains a speculation, but as new data emerge they point suggestively more and more to man as one of the major factors, at least locally. Probably climatic changes were regionally a contributing factor, and in some cases also geographical changes.

South America may turn out to give some clues to the enigma of Pleistocene extinctions. Man arrived late to this continent, where the disruptive effects of Pleistocene glaciation were relatively slight. Yet there is a spectacular Pleistocene extinction of large mammals in South America. The explanation in this case seems to be clear. It was an effect of a new intercontinental connection, the re-establishment of the isthmus at the end of the Tertiary. Fifteen families of North American mammals spread into South America, where the effect was catastrophic and resulted in the extinction of the unique notoungulates, litopterns, and marsupial carnivores and a great reduction of rodents and edentates.

To what extent man took part in the elimination of nearly all very large mammals of South America is partly obscure. Radiocarbon data from this continent are still very meager. But as far as we know, man arrived too late to be responsible for all the Pleistocene events on the South American animal scene.

What is clear is that the native South American fauna was unable to compete successfully with the invaders crossing the Panamanian bridge. Hence, in South America we are facing an ecological situation that was released by geographic rearrangement in the Pliocene, had dramatic extinction effects in the Pleistocene, and is still going on in recent time.

Australia is another continent where man arrived late. So far it does not seem that the earliest Australians had anything to do with the extinction of a number of Pleistocene giant mammals and birds, but also on this continent radiocarbon dating is still in its infancy.

If we again take the present-day pygmies of the Zaire forest as an example of early human predation, we find that the animal populations within a clan's territory are temporarily so thinned out by hunting that even a clan consisting of only a few families must change territories several times a year. The animal populations in an area abandoned by the pygmies soon recover in number, the hunters return, and the cycle begins again. So it has gone on for thousands of years. It is, however, important to recall that the pygmies and their quarry are living in the equatorial rain forest, an extremely rich biocommunity in which reproduction goes on throughout the year. The productivity is tremendous.

In savannas and in temperate regions the mammalian fauna is more vulnerable. The driving of ungulate herds over precipices and intensive trapping, for example, may in the past have had some effect on the numbers of slow-breeding larger animals. We know, for example, that in several areas in Europe the fossil remains of three species of Pleistocene elephants and one of rhinoceros contrast greatly in localities where man was present or not. Where man was absent, individuals of *Elephas trogontherii* and *E. primigenius* fifty years old or more predominate among the elephant herds, amounting to 78 percent and 62 percent respectively. Where man was present, the percentages for the same age groups dropped to 25 percent; and to 17 percent for *E. antiquus,* while younger age groups predominate. At a Paleolithic site in Europe, more than 70 percent of the rhinoceroses caught were young animals. This situation may, however, reflect that man was hunting young animals selectively.

The bow and arrow did not appear until a late stage of man's cultural evolution, the Mesolithic.

It is almost certain that the Paleolithic and Mesolithic food collectors moved regularly to areas where game and other sources of food were abundant. This shifting of forage grounds resembles the habits of grazing, browsing, and carnivorous animals. This is eco-

logically important, because it indicates a rational use of land: one
that did not destroy the resources of the various habitats. Thus
the influence of man on his environment was only local and temporary.

With a few exceptions, it is unlikely that man was the ultimate
cause of the extermination of the large late Pliocene and/or
Pleistocene mammals even though he certainly had evolved into a
formidable tool- and fire-using predator. Not until man ceased to
be a food collector and changed into a food producer did he become a destroyer and exterminator.

Among surviving orders of mammals it is the odd-toed ungulates (*Perissodactyla*) that show the highest extermination rate.
Not less than 152 genera of this order have been wiped out
(known from fossils) and at present only five genera with fifteen
species still exist. They are horses, tapirs, and rhinoceroses, of
which eleven species are declining toward extinction owing to
man.

Man as Pastoralist and Cultivator

In the cultural evolution of man, the stage as a food gatherer
and hunter was, in general, followed by a nomadic pastoral stage.
This new mode of living developed in some areas after man had
learned how to domesticate some herbivorous mammals, about
eight thousand years ago. This in turn led to agriculture (but already c. 7000 B.C. plant cultivation had begun in the Near East).
Man became a settled cultivator, but nomadic and sedentary pastoralism persisted in many areas or occurred in combination with
cultivation. In some areas this preindustrial use of land has continued almost unchanged since time immemorial.

Thus, the domestication of plants and animals was a decisive
factor for one of man's most important stages of development.
The animal kingdom was already an important source of food for
primitive man. It also provided him with other raw materials, the
importance of which, in certain parts of the world, probably increased in relation to long-term climatic changes. Falling temperatures created new uses for such material. Man with his intellectual
capacity had better prospects of adaptation to climatic changes
than many animal species: the distribution of man today is evidence of this. Gradually a symbiotic relationship arose between
man and his domesticated animals.

Although man's interest in animals has always been—and still is—primarily economic, magic and religion have played a role in it. This, however, has occurred chiefly during the phases of man's direct interaction with his natural environment. This is seldom so obvious as in the domestication of animals. The background of domestication has often been an interaction of biological phenomena that are not always due to the deliberate action of man.

On archeological and paleontological as well as biological grounds, the late British zoologist Frederick E. Zeuner (in 1963) concluded that domestication arose of itself as an outcome of natural circumstances rather than as conscious exploitation of a species by man. There is strong evidence that this view is justified, although it is hardly likely that the process was the same for all domesticated animals. As always in the course of evolution, chance has probably played an important role.

Many theories have attempted to explain why man began to domesticate animals. Nearly all of them assume that the fundamental cause was a utilitarian one—that man needed certain animals for economic and/or religious reasons, and therefore attempted to tame and domesticate them. According to Zeuner this ignores the fact that during the Mesolithic period, when domestication began, it would have been much simpler and more economic for man to hunt and trap animals, as his forefathers had done, than to involve himself in experiments of taming and domesticating unwilling animals that would not benefit him for his efforts until some generations later. If we start with purely biological factors, we find, Zeuner maintains, that domestication seems more an inevitable process. The social relation of domestication is not restricted to man. Other species of the animal kingdom also practice slavery or domestication as a part of their physiobiological environment.

Pastoralism evolved in temperate and/or subtropical regions, where fluctuating climate was an important factor in forming the new habitats. From these more northern latitudes the pastoral economy spread at a very late stage to tropical regions. However, the combined farming and stock-breeding economy developed into a secondary, nomadic pastoralism in wide areas of Eastern Asia.

Pastoralism as a dominant economy had been essentially a phenomenon of Old World temperate and subtropical areas. After it had spread to the tropics, it was generally confined to open lands. It has been postulated that pastoralism is usually not found in rain forests because they do not produce large quantities of grass. However, in Africa man had conquered the savannas long before he became a pastoralist. It was in the savanna that he started to base his economy on domesticated animals, and both partners remained there.

As a pastoralist, man with his domesticated goats, sheep, and cattle became a powerful competitor of the wild animals—chiefly by changing the habitats considerably. Excessive grazing in temperate regions may destroy many fertile areas temporarily, but in the subtropics and the tropics it can change grasslands into deserts with no possibility of regeneration as long as the present climate prevails. In temperate areas moderate grazing may even maintain and improve habitats for other animals, particularly birds.

With the development of preindustrial agriculture, man became a formidable reshaper of the earth, a kind of geologic factor. Forest destructions, fires, irrigation, terrace building, and other encroachments entirely upset the soil structure, the vegetation cover, and animal populations. Drainage came later.

This was the price paid for establishing a basis for what we call civilization. The social, cultural, and economic benefits to man have been very great indeed, but only periodically. In the perspective of thousands of years we can now see how civilizations and powerful empires on several continents have collapsed because of destruction of the environment.

It is chiefly in the subtropical and tropical parts of the world that pastoralism and cultivation impoverished the environment to a tremendous degree. The conversion of productive savannas to barren wasteland has gone on ever since man domesticated grazing and browsing mammals and directed the herds where he wanted them to be. Although nomadic pastoralism was and locally still is based on a system that in many respects resembles that of wild grazing animals, that is, utilizing the vegetation where it can—in time and space—support the herds, it is nevertheless because of nomadic pastoralism that most man-made deserts have been formed. Forests also have been greatly modified during centuries and millenniums by man and his domestic animals. These environmental changes are particularly profound in Africa, Asia, and Europe, where man has been longest in action, but even the Americas, Australasia, and the Pacific Islands have seen marked physiogeographic alterations despite the relatively short time man has been there. We will come back to this subject in our regional chapters. The temperate parts of the world have also been greatly affected and almost entirely converted into man-made lands, but there the capacity of the environment to resist has been astonishingly high during very long periods. But the fortunate circumstance will not last for ever.

THE LAST IDYLL

In other times man considered nature his enemy. This was understandable as long as he had to compete with other animals. But when he became increasingly a dominant species, developing his power to use living and inorganic nature to what he presumed to be to his own advantage, his approach to the land around him was still antagonistic. This attitude, however, gradually changed with man's growing feeling of superiority. When he no longer feared nature, he began to plunder it as if it were inexhaustible. He has gone on doing this ever since. This approach is reflected in man's classical view that nature is something opposed to civilization. Man seems to have forgotten at an early stage that he is subject to the same natural laws as other living organisms. But never in the history of man has his unrealistic biological behavior been so paradoxical as in our time.

The land has suffered most wherever civilizations have been established the longest. Thus the rate of destruction of nature was and is very different in various parts of the world, depending on the degree of civilization and the density of the population. As Plato and other writers testify, the vegetation of the Mediterranean and the Middle East was already largely destroyed as far back as 2,500 years ago. Most other parts of the world were at that time still in a virgin stage or at least had a harmonious balance of nature, in spite of the fact that man was already dispersed over vast areas.

However, man rapidly increased his impact on the environment and became more and more aggressive and dangerous. His expansion during the last three thousand years has led to a tremendous misuse of the land and the extermination of other species. Particularly vulnerable to man's ravaging were mammals and flightless birds on isolated islands. As far as we know, at least ten species of insular birds were exterminated during the seventeenth century alone. One of them was the famous dodo (*Raphus cucullatus*), a large flightless bird on Mauritius. Many more went the same way during succeeding centuries.

Despite man's drastic effect on the natural environment everywhere, his hegemony over the terrestrial animals was far from being total. Only three hundred years ago there was still a surprisingly rich plant and animal life in most areas. On the whole, the animals were still masters in the forests, on the savannas and prairies, in the mountains, along the shores, and in the streams, lakes, and seas. In many areas the countryside was so varied and rich that there was room for both animals and human beings. This idyll lasted until the beginning of the eighteenth century and, in some regions, until the explosive industrial development at the beginning of the present century.

It is true that during thousands of years man struggled with the surrounding forests, creating cultivated meadows, steppes, heaths, scattered groves and coppices. All these types of man-made landscapes were gradually filled with the fauna adapted to them. But up to the nineteenth century these adaptations were not so great as to alter the overall picture of the animal world.

Imagine, for example, the once glaciated parts of Asia and Europe only a century and a half ago. Forests dominated them as now but they were less uniform than they are today; they had kept their individuality and character. Coppices were numerous, for the regular leaf harvest that created them was of great importance in the old agricultural economy. In vast areas the soil was still untouched. Thousands of lakes, marshes, and bogs, the legacy of the great last ice cap, covered the countryside. Through forests, woods, and meadows, glittering streams and brooks ran freely. In spring they overflowed and flooded the meadows around them. As summer approached, the low-lying fields of sedge, horsetail, and rush were transformed by the sun into natural meadows, which were mown yearly to make use of everything that could serve as fodder for the livestock during the winter.

It was to such a countryside that the wild fauna was adapted in large parts of the Northern Hemisphere. This fauna consisted of much the same species as today, but it was much richer and it was distributed over much larger ranges. In those days man was more settled, his routines less subject to change, and the changes were not so great that Nature could not adapt herself almost immediately to the new conditions.

This situation ended with the expansion of industry, the draining of marshes and wetlands, the exploitation of forests for timber, the harnessing of rivers and lakes for hydroelectric power, the pollution of waters, the dumping of slag and waste on fertile lands, and so forth. The natural environment, which had been fashioned during thousands of years in a way acceptable to most living creatures, was violently transformed by just one species.

In North America, so rich in natural resources, man had lived in harmony with nature ever since his arrival on the continent. Then followed the invasion of Europeans, with the consequence that no continental area has ever been so rapidly destroyed. Within the last two centuries the American landscape has been changed on a tremendous scale and with incredible violence. It has led to rapid profit, but later generations will suffer from the loss of ground capital.

In the tropics, where man had existed longer than anywhere else, the change in the situation of animal life since the beginning of the nineteenth century has been incredibly drastic. A magnificent array of Africa's large mammals roamed on the savannas in countless numbers. The mountains and hills were covered by forests rich in animals. But south of the African tropics, on the velds of South Africa, the repercussions of the white man's expansion were evident already 250 years ago. Several species had been exterminated, and others faced annihilation.

It was not long ago that the steppes of Asia and Europe and the arid regions and semideserts of Africa and Asia were still populated by animals showing a remarkable ability to adapt to the harsh conditions of such areas. The pampas, llanos, and campos of South America and the slopes of the Andes harbored a rich fauna of mammals and birds. So did Australia and the arctic tundra and islands. The seas abounded in the largest animals that have ever lived—whales. Together with dolphins, porpoises, seals, walruses, and other marine mammals, they converted various food items of the sea into fat, proteins, and skins, an incredibly rich natural resource.

These are only a few examples of the immense organic resources in that early time. They represented a heritage for which the most powerful of animal species, man, was responsible to future generations—a responsibility that he completely ignored.

THE GREAT RETREAT

Three hundred years is only a split second compared with the eons during which various life forms have been evolving on earth.

But the last three hundred years have been sufficient for our own species to reshape the face of the continents. This is often considered a praiseworthy achievement, and is called progress. Of course, it is progress from a technical or cultural point of view, but considered globally and in long-term perspectives, it is not economic progress. In terms of national product, imports, exports, and living standards in relation to the world population as a whole, the outlook is very negative. But to view man's social and cultural development only from an economic angle is a confession of spiritual poverty. Increasingly, in modern, highly organized societies, man turns to living nature for relief. It affords him recreation and inspiration just as do art, sport, and other diversions. As more and more people become urbanized or live in villages and in concentrated areas, this trend back to nature will become more pronounced.

There is still time to save much of the world's disappearing natural resources and wonders, but whether this will be done depends entirely on man himself. To save them we must understand how much of the world's natural resources has been destroyed by man in so short a time.

Erosion and Habitat Alteration

In large parts of the world, erosion is man's greatest and oldest conservation problem, although often he seems quite ignorant of it. This is tragic, but not astonishing, for this catastrophic process has been going on in the Mediterranean region, Africa, and Asia for thousands of years. And man, with his domestic animals—the goat in particular—is responsible. We cannot blame the climate. In the Near East, with its naked, drastically eroded land, it was recently found that when some areas were evacuated (by Arabs, Israelis, and their domestic animals, due to war), plants never seen there in the memory of man began to reappear on barren earth.

In the mountains of Italy, both the Alps and the Apennines, 80 percent of the pastures are said to be damaged by erosion, originally due mainly to grazing animals. Without a protective cover of vegetation, the soil is washed away and the rock left bare. Still more terrible scenes face us on the sierras of Spain and on the plateaus. In Spain between 60 and 80 percent of all land used for agriculture and animal husbandry is damaged by erosion. Not even terracing has been able to stop the erosion, for there is not a single blade of grass left on the hills above, and rainwater relentlessly washes all the soil from the slopes. The amount of damage caused by goats in the Mediterranean area is incredible, and the loss to man cannot be expressed in figures.

Destruction of land by goats began as soon as these animals were domesticated, and the terrible consequences of their ravages can be seen everywhere in the Mediterranean countries, the Near East, and Africa. The combination of man and goat destroys the environment to such a degree that both species are compelled to move on after they have turned a dwelling place into a desert. And so the process of destruction has gone on with the results we see today—eroded landscapes devoid of vegetation. In such areas it is not uncommon to see goats climbing into trees to eat the leaves. But they do not do this until the ground around the trees is bare; in other words, it is the final phase in their work of destruction. As long ago as 2300 B.C., the goats at Ur had begun climbing trees, as can be seen in art from royal sepulchers there.

The goat was probably the first ruminant to be domesticated, possibly ten thousand and certainly at least eight thousand years ago. The origin of the tame goat is not yet clear, although its wild ancestors still exist. Complicating the problem is the fact that many species may be mixed up in the history of the tame goat.

For thousands of years the goat has been regarded as man's most useful animal. In reality the tame goat is man's worst enemy. Over great stretches of Europe, Asia, and Africa, man's association with the goat has been disastrous to all living organisms and the whole landscape.

In the tropics, too, large herds of cattle can, by excessive grazing and treading on young plants, turn flourishing tracts into deserts. This has occurred in many places in Africa. These cattle, which are out of place in these areas, have probably not been there for more than about five hundred years. During this brief period, cattle and goats, with the help of man, have destroyed relatively larger areas of tropical Africa than goats have destroyed in the Mediterranean areas and the Near East in about eight thousand years, which indicates how vulnerable the tropical landscape is.

There are no natural deserts in India, but desertlike tracts are not lacking there today. They are all the consequence of man's mismanagement of the land by too intensive animal husbandry. As soon as these deserts are left in peace by man and his domestic animals, the woods return. But there is no continent which, in proportion to its size, has been so terribly damaged by man as Australia, where one abuse has led to another, destroying the native flora and fauna. Almost everywhere in the world, erosion has been preceded by excessive grazing. In North America the process has been so rapid that it has taken only a few decades, not centuries. A great struggle is taking place in the United States between champions of conservation and politically powerful livestock breeders over the need to reduce the number of cattle in order to prevent further destruction of the soil and begin its rehabilitation. Exactly the same problem, and the same fatal conservatism in cattle breeders, is found in the developing nations of Africa and Asia, although it is less surprising there than in a technically enlightened country like the United States. In the latter, as Raymond F. Dasmann (in 1963) has pointed out in *The Last Horizon,* the lack of social responsibility in those who destroy the land is manifest. As long as landowners and cattle breeders use their income in a way comfortable with contemporary conventions, they may continue to violate productive nature and are even regarded as good citizens. There are few who realize that their work will in the long run prove ruinous and will impoverish future generations. To a biologist, it is a great crime to turn a productive landscape into a naked ruin, where neither man nor animals can live. And still, a stock breeder is considered a very respectable member of society, which is evidence of society's appalling indifference, lack of knowledge of biology, and, in this case, excessive respect for the right of ownership.

Too often wild animals are blamed when things go wrong owing to man-made factors. An example of these is termites. The important role of these insects in ecosystems is still not fully understood. Some species of termites, at least in Africa and Australia, increase greatly owing to land denudation caused by the overgrazing and overtrampling of livestock. Together with the latter certain termites keep the soil bare, but soon the domestic animals must give up using the land because of the lack of vegetation; and finally also the insects die out, probably from food shortage. Then grass cannot grow there for decades, probably as long as thirty-five years (Watson and Gay in 1970, Newsome in 1971). This unnatural abundance of termites correlated to extensive grazing of livestock is known from the Karoo in South Africa and a mulga (*Acacia aneura*) ecosystem in Australia. In both areas the termites are therefore considered as pests; but it would certainly be more objective to declare the livestock as pests because they induce the deterioration and are the real troublemakers in these ecosystems.

But it is not only animal husbandry that may destroy the fertility of the soil; in many places, farming, particularly in the tropics, leads to the same results. First the forest vegetation is removed and the wild animals are driven away or killed off. Then farmers come. After a few years the fertility of the soil declines, the crops get poorer and poorer until nothing at all can be harvested. Moreover, where the vegetation no longer protects the soil, the soil is carried by the water runoff and on its way silts up ancestral water holes, lakes, rivers, and other permanent waters, eliminating an inestimable resource essential for the health and function of a living landscape. The processes of silting up inland waters contribute greatly to the poor retention of the precipitation when it falls and reduction of subsoil water supply. Fertile topsoils blow away or are washed out to the sea, owing to overgrazing by domestic stocks and cultivation. Such erosion also occurs along riverbanks; disastrous erosive effects soon follow. Gully erosion is a tragically common phenomenon in man-altered lands in the tropics and subtropics. How much more valuable the land was in its original state! Its productivity of timber and wildlife would have remained at a high level without any investment in capital and labor. Many scientists, particularly in Australia (Newsome in 1971) but also in Africa and Asia, think that there is no productive or "safe" way to graze dry range lands by livestock. They believe that domestic grazing can only lead to ecosystem degradation. Certainly the evidence is in their favour.

For ages, man in many parts of the world has proceeded on the assumption that forest land, in lowlands as well as highlands, in the temperate zones and in the tropics, is economically inferior, or completely worthless, and should therefore be cleared away to make room for pastures and fields. In the temperate zone this view has been superseded by a realization of the ecological and economic value of woods. In the tropics, however, the old attitude still prevails, as is often evident in agricultural projects in developing countries. Such a view is not only fatal to the supply of water and eventually farming, but it is completely ignorant of the value of tropical forest. Apart from the fact that the rain forest is climax vegetation, which is the maximum vegetal achievement of the earth and therefore of very great scientific interest, its very rapid turnover and enormous fertility will probably allow for successful exploitation, in spite of the fact that hundreds of species of trees mix together. Tropical Africa has in its forests a natural resource that, far from being wasteland, could be most beneficial. But in Nigeria 74 percent of the forests have been cut down within a few years. It is unrealistic and almost criminally shortsighted to propose clearing away rain forests on the theory that agriculture (chiefly in the form of shifting cultivation) will give better returns. The evidence indicates that such theories are not thought through but are mere improvisations.

Mountains and hills are particularly vulnerable to vegetation destruction and erosion, to which enormous areas of the world bear witness. The rocks lie bare; previously permanently flowing streams and rivers have become dry. The water is no longer retained and slowly distributed to lowland soils and does not feed the water tables to maintain their levels.

Man has long used fire, but not until it was adopted by livestock breeders and farmers was it utilized for widespread destruction of nature. Vast areas of forest land have thus been destroyed on all continents.

For thousands of years Africans have set fire to grass in order to maintain or develop the savanna vegetation. There are many who claim that without fire there would be no savannas in Africa today. It is likely, however, that several factors are responsible for natural savannas. In the transitional zones between savanna and forest, it is probable that grazing animals in combination with natural fires (caused by lightning, for example) prevented forests from encroaching. On savannas far from forests, grazing alone was very likely sufficient to create such an environment, provided, of course, that soil and climate were suitable.

Only sixty years ago, the savannas in tropical East Africa—in Uganda, Kenya, Tanzania, Zambia, and Rhodesia—were steppes of billowing grass where innumerable herds of wild hoofed animals, from tiny duiker antelopes to mighty elephants, grazed. And so it had been for thousands of years. Many people alive today can tell of a time when the area supported wild hoofed animals in such great numbers that no parallel could be found on earth. This area has been reduced by half, and the number of wild animals has dropped by about 75 percent.

During the same brief period, the cattle and goats of Africans have increased enormously in numbers as a consequence of the cessation of tribal wars, the progress of veterinary medicine, irrigation, and so on. These seemingly beneficial steps have had a quantitative, not a qualitative, effect on the stock of animals. The frequency of death by starvation among them is rising again. Most pastures of Masailand, comprising large parts of Kenya and Tanzania, lie waste, owing primarily to excessive grazing and trampling, and secondarily to wind and water erosion after the protective carpet of vegetation has disappeared and water-accumulating forests have been burned down. This process goes on inexorably, for when the Masai have turned one region into a desert they move with their herds to new pasture lands and there repeat the destruction.

An area of about 2,300,000 square miles of tropical Africa harbours tsetse flies, which suck the blood of mammals; some species of these flies infect cattle with African sleeping sickness— nagana. With few exceptions, however, the wild animals are immune against infection carried by tsetse flies and other blood parasites, while tame animals invariably die if infected. This means that an area of tropical Africa almost as large as the United States cannot be exploited for cattle breeding without very expensive clearance of forest land and brush to get rid of environments that shelter the tsetse fly. This has often led to the extermination of the large mammals in the region, for although nagana is not fatal to them, they may carry this disease.

Such large-scale transformations of the landscape have occurred in many parts of Africa, especially in Rhodesia. Experience has shown that with a few exceptions these great investments and all the labor have been in vain. Tame cattle, it is true, take the place of wild animals in the areas freed of tsetse flies, and at first find a rich supply of food. But the vegetation cannot survive the intensive grazing and trampling. Rain and wind, given greater freedom by forest clearance, wash and blow away the very thin layer of fertile soil, now unprotected by plants. Cattle die of starvation or, owing to impaired physical condition, of ordinary sicknesses not normally fatal. In a short time the region becomes a semi-desert where neither tame nor wild animals, much less man, can find nourishment. The same region in its former state, with its original vegetation, tsetse flies, and wild hoofed animals, was an ecological unit and economically very productive. The steps taken made the area useless for decades and perhaps centuries.

On marginal lands unsuited for agriculture and pastoralism, wildlife utilization in various forms would have been a better kind of land use and would not have resulted in habitat deterioration. In the tropics a high proportion of human inhabitants still subsist completely or partially on hunting and food gathering, an economy essentially based on wild-animal proteins. In addition, such hunting yields hides and can locally develop to an industry.

The last twenty years have seen a drastic decline of populations of large wild herbivorous mammals. All evidence indicates that this decline is due to habitat deterioration and overexploitation. The environmental degradation is all over linked to human activities. In the African tropics habitat manipulations, especially by harmful burning, by overstocking, by cultivating, or by creating artificial water supply in the form of bore holes and wells, often have catastrophic results. Large concentrations of livestock in areas up to ten miles or more surrounding the artificial water sites cause heavy overgrazing and a general environmental degradation. The perennial grass cover disappears, the water table lowers, rivers and natural springs dry up. The ecological balance is upset and the whole region changes from grasslands to deserts. Particularly frightful environmental effects of water bore holes and wells can be seen, for example, over wide areas in Botswana and Tanzania, as a result of unwise "aid projects" to these countries.

Where shallow underground water is found at depths from three-and-a-half to thirty meters, the soil and the vegetation often offer excellent forage; but where bore holes are dug, the daily walking of cattle alters the habitat to such an extent that grazing becomes nonexistent for miles away from the watering point. Erosion follows and the land is degraded.

The provision of artificial water supplies for livestock is in many developing countries offered and executed by international and national aid agencies as projects for development. There is in many countries clear evidence that such schemes result in rapid and severe land deterioration. They are, in part, a disservice to a country rather than an aid. Yet, programs of sinking bore holes in arid regions for domestic animals are encouraged and continued. The long-term productivity of a region goes down instead of being maintained for optimal use of future generations. Such "development" is not viable.

Also, in subtropical and temperate parts of Australia, watering points were established in order to improve the land productivity. They originally led to an initial increase of domestic stock numbers, but here as elsewhere degradation followed. However, the deterioration was punctuated by great climatic variations and droughts, which were blamed as the prime cause. The land deterioration in Australia was in some areas a relatively slow process often spread in time over a few human generations, who apparently for long periods believed there were no environmental alterations at all.

Unfortunately, the impoverishment of the soil of tropical Africa has been going on for many hundreds of years, with the combination of man, cattle, and goats destroying the land at an ever accelerating rate. The course of destruction is nearly always the same: Forests are burned and cleared, tame animals kill the vegetation, erosion completes the devastation in the valleys, and then the process is repeated higher and higher up the mountain slopes. Where forest land survives, there is still life in the landscape, although often it is in its death throes. Where the forest has disappeared completely and every blade of grass has been gnawed off, the mountains are sterile rocks and the plains below are deserts. Only a hundred years ago or so, rain forests clothed the same mountain slopes, and the plains were covered with luscious grass. Both forests and plains supported an animal life which, in numbers and richness of species, exceeded that of every other region in the world. This unique natural resource, the main producer of proteins, has been destroyed and replaced by desolate tracts over vast areas of Africa. And this devastation is still going on. Smoke can be seen everywhere, lying like a shroud over the mountain slopes of Africa, spelling the doom of man. Unless a radical change occurs very soon, much of Africa will soon be a gigantic desert in which only the afro-alpine vegetation on the highest mountains and the gallery woods along the great rivers will be green oases. And paradoxically, it is only because of the deadly tsetse fly that fertile land in biological equilibrium still survives in large parts of tropical Africa.

A global trend for hundreds of years is for productive lands through bad management to alter to marginal lands and for marginal lands to turn into unproductive lands. This tragic deterioration includes also the waters and is particularly pronounced in tropical and subtropical, semiarid and arid lowlands and highlands. There, present generations of man are destroying a precious resource capital without leaving anything for their successors.

All this destruction of soil and vegetation, particularly in the subtropics and tropics, has been disastrous for wild animals. They have been compelled continuously to retreat to other regions where conditions are still suitable for them. The destruction of environments has in general done more to reduce their number and distribution than hunting.

The Slaughter of Animals

In many parts of the world, the stocks of wild animals have suffered from too intensive hunting, which has even led to the extermination of several species. Automatic firearms have resulted in an ever-growing hunting pressure, which only in a few countries is under control. It is usually by shooting that the last of a species are killed. In other cases, however, shooting is regarded as the main cause of the extermination or decimation of certain species. The Antarctic is the only continent where, as far as is known, no animal species has been exterminated by man. The massacre of the bison of North America was a disgrace to mankind. The slaughter of buffaloes, antelopes, and other hoofed animals in East Africa and Rhodesia that took place because it was believed that this would get rid of the tsetse fly was, as we have seen, a mistake. In Rhodesia alone, about six hundred thousand hoofed animals were killed. Similar massacres took place in other regions, and the fauna there received a blow from which, numerically, it has never recovered.

Of all birds, none has been so persecuted by man as birds of prey and owls. Extermination has been the goal in many countries, and unfortunately this goal has been achieved. Only a few birds of prey and owls in Europe, for example, have been able to maintain their distribution range during the past hundred years. By all possible means—shooting, trapping, poison, and robbing nests—man has for centuries destroyed these birds. Several species have also been subjected to pressure by changes in their environments due to the transformation of a natural into a cultivated landscape.

For generations, farmers, fishermen, and huntsmen have regarded birds of prey and owls as enemies that must be suppressed. Regular campaigns have been organized against these birds. Bounties have been paid—and in some countries are still being paid—for killing them, and such ruthless destruction has been encouraged in other ways. Man's view of birds of prey and owls has until quite recently been based on a complete misunderstanding. Predators have been regarded as harmful competitors or simply as cruel creatures because they kill their prey in order to live. The ecological role of birds of prey and owls as stabilizing and controlling factors in animal populations in nature has been denied. Most species live on small rodents, and their occurrence in a region depends on the supply of prey, not the other way round. It is a tragedy that when human beings have finally begun to realize the value of birds of prey and owls, pesticides are being used more and more widely, and are taking their toll of these birds to such a degree that several species are facing extinction.

The Misuse of Water

For centuries man has regarded marshes and any land periodically flooded by the sea as Nature's rubbish heaps. Waterlogged ground has been considered worthless, and innumerable attempts have been made to drain such land. Much fertile land has been won for agriculture by this process; but far too frequently such drainage has failed, causing an enormous waste of natural resources and public funds. Not only have all the expected gains failed to materialize, but both the natural and artificial productivity of the land has been reduced and its power to support the surrounding population impaired. The subsoil water sinks, formerly fertile fields lose their productivity, fish and other wildlife become scarce or disappear completely. These consequences of drainage become more pronounced with each passing decade, for it is not until twenty or thirty years have elapsed that the disastrous effects become fully evident. What is clear to every ecologist —the relation between the supply of water and the long-term productivity of the soil—has been ignored.

During the past 150 years, the practice of draining shallow lakes and marshes was so common in North America and Europe that one is justified in speaking of a passion for drainage. In the United States, for example, more than three-quarters of all the marshes and shallow lakes in the country have been drained. There are no reliable data available for the various countries of Europe, but the trend has prevailed there.

Furthermore, the remaining lakes and watercourses have been shockingly misused by the authorities. Such waters have been used for decades for sewage disposal by municipalities and industrial plants. It has clearly been assumed that the self-cleansing capacity of rivers and lakes is unlimited.

The danger of unsuccessful drainage often becomes evident in the reduced productivity of the surrounding regions. The effect of draining must, however, be seen in an even wider perspective, particularly in those areas where lakes have been drained on such a large scale that the natural system of marshes of a whole continent, such as Europe and North America, has been altered. Marshes and lakes are extremely important components of the natural resources of a region, of man's standard of living, and in the long run of his very existence. The present affluence of Europe and North America is due largely to the supply of water.

Also in the tropics and subtropics, swamps and lakes are of great importance for environmental health and productivity. They are integral parts of well-balanced ecosystems and as such sensitive to disturbances by unnatural factors. An example of this ecological fragility comes from the Caprivi Strip between Angola, South-West Africa, Botswana, and Zambia, where the reduction of hippopotamuses in a swamp by shooting caused the drying up of a river on which many villages downstream depended. The hippos' regular movements along certain trails on the swamp kept the aquatic vegetation from choking the channels through which water flowed to the previously permanent river.

Apart from their great economic value, which can be expressed in monetary terms, marshes and shallow lakes represent many values of a scientific, recreational, and aesthetic nature—in other words, social values. It must be considered in the public interest to preserve waters that provide man with healthy pleasure and relaxation in the form of open-air activity—swimming, fishing, hunting, and the study of nature. For thirty years or so, the bird lakes and wetlands of North America and Europe have been by far the most popular for excursions of people interested in nature. Very frequently it is just the wetlands with a rich variety of life that are drained or threatened with drainage. Great historical value must also be assigned to marshes and shallow lakes, for they are the remains of a former landscape rich in water and marshes. It is at least as important to preserve representative relics of types of landscape as it is to keep medieval buildings in repair at enormous cost. Marshes and shallow lakes are always in the process of evolution; they are never static. This is especially true of regions formerly covered by the inland ice sheet. All stages of wetland evolution should therefore be preserved. In 1955 the National Wildlife Federation in the United States began an information drive to save America's wetlands. It did much good, and during recent years the federal government has taken energetic steps to save remaining marshes and shallow lakes.

The damage caused to nature in many countries on all continents except Antarctica by the construction of hydroelectric generating stations and dams is enormous and generally irreparable. The consequences of great dams are appalling, not only for the watercourse itself, but for the whole of the surrounding district. The landscape may be changed radically. The fauna and flora are exposed to sudden, fundamental changes, which must be fatal in the long run. We do not know with certainty how the climate around regulated water is affected, but there is strong evidence that it changes negatively. In tropical and subtropical regions, also in some temperate ones, dams for various purposes are only temporary solutions, because they will gradually silt up. Living natural resources such as large deltas, often rich in wildlife, and vast, economically valuable areas of forest land are drowned. The spawning places of many species of fish are destroyed and reproduction ceases. In many watercourses the fish cannot move upstream or downstream. To replace the loss of valuable fish, especially various species of salmon, which cannot breed naturally when its environment is changed by man, artificial breeding is resorted to; this, it is claimed, will in future balance the loss of natural reproduction. It should be biologically possible to achieve the reproduction of salmon artificially, but at the same time great and costly risks are being taken.

Many biological problems remain to be solved. Diseases of fish in artificial breeding ponds have not been eliminated; on the contrary, furunculosis is increasing at salmon-breeding stations. Furunculosis is a contagious disease to which salmonids are most susceptible. Infection spreads quickly where the fish population is dense, and all the fish at a breeding station may die. Although this disease seems usually to have little effect on populations of wild fish, and is not so virulent in the cold water of northern latitudes, experience in Germany and Switzerland has shown that it causes large losses among salmonid fish also in free waters. Populations of such fish living in rivers in Switzerland have been wiped out completely. At present this disease is kept more or less under con-

trol in the breeding ponds by treating the fish with sulfa drugs, and
it is claimed in California that furunculosis is under complete
control.

In the seas, too, man has gravely misused the living natural
resources—the great marine mammals above all. Several species
of whales are on the verge of extinction. The blue whale, the largest
mammal ever known, is near extermination as a consequence of
ruthless hunting, which some states long have refused to prohibit.
The same is true of other whalebone whales. It would be a pity if
these unique giants of the animal world were exterminated.

Excess fishing has in certain areas reduced the stock of fish in
the sea and is also taking too heavy a toll of adult fish, so that
reproduction of local populations is jeopardized.

But damage in the sea is not caused only by ruthless hunting
or fishing. Frequently, oil pollution from ships at sea causes death
to innumerable sea birds. It is also believed that the drifting fields
of oil affect mammals, fishes, and other marine organisms. And
contamination of the floor of the sea by oil has seriously injured
various bottom animals. Other kinds of marine pollution are also
a threat to the life organisms of the sea.

Introduction of Exotic Species

The introduction of a foreign species of animal often injures
the local environment. Economically, such an introduction may at
first be profitable and seem successful, but in most cases as time
goes by one disadvantage after another begins to appear. Not infrequently the result is a catastrophe, an ecological collapse. There
are, of course, examples of seemingly successful introductions
where the economic return seems to have been very large locally,
but we do not always know what these regions would have produced if the productivity of the native, original habitats had been
fully exploited. And exotic species may easily spread to other regions where they may prove harmful. To prevent this, continual
control measures must be undertaken. The most famous example
of a disastrous foreign introduction is that of the wild rabbit into
Australia. Its history is this: Introduced in 1859; within three years
the animal was regarded as a national calamity; for a hundred years
various measures to get rid of it, including the introduction of
other animals, were tried, but to little effect; in 1950 a virus disease, myxomatosis, was introduced and killed off a large part of

the rabbit population, but six or seven years later the rabbits began to become more and more resistant; today the percentage of survivors is getting greater after each outbreak of the disease. It is impossible to say how much damage, ecological and economical, the rabbit has caused in Australia. On grassland the rabbit has about the same ecological effect as sheep, and grazing pressure is thus very high.

Australia is one of the regions of the world that has suffered most by the introduction of exotic species. Others include such islands or archipelagoes as New Zealand, Hawaii, and those in the Caribbean Sea.

Pesticides

The use of poisonous chemicals in nature is now so widespread that it is the most urgent and serious problem in the conservation of nature in many countries and one of the most important problems facing man today. Birds and aquatic mammals especially have suffered severely, and what has happened to them physiologically and genetically may be taken as indications of what can happen to man. There is so much convincing evidence in various countries of the gradual but fatal effects of pesticides on the bird fauna, that it would be irresponsible to remain passive. Many birds of prey and owls, as well as marine birds, are the final link in a food chain—just like man—and therefore rapidly become victims of pesticides.

Spraying woods with DDT or other biocides from the air may cause serious changes in environments. Such spraying has, for example, already had disastrous effects on the stocks of fish in rivers and lakes. If such spraying is continued it will threaten fish populations, another of man's most important natural resources.

Hitherto only environments on and above the surface of the earth were impoverished; now pesticides enable man to invade the water and the subsoil, where pesticides are stored and accumulated. The poorness of the number of animal species is becoming more pronounced, and this is a main reason why the natural biological interaction between various species has ceased. As a consequence, species that are harmful from our point of view proliferate, and man attempts to counteract them with poison. In the long run this will create "biological vacuums," which will favour the species we wish to eliminate, for unfortunately they will become more resistant to poisons and have a greater ability to reproduce than the species that normally control them. It is tragic that many agricultural experts do not notice or do not understand the relation between the increase in parasites on crops and the decrease in the variety of fauna.

Explosion of Human Population

Man is the only creature on earth that deliberately overexploits the environment on which he is dependent. This unique phenomenon may be related to the fact that he has, so to say, postponed the negative effects by solving one biological problem after another with his technical inventiveness and his advances in medicine. In this way he has modified for the time being a natural mortality rate formerly regulated by his environment.

Among plants and animals there is, in the course of evolution, a tendency to strive toward maximum productivity in relation to the environment on which they depend. It would therefore be advantageous for animal species, including man, if they were able to keep their numbers at an optimum level. It follows that mechanisms regulating the population improve the prospects of survival of the respective species. During the past decade, the theory of automatic environmental control of the population level in various species has been accepted by an ever-growing number of ecologists and students of population dynamics. Although there is strong evidence to support this view, the problem is very complex.

The physiological machinery of an individual animal works throughout its life in a fascinating and purposeful way to adapt its functions to ceaseless changes in its physical surroundings. The whole population of a species works in the same way. To achieve a favourable balance between the population of a species and the resources of the environment, a control system has evolved. Here man's behaviour and attitudes enter the picture in an irrational way.

As far as the world's resources of food are concerned, we know that they are at present insufficient to supply all individuals. This insufficiency is due largely to the mismanagement of the natural resources of the earth coupled with overpopulation. Every day, every hour, the situation is changing for the worse as the number of human beings increases. Even though man is thus sawing off the branch he is sitting on, he will not suddenly die out as a species, for his distribution over the earth and the number of his sources of nourishment are almost unique in the animal kingdom. For the same reason, the process moves slowly, but it has already gone quite a long way. And the human population explosion is bringing us ever deeper into a crisis whose consequences may be fatal to many.

.Ample data on primitive human populations show the same pattern of automatic factors controlling population crisis found in animals. But modern man has moved so far away from this relationship that he now seems quite independent of the natural laws of the animal world. However, as a species we may be much nearer the deadline when nature strikes back than we imagine. The biological dynamics of population cannot be permanently checked by man.

The explosion in human population is primarily responsible for the great destruction of nature now going on. Mismanagement in its turn leads to more hungry people and to a reduction in the wild fauna. This means that we are losing one plant and animal species after another. What will coming generations think of this tragic shortsightedness? It is highly probable that the plant and animal treasures of nature will be appreciated in quite another, less materialistic way than at present. We can already see evidence of this in the form of a growing interest in nature. Very little of nature in its pristine state remains on earth, but what is left may become man's salvation, teaching us how we can replace what man has destroyed.

We now turn our attention to animals already extinct or threatened with extinction in various parts of the world. Since these animals are entirely dependent for their existence on their environments, which are being tampered with unceasingly by man, the struggle is one in which man is the aggressor and the animals are in retreat. We must not forget that through the evolution of his brain man, alone of all animals, has power over the world and all of life—an enormous responsibility.

CHAPTER TWO

Africa

No other continent has such a wealth of wild animals as Africa. More species of terrestrial vertebrates live there than anywhere else on earth, and the density of large mammals on some of Africa's savannas is unparalleled. The reason for this is probably that Africa's fauna is of a very great age; it has had countless eons in which to become adapted to various types of habitats. Repeated changes of climate, continuously altering the landscape, have caused dislocations in the distribution of plants and animals. These dislocations in turn have favoured speciation and the evolution of species in special directions. To this must be added an evolutionary phenomenon typical of all the African fauna—by competition the animals have become fitted to utilize all the possibilities offered by the rich environment. This has enabled numerous species to live side by side in the same habitats and in harmony with the vegetation by utilizing different niches.

Now this splendid and remarkable fauna is disappearing, partly as a result of the influence of man. The latter with his livestock, fire, and cultivation has in a shorter time had a more profound effect on Africa's vegetation and fauna than long-term climatic changes during thousands of years. The animals most threatened are the large mammals, which ever since the arrival of white men in Africa have been killed in incredible numbers or heavily reduced in numbers owing to habitat destruction. It is easy to understand why the average person outside Africa feels no uneasiness about the animal life of Africa, for he has long been exposed to excellent documentary films showing the rich wildlife on the open shimmering savannas. These along with many popular movie and television stories have given the impression that all is well with the nature and animal life of Africa.

As long as there were few human beings on the African scene, their behaviour had little effect on the forests or the savannas. All this has changed radically. The living space of animals is shrinking steadily, and they are retreating to the few remaining types of country suitable to them. The competition between them is much keener. Some animals adapt themselves to the cultivated landscape; the rest perish or go elsewhere. There are no other alternatives.

Africa is estimated to have had a population of 120 million people at the beginning of this century; today there are about 345 million. In another thirty years the population will probably be twice as great. Even so, the population density of Africa is not very great compared with that of Europe or Asia, for Africa consists largely of hot deserts, in many places quite uninhabitable by man. While human beings are rapidly increasing in number, they with the help of their livestock are destroying the environment on which they ultimately depend. Domestic cattle are rapidly turning once flourishing and productive regions into deserts and semi-deserts. In tropical areas human activities during recent centuries have reached the verge of a catastrophe, particularly since many states can produce little that does not depend on the fertility of the soil. This means that the productivity of the soil must be restored over wide areas and it must be exploited rationally.

It is almost incredible that Europeans in Africa during about a century of colonialism have been blind to the ruthless destruction of nature by cattle. There are two main reasons for this destruction. In the first place, the exploitation of land has been based strictly on European principles, with tame cattle considered the most economic producers of meat—a view that coincided with traditional African livestock breeding. In the second place it was assumed that the destruction of the soil of Africa was due only to climatic conditions. It was not realized that tropical Africa was a climax region, where animals and plants lived in a kind of balanced interrelationship, an ecosystem resulting from millions of years of uninterrupted evolution. If one or several of the elements of this highly specialized and productive biotic community were disturbed, the whole system would collapse. It is true that Africa is just now passing through a protracted dry period, but the spread of the deserts is due primarily to the mismanagement of the land by man during the past five or six hundred years—in Sahara during as many as three thousand years.

This is clearly demonstrated in national parks and nature reserves, where the almost limitless productivity of plants and animals contrasts with the barrenness of nearby areas ruined by livestock. The contrast is made sharper by the fact that the nature reserves were often established in productively poorer areas.

Even though sun and heat are always regarded as characteristic of the African climate, it is mainly humidity and precipitation which determine the vegetation and thereby the character of a landscape. The amount of rainfall in various parts of Africa is often very impressive, but everything depends on how the rain falls and whether water is stored in the earth. Heavy, concentrated rain, so common in the tropics, often results in a large proportion of the rainfall running off the surface. High temperatures, low humidity, dry winds, and hot sunshine cause great evaporation. Since vegetation plays a decisive role in the distribution of rainwater and thereby in humidity, the consequences of forest clearance are nearly always catastrophic, for desiccation occurs not only in the area cleared but also at lower levels. Even the water table is affected. It is primarily by such destruction of land that man, with misguided zeal and on an enormous scale, has restructured the African scene. Traces of this can be be found all over the continent, and the destruction is going on at an ever increasing rate.

ANIMAL FAMILIES PECULIAR TO AFRICA

In terms of animal distribution, Africa consists of two faunal regions: the Ethiopian, which covers most of the continent, and the Palearctic (chiefly Eurasian), which includes the northern part. Madagascar is often regarded as a separate subregion, but we shall treat it as part of Africa.

Africa is famous for big mammals of familiar species, but there are also many less conspicuous species belonging to unique forms. Several groups are found only in Africa or Madagascar: for example, tenrecs (*Tenrecidae*), otter shrews (*Potamogalidae*), golden moles (*Chrysochloridae*), elephant shrews (*Macroscelididae*), typical and woolly lemurs (*Lemuridae, Indridae*), the aye-aye (one species), anomalurids (squirrel-like rodents belonging to the *Anomaluridae*), the springhaas (harelike rodents, *Pedetidae,* two species), the aardvark (*Orycteropus,* probably only one species), hippopotamuses (two species), and giraffids (two species).

The birds are very cosmopolitan in their family relationships; that is, the majority of families also occur on other continents. In fact, there are only five or six families that are exclusively African: ostriches (one species), hammerheads (one species), secretary birds (one species), touracos, and mousebirds. Perhaps helmet shrikes should also be included in this category.

Exclusively African reptiles are the *Feyliniidae* (limbless skinks) and *Cordylidae* (spring-tailed lizards and plated lizards). In the amphibians only one family, the *Phrynomeridae,* does not occur outside of Africa.

On the African continent freshwater fishes have evolved along many diverse lines, resulting in a great richness of species and several families that are peculiar to Africa. This is the case with bichirs (*Polypteridae*), lungfishes (*Protopteridae*), *Cromeriidae* (one species), *Kneriidae, Phractolaemidae* (one species), elephant-snout fishes (*Mormyridae*), *Gymnarchidae* (one species), *Citharinidae, Mochocidae, Amphiliidae,* and electric catfishes (*Malapteruridae,* one species).

It is in the tropical areas that we find the largest number of species and most of the spectacular animals which have made Africa famous. The southern part of the continent is not so rich, but there the fauna includes a wealth of vertebrate species. The northern part of Africa with its extensive deserts is poor in vertebrates compared with the number in the south.

As already mentioned, Africa south of the Sahara is undergoing a drastic change. The original ecosystems are being increasingly undermined by man, and this change does not work in favour of animals, including man. This new feature of an old continent is a consequence of the fact that tropical Africa was one of the last areas to be colonized and influenced by Europeans.

THE COASTS AND ISLANDS

Mediterranean and Atlantic Coasts

The vegetation of the northern and southern coasts of Africa differs from that of the interior. The northern coast is in principle much like the Mediterranean shores of southern Europe except that it has suffered even more from man's destructive activities. Whenever Phoenicians, Romans, Frenchmen, or Italians settled along the coast of North Africa, they improved the environment, stabilized it, and allowed it to flourish, but these efforts were cancelled by the anarchic impact of invading nomads and conquering Arabs. The latter brought on desertlike conditions, clearly demonstrating the ruinous ecological effect of nomadic pastoralism.

Most of North Africa is today semidesert, but the topographic diversity gives the Mediterranean coastal strip a variety of habitats. There are stretches of maquis vegetation, small woods, and on the slopes of the Atlas Mountains, some temperate forests. The deteriorating valley of the northern Nile still has green areas. There are still many forms of life in the semidesert, but seen in the perspective of thousands of years, the impoverishment of the fauna is striking. This is also true of the marine animals of northern Africa.

Only a century ago the Mediterranean monk seal (*Monachus monachus*) was distributed along the African coasts of the Mediterranean and southward along the Atlantic as far as Senegal. It also occurred along the European coasts and islands of the Mediterranean as well as islands in the Black Sea. Persecution and disturbances by man led to a severe decline. Pollution may also be involved, at least in the Mediterranean, where waters have been rapidly deteriorating for several decades. A 1962 report to the IUCN estimates the entire population of the Mediterranean monk seal as less than five hundred animals. Apparently the greatest numbers are present along the western coast of Africa down to Cape Blanc. This seal is protected in France, Italy, Yugoslavia, Greece, Bulgaria, and Rio de Oro in Africa, but illegal shooting goes on. The species is also continuously disturbed in the caves where it breeds.

At present the Barbary stag (*Cervus elaphus barbarus*) is confined to a small area of the Mediterranean vegetation belt of eastern Algeria and western Tunisia. This race is of zoogeographic interest, because it is of the European red deer and the only deer in Africa. Up to recently, geologically speaking, this deer, as indicated by fossil remains from the middle Pleistocene epoch, was distributed southward to the central Sahara. Apparently the range of the Barbary stag was similar to that of the Quaternary forests which once covered large areas of this part of Africa. In Roman times the Barbary stag was still common all over Tunisia, northern Algeria, and parts of Morocco.

The decline of the Barbary stag resulted from the destruction of forests and extensive hunting. Recently it suffered grievously during the Algerian war, when poaching and slaughter were uncontrolled. Jacques Blondel has reported that the electric fences erected on the Algerian-Tunisian border killed many of these deer. It is also hunted with silent dogs, which quickly run it to earth, particularly when the victim is a pregnant female. In 1964 the population in the Tunisian part of the Barbary stag's range was estimated at about 150 animals. Although the animal is here protected by law the control is inefficient. A new reserve was established in 1966.

The Barbary serval (*Felis serval constantina*) had formerly a wide range in northern Africa but is at present limited to forests in Algeria where it is very rare.

A rapidly decreasing bird is the famous waldrapp (or hermit ibis, *Geronticus eremita*), that today breeds in colonies in Morocco and Algeria, as well as at one site in Turkey. Possibly it also exists in Syria. Two hundred years ago this bird occurred in Central Europe, and the ancient Egyptians were sufficiently familiar with it to use it as a hieroglyph, so it must have been common in Egypt some thousands of years ago. The colony in Turkey has decreased from 530 pairs in 1953 to forty-five pairs in 1967. The total population is believed to be much less than a thousand pairs.

The long-toed pigeon (*Columba trocaz*) is known from Madeira and the Canary Islands (Tenerife). The nominate race (*C. t. trocaz*) inhabits Madeira, where it is extremely rare, while *C. t. bollii* was last observed in Gomera in the Canary Islands in 1949 and on Tenerife in 1956. It is doubtful whether the latter race still exists. The destruction of laurel forests and excessive shooting seem to be the reasons for the decline.

On the Canary Islands the Eastern Canary Islands black oystercatcher (*Haematopus moquini meadewaldowi*) became exterminated in 1914.

The islet of Raza in the Cape Verde Islands off the West African coast is the home of a unique bird, the Raza Island lark (*Alauda razae*). Even a slight habitat change may be fatal to such a small and specialized population.

Islands in the Gulf of Guinea

Located off Camcroon and within the equatorial-rain-forest belt of Africa is the island of Fernando Po. Found only on Fernando Po are the Fernando Po speirops (*Speirops brunnea*), a white-eyed warblerlike bird, and Fea's chameleon (*Chamaeleo feae*), both of which live in a mountainous area. The bird is rare and known only from five specimens collected between 1903 and 1955. The chameleon is also rare and decreasing.

Southwest of Fernando Po lie two other isolated islands, Príncipe and São Tomé. On the former the local race of the olive ibis (*Lampribis olivacea rotschildi*) was exterminated in 1901, while on São Tomé a full species, a grosbeak weaver (*Neospiza concolor*), has not been observed since 1888. Three expeditions have searched in vain for the latter bird, which is now almost certainly·extinct owing to habitat destruction.

South Africa's Coastal Belt

The coastal zone of the southernmost part of Africa, from immediately north of Cape Town on the Atlantic side to Port Elizabeth on the Indian Ocean, is unique in many ways and above all in its flora. The South African spring changes character with the latitude, but nowhere else can one see such a glorious display of flowers of various hues as on the slopes of the Cape peninsula between the blue stretches of the Atlantic and the Indian oceans. The amazing wealth of species, including plants found nowhere else on earth, and species related to some found in Australia and South America, is characteristic. Around the Cape, distinct plant associations dominated by one or a few species have given place to an incredibly complex mosaic of plants. Generally speaking, it is low vegetation of the maquis type, strongly reminiscent of that seen on mountain slopes around the Mediterranean. Unfortunately, large areas are now dominated by imported trees and plants, which are spreading at the expense of native species and gradually destroying the unique qualities of this corner of Africa.

Among vertebrates, only the birds can compare in singularity with the flora of the Cape. Several species of birds are found only in the South African maquis landscape; for example, the sugarbird (*Promerops cafer*), which is adapted to *Protea* shrubs. Similarly, the sunbird (*Anthobaphes violacea*) is here adapted to the blossoms of *Protea* and *Erica*. Other species similarly isolated in their distribution are a warbler, *Bradypterus victorini,* and the Cape bulbul (*Pycnonotus capensis*).

As a result of agricultural development and urbanization, the fauna of the coastal belt of South Africa has lost many of its habitats. Moreover severe "predator control" and heavy hunting pressure have reduced drastically the number of animals, especially almost all the large mammals. This is partly a result of the early European settlement, established in 1652, which saw the beginning of a fearful abuse of wildlife.

Mammals restricted to the coastal belt of the present Cape Province were soon endangered. The very beautiful bontebok (*Damaliscus dorcas*), an antelope that occurred around Cape Agulhas, was hunted intensively and driven to poor grazing lands. It became extinct in a wild state and almost disappeared entirely from the African scene, only a few surviving on the open plains between Bredasdorp and Swellendam. In 1930 the numbers were down to about twenty. In 1931 the National Bontebok Park, with seventeen specimens, was established here but in 1960 the animals and the reserve were moved to an area near Swellendam. When I visited the national park in 1961, it had seventy-two bontebok and they seemed to be thriving. In 1965 they had increased to 150. Including herds on private lands, the whole bontebok population was estimated in 1962 at about six hundred animals and in 1971 at eight hundred. Its near relative, the blesbok (*D. d. phillipsi*), which occurred north and east of the bontebok, was also hunted indiscriminately and fenced off from good grazing areas, so it, too, was near extermination; but conservation measures have altered this trend, and this race is now no longer in danger.

The fate of the bluebuck (*Hippotragus leucophaeus*), which had a very limited range in the Cape Province, was more tragic. It first became known during the period 1705–13 but by 1774 was already rare. The last bluebucks were shot in 1800. Only four stuffed specimens are preserved in European museums.

Among the coastal birds of South Africa, two species, the sugarbird and the white-winged seedeater (*Poliospiza leucoptera*), are highly specialized feeders and therefore particularly vulnerable if their limited habitat is threatened. Both species are adapted to *Protea* bushvelds, which are found only on mountain slopes near Cape Town. This type of biological community is being rapidly destroycd by fires, farming, and building. The sugarbird, which belongs to the only avian family peculiar to South Africa, is a beautiful bird with interesting habits, and an integral part of an extraordinary habitat.

The geometric tortoise (*Testudo geometrica*) is one of Africa's rarest reptiles. It was thought that the species became extinct about 1910, but in 1946–47 and 1958 specimens were obtained. It occurs in a small area to the north and east of Cape Town, where it will be protected in a special reserve.

The East African Coast

The East African coast from Mozambique and Madagascar northward to the Red Sea is the habitat of a curious aquatic mammal, the dugong (*Dugong dugon*). It is often thought to be the creature that gave rise to legends about mermaids. The dugong inhabits shallow coastal waters in tropical and subtropical seas of the Old World. It has a wide range: along the coasts of the Indian Ocean and the western Pacific from East Africa in the west to the Solomon Islands and New Caledonia in the east. Because of its aquatic life it is not easy to estimate the number of dugongs. However, the general impression is that the species is rapidly decreasing almost everywhere. There are several reasons for this decline. The dugong is hunted for its edible flesh, hide, and oil. In some areas it also has a reputation as an aphrodisiac. It is accused of preying on fish but it is in reality a marine-grass eater. Its habitats have been altered; in Australia, for example, the grass beds it frequents have been silted up or are disturbed by boat traffic. The dugong, moreover, breeds very slowly, having a gestation period of about a year.

In Kenya fishermen catch the dugong in nets. In Ceylon no less than 371 animals were taken in 1957–59. Few now remain around Ceylon and Malaysia, but in Australia its numbers are on the increase after a long period of scarcity. There are laws protecting the dugong in Mozambique, Tanzania, Kenya, Australia, and other places, but in most places except Australia they are difficult to enforce.

On the island of Zanzibar lives an interesting local race of the red colobus monkey (*Colobus badius kirkii*), whose population is thought to number only about two hundred. Since no high forest is found any longer on Zanzibar, the red colobus frequents the low and thin coast bush, but it also occurs in the Jozani Forest Reserve. Apparently it was already rare in 1868, when it was investigated by its discoverer, Sir John Kirk. It is believed that capture of the red colobus for sale to tourists and the replacement of natural forest by plantations have contributed to the animal's decline. It is protected by law, but the control does not seem effective.

The status of another rare animal on Zanzibar, a local subspecies of the suni (*Nesotragus moschatus moschatus*), is most uncertain and very little known. This tiny antelope, whose shoulder height is about a foot, is very vulnerable to illegal hunting. The Zanzibar leopard (*Panthera pardus adersi*), an island race of this big cat, is gradually disappearing because of human persecution. In 1971 leopards were still regularly trapped on Zanzibar.

THE DESERTS

Today deserts, subdeserts, and arid scrubs cover about 43 percent of Africa. In the north there is the immense Sahara Desert, in the south the Namib and Kalahari deserts, as well as the Karoo subdesert steppes, and in the east the Nubian, Danakil, and Somali deserts. The man-made subdeserts in Kenya, Tanzania, Botswana, Lesotho, and elsewhere should also be mentioned.

In dealing with endangered animals of extremely dry areas, we shall find that many species were originally not at all true desert animals; they have simply been driven out into the deserts by man, or man has changed their verdant areas into near-desert.

It is often theorized that the advancing deserts of Africa reflect a continuance of the shift from the last pluvial period into a dry period. It is true that the Sahara extends slowly southward year after year, the Karoo subdesert scrubs move eastward, and in Botswana and East Africa the metamorphosis of savanna into arid lands is frighteningly rapid. Moreover, lakes and swamps are drying up, rivers in which water ran throughout the year are often dry, and so on. Presumably climate contributes to these changes, but it is likely that human activity is the factor ultimately responsible for them. Destruction of natural vegetation by burning, overgrazing, overcultivation, and overdevelopment, as well as the cutting down of forest, has caused a loss of water resources. The accelerated runoff of water has catastrophic results; for this man alone is responsible.

Despite the unfavourable conditions in the desert, it is astonishing how many plants and animals are found there. Plants become adapted to arid conditions in a variety of ways. Some perennials live through the dry seasons in a kind of "coma," while others survive as seeds for months or years, then germinate and grow as soon as rain begins to fall. A third group keeps alive underground during dry periods as bulbs or rhizomes. Some species can accumulate water and thus grow even in the middle of a dry period.

Animals have solved the problem of water supply in a desert climate in various ways. Many species living in deserts show a great array of physiological mechanisms enabling them to withstand shortage or absence of water in areas of high temperatures. Behavioural adaptations also help these animals to make optimum use of the available moisture. Most animals found in Africa's deserts are species that are able to survive without drinking water for long periods. Many desert animals need astonishingly little water, and some species—small rodents, for example—have developed an ability to extract water from dry food. Desert reptiles save water by not emitting any fluids. Some mammals and reptiles remain dormant all day and become active during the cool hours of the night. And no fewer than 72 percent of desert mammals live underground.

Although plant and animal life is activated to a surprising degree during the short rainy periods, the problem of water supply is still a very serious one for most animals, for the rainfall seldom accumulates on the surface of the earth. Certain flying insects and birds make long migrations in order to drink. Some desert species, even larger mammals, do not need to drink at all, but most of them drink surface water when available. Many desert ungulates obtain moisture from green grass, browse roots, and bulbs. This feature emphasizes how productive these species are as a protein resource in areas with harsh environmental conditions. Examples of large desert mammals that can live for long periods without water are the dromedary and the addax antelope. The latter is probably capable of existing without drinking water at all. This is also the case for smaller antelopes, for example, the dorcas gazelle. The eland, the oryx, and Grant's gazelle can also apparently survive without drinking.

Besides adapting themselves to lack of water, desert animals have evolved a remarkable ability to tolerate high temperatures and hot sunshine. In addition, several reptiles can bury themselves in the sand at an incredible rate, thus escaping from their enemies as well as reaching a cooler place.

The Sahara and the Atlas Mountains

North Africa is dominated by the Sahara, the largest desert in the world. Along the Mediterranean there is a narrow strip of littoral vegetation, although the deserts have broken through at many places. The desert extends from the Atlantic to the Red Sea, but it is not everywhere flat, sandy, and lifeless. Some parts of it do get a little rain, which occasionally or periodically encourages plants to grow. There are mountains in the heart of the desert, such as those at Tibesti that climb to a height of 11,000 feet, or extend in a chain, as do the cedar-clad and snow-capped Atlas Mountains in the northwestern corner. (Parts of these mountains are covered with forests and thickets, and these of course have their own kind of vegetation and wildlife.) In the east the mighty Nile creates a strip of vegetation amid the sand. But as a whole the Sahara is barren country, a sea of sand with a few oases.

It was not always thus. During the last Ice Age in northern Europe and Asia, the climate was damper in the Sahara, and it was not until geologically recent times that the desert became dominant. There is also evidence that in a not-too-distant past— six thousand to two thousand years ago—parts of the Sahara consisted of steppes with perennial grasses supporting an abundance of mammals of a kind found in the African tropics to the south. The drying up of the Sahara at the end of the Pleistocene certainly contributed to the disappearance of many forms of wildlife. But man, too, is involved. We know from cave paintings in the western Sahara that herds of domestic stock once lived here along with large grazing and browsing animals. The abuse of the soil and vegetation by domestic livestock through millenniums has ruined North Africa and changed to deserts even areas with a moderate rainfall.

In an earlier epoch, vegetation and animal life in the Sahara were in many ways similar to the forms of life now typical of the savannas and rivers of tropical Africa. It is very likely, however, that there was for long periods a desertlike belt, perhaps somewhere in the middle of the present Sahara, but apparently it was not large enough to prevent the dispersal of tropical animals from the savannas south of the Sahara. Between 4500 and 3500 B.C., hippopotamuses, elephants, giraffes, and rhinoceroses were common on the central parts of the Sahara, showing that there was ample grass, shrub, and tree vegetation to satisfy their enormous needs. Hippopotamuses wallowed in the rivers and crocodiles lay along the banks, and buffaloes and several species of antelope lived on the wide expanses of grass. At least part of the Sahara was thus grassy tree savanna in relatively recent times. Around 2000 B.C. the hippopotamuses, elephants, and rhinoceroses began to disappear from the central parts of the Sahara, but as late as 1200 B.C. giraffes were still nibbling the leaves in the crowns of trees. In 1815 there were hippopotamuses in Egypt, and in 1750 both they and the elephant were still found around the lower Senegal River.

In the interior of the Sahara scientists have found fossilized profiles of humus-rich soil with pollen, calculated to be five to six thousand years old, from a cedar forest. As recently as two thousand years ago, there were forests deep in the Sahara where today there is nothing but sand, indicating that the vegetation along the coasts of North Africa once extended into what is now desert. In Morocco alone, forests covering more than one-third of the country have disappeared since Roman times.

What was the cause of the widespread desiccation of such a vast area? No conclusive answer can be given, but there is good reason to believe that man and his livestock were an accelerating factor in the process. It is a remarkable fact that whenever civilization in North Africa has flourished, the soil has begun to bear plants—before and during the Roman period, and in more recent times under French and Italian control—but during the long periods when the area was dominated by nomadic tribes, the soil deteriorated. The climate is, of course, a contributing factor, but it seems to be man, cows, and goats who began the erosion avalanche.

Unfortunately, not all the larger mammals of North Africa could take refuge in the tropics. Many could not escape or were not adapted to survive outside the subtropical region. Persecution by man left them in isolated pockets, chiefly in mountainous zones. There they were soon reduced in numbers and some were exterminated. Hunting in general was responsible for this decline, but it was only after the use of firearms spread to most tribes that several species were completely wiped out.

The Algerian wild ass (*Equus asinus atlanticus*) is one of the animals that vanished before the discovery of guns. It became extinct in Algeria some time after A.D. 300. This wild ass was so well-known in Algeria during Roman times that a mosaic in a Roman villa shows a hunting scene in which a mounted Numidian is throwing a lasso at the animal. It is also known from rock paintings in Algeria. The domesticated donkey probably derives from this extinct race, since all true asses are of purely African origin. Only two other races of this species remain in a wild state, the Nubian and Somali wild asses, and both are very rare.

The next large mammal to disappear was apparently the Atlas bear (*Ursus crowtheri*), described as a species from a specimen killed before 1841 at the foot of the Tetuan Mountains. Fossil records of bears from northwestern Africa are known, and there are many accounts of the occurrence of bears from Roman times until the latter half of the nineteenth century. This was the last of the bears in Africa.

The bubal hartebeest (*Alcelaphus buselaphus buselaphus*) was once a common antelope across northern Africa from Morocco to Egypt. In 1850 large herds were still encountered in mountainous areas of central Sahara, and some were reported as late as 1867 from the mountains in the Tuareg country. There have been no reports of this antelope during the last forty years, and it is now considered extinct.

The same fate seems to have befallen the rufous gazelle (*Gazella rufina*), a species never seen outside the Algerian-Moroccan border region of the Atlas Mountains. Discovered in 1877, not very much has become known about it, except that it probably lived in mountainous forests. In 1925 the species was reported to be well-known to furriers in Oran. There have been no substantiated reports of it since then.

The disappearance or decimation of several species of antelopes was followed by a decline in their predators. Of course, habitat changes and persecution by man was also involved in this process. The Barbary lion (*Panthera leo leo*) was once quite common in North Africa, including the Mediterranean littoral. Lions for the Roman arenas were constantly shipped to Rome, where according to Pliny hundreds at a time were exhibited. From Libya to Morocco, lions still existed about two hundred years ago and were even fairly numerous in Tunisia. But the last Tunisian lion was killed in 1891. The history of the lion in Algeria is similar, with the last one also killed about 1891. In Morocco the Barbary lion survived to at least 1922 in the Middle Atlas, but now the nominate race of the lion is gone forever.

The Barbary hyena (*Hyaena hyaena barbara*) is a race of the striped hyena, which is chiefly a tropical species. In northwestern Africa the local subspecies is restricted to mountainous regions of Morocco, where the population is estimated to be less than four hundred. This hyena is persecuted for many reasons, all based on superstition and misunderstandings. The Barbary hyena is accused of preying on sheep and goats. It is also killed because it is credited with magical qualities: the hairs are used as a talisman, and the brain is said to have a beneficial power. The Barbary hyena has been totally protected in Morocco since 1955, but the law does not seem to be effective.

This is also true of the Barbary leopard (*Panthera pardus panthera*), the northwesternmost race of a species that is spread over vast areas of Africa and Asia. In this corner of Africa the leopard is restricted to certain Atlas Mountain areas of Morocco and Algeria and perhaps Tunisia. The decrease of the Barbary leopard has been very rapid during the last decade, primarily because its skins have a great commercial as well as trophy value. It has been protected since 1948, but those who kill the animal claim that they were acting in self-defense or to protect livestock. Leopards in North Africa seem to prey almost exclusively on Barbary monkeys and wild boars. The population of the Barbary leopard in Morocco, where most of them live, is believed to be about one hundred animals.

Some antelopes of the genera *Oryx* and *Addax* are found in arid regions of Africa and western Asia. They are remarkably adapted to harsh conditions and therefore have a great value as a protein resource. The scimitar-horned oryx (*Oryx tao*) is one of these antelopes. During the Middle Ages this nomadic oryx was the most characteristic animal of southern Morocco and probably the most numerous larger mammal of the semideserts just south of the Sahara. It was distributed from Mauritania in the west to the Red Sea in the east. At present it occurs only in Mali, Niger, Chad (about five thousand animals), and Sudan. In 1958 the entire population was estimated at about ten thousand. Together with the addax it is today considered the most endangered of the African antelopes. Arab horsemen armed with modern guns hunt them constantly. Oil prospectors and soldiers also persecute the animals, using vehicles and even automatic weapons. Some reserves have been established, but unfortunately they do not provide a safe refuge for nomadic antelopes.

Threatened even more is another desert antelope, the addax (*Addax nasomaculatus*). Like the scimitar-horned oryx, its range about a hundred years ago covered a wide area of North Africa— almost the whole of the Sahara—but today it is found only in Rio de Oro, Mauritania, northern Mali, and Chad. There are also a few herds in Algeria, southern Libya, and northern Sudan. It is very rare everywhere except for an uninhabited and almost waterless area in Mauritania and Mali in the western Sahara. According to Professor Théodore Monod, this antelope was still numerous in this region in 1963, but it was being constantly hunted by the nomads. In 1958 the estimated number of the addax in about two-thirds of its distribution range, the western Sahara, was about five thousand. In 1966 the same number was maintained. In Chad there were about four thousand addax in 1964, but in 1970 the species had decreased to about fifteen hundred.

It is tragic that the destruction of the addax is on the increase. Constant overhunting from motor vehicles constitutes a great danger to the future of the addax. Again, man is wiping out one of his best food resources. The addax is one example of how miraculously a large animal can survive in great numbers and build up a considerable weight, converting almost nonexisting desert vegetation into meat. It is an almost incredible sight to see a herd of these relatively large antelopes on an expanse of sand where not a stem of grass or drop of water can be seen within hundreds of miles and where there is not the slightest shade from the burning sun.

The status of several gazelles in northern Africa is precarious or uncertain. Two races of the dorcas gazelle occur between Morocco and Spanish Morocco. They are the Algerian dorcas (*Gazella dorcas neglecta*) and the Moroccan dorcas (*G. d. massaesyla*). Both are considered to be rare. François Edmond-Blanc (in 1962) found small herds of seven or eight of the Moroccan dorcas in the "total desert" of Borkou, but farther south where the pastures were better, for instance, at Bagaba, he observed "several hundred." The Atlas gazelle (*G. cuvieri*) is also very rare. It was formerly abundant throughout the Atlas Mountains where it is now restricted to forests and high plateaus (it is not a desert species). This species has been mercilessly pursued by the local tribesmen, who now hunt with modern rifles and often from automobiles. In 1932 it was already said to be one of the rarest of all gazelles. Today only some small herds are left in various parts of the Atlas Mountains, and it has probably been exterminated in Morocco. In 1961 about two to three hundred animals were estimated to exist in Algeria and rather fewer in Tunisia. No protective measures seem to have been taken. The slender-horned gazelle (*G. leptoceros leptoceros*) shows the same serious diminution, again due to slaughter by the Arabs. This species, once the most common of all the gazelles living in the Saharan deserts, no longer occurs in most areas of northern Sahara, and it is rare in the southern parts. Edmond-Blanc searched for it in vain during a 1962 expedition to the region of Bagada in Chad, which had been one of its last strongholds. The sand gazelle is particularly valuable because it can exist in deserts that can hardly support any other ungulates. Finally, the mhorr gazelle (*G. dama mhorr*), a very rare subspecies in southwestern Morocco and the northwestern Sahara, is believed to be close to extinction. In 1971 only twelve individuals existed. They are now under control but it seems very unlikely that this subspecies can be saved from extinction. It was very actively hunted because it produced the precious bezoars used in Oriental medicine. Its near relative and neighbor, the Rio de Oro gazelle (*G. d. lozanoi*) has dwindled to a precarious level. Probably only about fifty individuals were still in existence in 1968.

Only a few species or races of birds in the desert region of North Africa are in danger of extermination. One of them is the North African ostrich (*Struthio camelus spatzi*), which has disappeared from the areas it formerly occupied in North Africa except for Rio de Oro and Mauritania. This valuable bird has been destroyed by hunting.

The bearded vulture (*Gypaëtus barbatus barbatus*), one of the Old World's bird treasures, is restricted to northwestern Africa from Tunisia to Morocco. It is rare everywhere within its split distribution area in Africa, Asia, and Europe. Although it lives among rocks in North Africa, it is not confined, as it is elsewhere, to the highest and most remote mountains. In northwestern Africa it is attracted by villages and shows a preference for human settlements, much as do the Egyptian vulture (*Neophron percnopterus*) and the black kite (*Milvus migrans*), and it lives mostly on refuse. The bird's tendency to associate with man prevails only in areas where it is not hunted, which means that it occurs in few localities.

Two other local races of birds that have become rare in north-western Africa, the helmeted guinea-fowl (*Numida meleagris sabyi*) and the double-spurred francolin (*Francolinus bicalcaratus*), occur only in western Morocco. They have become scarce because both are game birds.

The desert environment strongly influences the fertility and migratory movements of birds that live in it permanently. Several species have only one clutch a year, and the breeding period is often shorter than that of birds in temperate and tropical regions. Of the birds distributed on both sides of the Mediterranean Sea, the species in Europe normally have two clutches, while those in arid parts of Algeria and Tunisia have only one clutch. In addition, the average number of eggs are fewer in North African populations than in European populations of the same species. During certain years, the red-legged partridge (*Alectoris rufa*) does not breed at all and no pair formation takes place. This variation is thought to be correlated with the vegetation, which in turn is regulated by the extremely variable rainfall. This reduced reproduction makes the North African game birds particularly vulnerable to hunting pressure.

The Sahara Desert constitutes a considerable barrier for many migratory birds. In spite of this, many of them cross the area in both northern and southern directions. Such aquatic migrants as terns, ducks, waders, and rails, as well as passerines living in marshy habitats, have very little opportunity to feed while crossing the world's largest desert. Consequently, these birds tend to congregate in good feeding areas north and south of the Sahara Desert, where they can easily be molested by hunters. A network of reserves protecting such feeding areas should be established.

Nubian and Somali Deserts

For at least five thousand years the Nubian wild ass (*Equus asinus africanus*), formerly found in Sudan and Eritrea between the Nile and the Red Sea, has been pursued by man for domestication. But it was not until modern guns came into general use that the decrease reached alarming proportions. Much killing took place because the wild ass was accused by the nomads of consuming the grass, leaving too little for their goats. Man has always seemed blind to the fact that the deterioration in grazing lands

is due to the goats themselves. Today only a few small herds of
the Nubian wild ass occur in northeastern Sudan, and in 1971
it was observed in Eritrea near the Sudanese border. It should be
added that the immediate cause of the critical decline of the Nubian wild ass may be a lowering in quality of the strain due to
interbreeding with domestic donkeys. Though all African wild
asses have been completely protected by law since 1933, once
again there seems to be little enforcement of the legislation.

Much the same fate has befallen the Somali wild ass (*E. a.
somalicus*). In 1905 its number was estimated at about ten
thousand in the Maritime Hills of eastern Somalia alone. By 1965
it had apparently disappeared from Somalia except for two small
herds, which together numbered about ten to twelve animals. However, in 1969 about 125 wild asses were reported from Somalia.
The only other remaining population is about four hundred
animals in the Danakil subdeserts and the Awash basin of Ethiopia, which were observed in 1970. The species' sharp decline is
due to excessive hunting along with the wars that have unsettled
this part of Africa since 1935, and to competition for food and
water from livestock increasing in numbers. As a preservation
measure, the establishment of a well-controlled nature reserve in
the Danakil region has been suggested. If livestock is excluded
such a reserve could save the Somali wild ass. The Ethiopian conservation authorities look favourably on this proposal but unfortunately have not followed it up by taking action. The flesh of the
Somali wild ass is considered a delicacy; wisely managed, it could
certainly be a profitable natural resource, converting a subdesert
vegetation to excellent meat and hides of good quality. Several
tribes value the meat but they overexploit the resource. Moreover,
tourists in vehicles chasing the asses in order to take pictures
exhaust the animals to death.

In this connection we should note that the last members of
Swayne's hartebeest (*Alcelaphus buselaphus swaynei*), a race of
the extinct bubal hartebeest (see page 51), still exist in the Al-
ledeghi Plains and the Awash valley of Ethiopia, where there
probably are not more than two to three hundred. About sixty
years ago many thousands roamed the same plains. There is a
small population also at Nachisar Plains in the Lake District of
the Rift Valley in Ethiopia, where seventy-eight animals were
counted in 1971. The continued survival of this antelope is very
uncertain. Human persecution is again the reason for its disap-

pearance. The tora hartebeest (*A. b. tora*) in Eritrea and Sudan has also been reduced almost to extinction.

Even at the time of its discovery in 1885, the beira (*Dorcatragus megalotis*), found only in the arid coastal areas of northern Somalia and French Somaliland and in eastern Ethiopia, was considered a rare species. Since then its range has been the scene of many military campaigns, and the beira has suffered severely from armed local tribes and foreign troops. As far as is known, only a few individuals remain in northern Somalia and in eastern Ethiopia, where some animals were seen in 1970. Pelzeln's gazelle (*Gazella pelzelnii*) is nowadays limited to plains in northern Somalia and eastern Ethiopia, where it has seriously declined in recent years.

The Southern Deserts

Curiously, the Kalahari Desert in South-West Africa, Botswana, and South Africa is the home of a rich variety of higher mammals, consisting of nine species of larger herbivores. In reality, however, most of Kalahari, even in its southern parts, is an arid savanna varying from sand dunes and open grasslands to bush and tree savannas. Rainfall is erratic and surface water is only temporarily available in pans for a short time after the rains. The vegetation over wide areas of Kalahari has been altered by harmful burning and overgrazing by domestic animals, and the wild-animal populations there have been drastically reduced by persecution, but not by the natural human inhabitants, the Bushmen, who, although making extensive use of the wild animals, particularly smaller species, do not have an impact on them. Despite the pressure from other humans, great herds of up to a thousand or fifteen hundred springbok (*Antidorcas marsupialis*) and the splendid gemsbok (*Oryx gazella*), a South African oryx, along with other species of antelopes such as the greater kudu (*Tragelaphus strepsiceros*), red hartebeest (*Alcephalus buselaphus*), and eland (*Taurotragus oryx*), may be seen in and around the Kalahari Gemsbok National Park, where they have been protected since 1931. This national park in the desert and adjacent semiarid areas provides excellent evidence that great herds of grazers can live on extremely meager pastures without destroying their source of food—a situation diametrically opposite to that in desert and other arid areas where goats and cattle have been introduced.

The Namib Desert, extending about a hundred miles along the
Atlantic coast of South-West Africa, is probably one of the world's
oldest deserts, and has remained more or less unchanged since the
pluvial periods. The extreme specialization of animals to suit such
a habitat has most likely gone on for countless ages. As a result,
there is strong evidence that they are more genuine desert-dwellers
than those animals found in other deserts. There is no threat from
humans to the highly specialized vertebrates living in the Namib
Desert. However, one species, the Namib golden mole (*Eremit-
alpa granti namibensis*), was long on the official list of endangered
animals entirely because specimens were not collected until 1963.
It is not surprising that a subterranean animal which moves about
on the dunes only by night should not often be observed in a
desert not inhabited by human beings.

THE SAVANNAS

To the south, the North African desert turns into subdesert,
grass, and shrub savannas, and finally more or less dense tree
savannas. Still farther south, forests appear; such growths reach
their optimum development in the Zaire basin. In fact, Africa
both north and south of the equator can show all types of nature
from extreme desert to extreme rain forest. Savannas cover about
40 percent of Africa, in both subtropical and tropical regions,
and they vary greatly from region to region. Africa's savannas,
steppes, arid plains, and subdeserts stretch in an arc across the
continent. Beginning in East Africa between the latitudes 20° and
10° N., they fill practically the whole of Africa south of 10° S.,
with the exception of the Cape region. Some of these plains have
become or are becoming deserts; others are still fertile grass or
tree savannas, which in places turn into open forests. Thus a wide
variety of environments is included in what we here call savannas.

During the pluvial periods of the Ice Age, great forests spread
over wide areas of Africa now covered by savannas, but evidently
there were sufficiently large open areas during the forest periods
to allow savanna species to survive in unparalleled variety. After
the last ice sheet had melted from the Northern Hemisphere, a
new dry period began in Africa, and about twenty thousand years
ago the savannas started increasing in area. Only a century or two
ago, the mighty savannas of Africa provided scenes we today find
difficult to visualize. Numerous species of large and small ante-

lopes, mixed with giraffes, buffaloes, rhinoceroses, and elephants, lived on the various kinds of savannas. These plains were regions of biological equilibrium, highly productive climax areas, created by Nature herself through countless ages.

In this highly specialized ecological system, each organism was a necessary element in the perpetuation of the region. Different animal species made efficient use of the whole array of available niches within the habitat. The various species of hoofed animals grazed and browsed together, choosing different kinds of bulbs, grass, twigs, leaves, and fruits as food. Selection had eliminated competition, and in this way the effect of grazing was evenly distributed. With exceptions for species such as the eland, the oryx, the impala, the gerenuk, Grant's gazelle, and Thomson's gazelle, which need little or no water, herds congregated on the savanna regions around lakes, rivers, springs, and small water holes, for not many savanna species can live for long periods without water.

During dry periods most of these hoofed animals moved to other regions which had recently had rain and where the grass was plentiful and green. And so it went, all the year round. The hoofed animals followed the rain, changing pastures regularly, and as a consequence the grazing never destroyed the vegetation, which after the next rainy period was as fresh and green as ever.

The African savanna could support huge numbers of large meat-producing animals, which in turn were kept under control by beasts of prey. Although the wild hoofed animals a century or two ago were far more numerous than the tame cattle on the plains today, they did not destroy the land even in the course of hundreds of thousands of years. But in two hundred years, man, along with his goats and cattle, has managed to transform large parts of the flourishing African savanna into a desert, showing only a shadow of its former splendour and wealth. Tame cattle have probably existed in tropical Africa for five to six hundred years, and in some coastal regions even longer, but it is only during recent centuries that the destruction of land by man and his domestic animals has had such terrible consequences.

What has been said above about the fertility of the African savannas and the incredible number of wild animals on them may seem like a figment of the imagination, but it is not. Europeans visiting both the tropical African savannas and the South African veld have left eyewitness accounts of them. And the national parks and nature reserves remain as oases, rich in wildlife, in various parts of the savannas. Besides this, savanna fauna can still be found in some regions not yet destroyed by domestic animals, owing to the fact that African sleeping sickness, the nagana, spread by tsetse flies has prevented the breeding of tame cattle in those areas.

This disease, trypanosomiasis—usually called nagana in animals and sleeping sickness in human beings—is caused by microscopic flagellates (*Trypanosoma*) of several protozoan species, of which at least two and probably three are pathogenic to man. The trypanosomes are carried by tsetse flies (*Glossina*), of which there are numerous species. Two of them (*G. palpalis* and *G. morsitans*) are vectors of the human disease. That wild animals are normally not affected by trypanosomes, although they serve as hosts for them, is certainly a result of adaptation through natural selection, while man and cattle are not immune, despite two million years of the presence of humans in Africa. Hence tsetse flies and trypanosomiasis are an important part of the ecology in tropical Africa.

There is strong evidence that these tsetse regions will yield greater economic return for man if they are preserved in their present condition, with their stocks of wild animals, which are immune to nagana, than if, at enormous cost, men introduce tame cattle. Within a few years, the cattle are half starved, the vegetation is gone, the thin layer of fertile soil has been blown or washed away, and the subsoil water sinks over a wide area, even including places remote from where the damage was done. Neither animals nor human beings can live there, while gradually less land is available for the human population that increases explosively because modern medicine has reduced the death rate.

This ecological problem with its economic background is now one of the most urgent in Africa. It also concerns the future of man. If human beings are to remain in tropical Africa, the savannas must be kept in or restored to productivity, which on marginal lands, that is, about 90 percent of the savannas, can only be accomplished with the help of wild hoofed animals. The remaining 10 percent can resist grazing by tame cattle, and no change need be made there.

Thus, the sterile African plains of today are mainly the work of man. Only in a few such areas as the great national parks of Zaire can one find genuine natural savannas with flora and fauna undisturbed. One consequence of this is that the savannas in the

Albert National Park produce more meat per square mile in the form of large hoofed animals than any other region in Africa, and still the land is not degenerating.

The variety of types of savanna is almost infinite. One stage is the subdesert, where the sand is only partly covered by vegetation; another stage consists of a few wind-whipped thorny shrubs (mostly species of *Acacia*) on ground often covered by thin but permanent grass vegetation. Where there is still greater rainfall, the savanna becomes a grassy plain, with plant communities that vary greatly depending on ecological factors. Here trees are more frequent and also taller, but are still sparsely distributed. *Acacia* species are usually the most common, but in some areas mopane trees (*Copaifera mopane*) or *Borassus* palms or *Euphorbia* dominate. Baobab trees usually grow alone but may also be seen in dense groups. In more favourable situations, especially on elevations, the savannas are covered with open, light wood. The *Acacia* is the dominant genus, but *Brachystegia, Julbernardia,* and *Commiphora* may also form open woods. This type of wooded savanna is found in many parts of tropical Africa; for example, within a belt stretching north of the equator from the Atlantic to Sudan in Angola, large areas of Zaire, northeastern Rwanda, Uganda, Kenya, Tanzania, Zambia, Rhodesia, Malawi, Mozambique, and northern Transvaal, and locally in Botswana. Such savannas are still the most important haunts of elephants, rhinoceroses, buffaloes, giraffes, zebras, antelopes, and many gazelles. It is true that elephants and buffaloes are also forest and mountain animals with remarkable adaptability, but it is on the savannas that they are seen in large herds. Although many of these are herbivores who eat branches, twigs, bark, and leaves, thus exploiting all parts of the vegetation, most of them are pure grass-eaters. Many animal species differ in their preferences in grasses and their modes of grazing and therefore spread over wide areas.

It is rather easy to study the interaction between vegetation and fauna on the savannas, because unlike the rain forests, there is usually a wide-open prospect on them, so that the behaviour of the animals can be studied during the day, and the traces of what they do during the night can be clearly seen the following morning. As an example of the role of the many savanna organisms, we may consider the elephant. First, its habit of pushing over trees makes it possible for other plants to move in, but many years later these plants will again be overtaken by trees. This is part of the landscape dynamics. When, during dry periods, the elephant digs water holes in the parched riverbeds, it provides water for many other animals, from monkeys to mice, birds, reptiles, and insects, which would otherwise be compelled to move elsewhere.

The microclimate on the savannas varies enormously, depending on the density of the vegetation, the amount of shade provided by trees, and the like. The strata of the savannas most important for animal life are the layer of humus, the surface of the soil, and the grass. Trees play a far less important role as biotopes on the savanna, but are naturally exploited by many animals, mainly birds, reptiles, and insects. Animal life beneath the surface of the soil is no less important than the fauna on the surface. Termites in particular play a very important role in the ecology of the savanna.

These are some of the elements in the rich plant and animal associations of the African savannas. It is a very complex ecological balance, but its productive result is tremendous. This should be utilized properly and preserved wisely. Tragically, we are doing exactly the reverse.

It is deplorable that many Africans continue to misuse the land, but it is criminal that many European agronomists and veterinarians encourage people in Africa to do so. Experts from Europe and North America sent to advise Africans on how to increase livestock often do not understand African tropical ecology. These experts have been educated in temperate regions where cattle, sheep, and goats are believed to be cheaper producers of meat than wild animals. They also appear to assume that African soils can be treated in the same way as temperate soils. They do not appreciate that wild animals are being used extensively as an esteemed protein source throughout Africa, that is, where there is still any wildlife left.

The greatest losses through human misuse have occurred in northern, western, and southern Africa. But East Africa has by no means been spared, although the loss of animals has been proportionately less there than elsewhere, except for equatorial Africa. In fact, according to Caldwell (in 1948), it is probable that during the last fifty years the game areas in eastern Africa have been reduced by half and the game animals within many of those areas reduced by 75 percent. This was said twenty-four

years ago, and what has been destroyed since then is really frightful.

This elimination of a highly useful resource is a tragic development in a continent where human populations suffer from lack of
protein. Yet traditional hunting for meat and marketing of wildlife products are much more widespread in Africa than governments seem to realize. In Nigeria alone—a country depleted of
wildlife owing to forest destruction—the value of utilized wildlife
meat was estimated at fifty million dollars for the year 1966.

Poaching in Africa is, in general, not a simple killing for meat
but an industrial killing for profit that can be made from the sale
of meat and hides and such by-products as rhino horns, elephant
ivory, and tails for flywhisks. Poaching has become a widespread
money-making enterprise, using modern transports and an arsenal
of weapons, snares, and traps, but nationally it is an economic
waste.

Veld and Plains of South Africa

Generally speaking, southern Africa's veld may be divided into
two types, in both of which grass is the dominant vegetation. There
are about ten thousand species of grass in the world, divided into
620 genera, of which no fewer than 170 are to be found in South
Africa. In their original state, grassy plains may be described as a
sort of gigantic symbiosis expressed in the nutrition chain, *savanna
vegetation-herbivores-predators*—a fruitful coexistence of vegetation and animals. Only a few fragments of the former richness
and productivity of the savannas remain. Plows and tractors have
transformed the savanna into farmland, where few wild animals
and plants can live. In many places the change has been successful and good crops can be harvested in the temperate climate. But
like a blight, desert sand is advancing inexorably year after year
from the southwest toward the northeast. More than one-third of
South Africa has already been conquered by deserts and arid
shrub steppes—the subtropical Karoo, as the region is called. The
vegetation in the semideserts is capable of regeneration if it is
helped by excluding goats and cattle, although their destructive
effect is not always as rapid as in the tropics farther north. Patches
of grass savanna and remnants of the herds of antelopes which
once grazed over practically the whole of this part of the continent

are therefore still found here. Let us now consider the wildlife that has disappeared or is almost gone.

After settling in South Africa more than three centuries ago, Europeans spread inland from the coast. There they found rich grasslands and a wealth of wild animals. Intensified farming and the raising of cattle and sheep led to the occupation of more land and the driving out of the wild mammals. The opening up of the country to settlers increased the demand for meat. Many men became professional hunters; others killed for fun. Hecatombs of wild mammals fell before the guns. The intensive exploitation of the land produced a serious decline in grass cover and soils along with the wildlife.

The subdesert Karoo has expanded to its present size as a result of long overuse by sheep and goats. The former grasslands of the Karoo seem to have existed in a less arid climate. The removal of grass cover appears to have reduced the climatic moisture and thus upset the whole ecology of the area. Soil erosion increases. Here again, highly productive lands have been turned into dying lands as far as the production of proteins is concerned. This change of the land is not caused by climatic deterioration but is due to alterations induced by man's misuse and severe overgrazing by livestock.

The disappearance of the bluebuck and the almost total extermination of the bontebok in the coastal region have already been noted. The next mammal to vanish in South Africa was the Cape lion (*Panthera leo melanochaita*). This race lived in the Cape Province and Natal. During the eighteenth century many statements indicate that the Cape lion was not uncommon around Cape Town, but the last of these lions were killed in Cape Province in 1858 and in Natal in 1865.

The next victim of man's activities was the famous quagga (*Equus quagga quagga*), a hoofed mammal whose rear parts were striped like those of a zebra. In 1775 the quagga was still found near the coast of Cape Agulhas. In 1812 troops of thirty to fifty quaggas roamed the plains between Fraserburg and Hanover, which today are the Karoo subdeserts. In those days when the grasslands were full of life, the quaggas frequently associated with white-tailed gnus and ostriches. The European farmers hunted the quagga heavily, using the meat to feed their African workers. In about 1865 they began to kill the animals for their hides, which were in great demand in the coast district and among the Boers for grain sacks. The last wild quagga was probably killed in 1878. Several quaggas were brought to Europe and kept in zoological gardens, but no serious attempts to breed them seem to have been made. The last one died in Amsterdam in 1883.

Another race of the zebra and a relative of the quagga, the bontequagga (*E. burchellii burchellii*), is said to have abounded in countless thousands when European hunters and settlers penetrated into the plains north of the Orange River. By the 1850's it was very rare, and by about 1900 it had been wiped out on the African plains. The last specimen died in a London zoo about 1909.

The Cape red hartebeest (*Alcelaphus buselaphus caama*) was very abundant in the Cape Province and Natal at the end of the eighteenth century. Owing to intensive destruction by farmers this antelope had already in 1811 become much less common. By 1876 it was one of the rarest animals in the Cape Province, and some years later there were none left. Whether a small herd living on a farm in Natal represents this subspecies or the northern red hartebeest (*A. b. selbornei*) (of which there are about 550 individuals left in South African national parks) has not yet been determined. Most authors seem to agree that the Cape red hartebeest is extinct.

Another group of animals, including elephants, rhinos, hippos, and several antelopes, was eliminated from southern Africa but still persists in the tropical parts of the continent and in some national parks and reserves in South Africa. Some species still hold out in small, scattered populations or have been locally reintroduced. The elephant, for example, is today existing in only two isolated populations in the Cape Province, where eleven animals live in the Knysna Forest Reserve and another group of fifty-seven in the Addo National Park.

One of the oddest of Africa's mammals is the white-tailed gnu (*Connochaetes gnou*). Formerly it ranged all over the grassy veld and the Karoo steppes of the Cape Province and on the high veld of the Orange Free State and the Transvaal. Two centuries ago it was probably the commonest species of all the larger ungulates in this area. Although there were vast herds of these gnus, they could not withstand the terrible slaughter that began at the end of the eighteenth century. Probably not a single white-tailed gnu was left alive in the whole of Transvaal by the end of 1885. It would certainly have been totally exterminated if it had not been saved by some farmers in the Orange Free State, who carefully protected what was left of a few herds. However, they were not protected by law because they were on enclosed lands.

Efforts to remedy this situation have now been made. Within the white-tailed gnu's normal range it is now preserved in a national park (Mountain Zebra National Park), two provincial reserves in Natal, and on three private estates. In 1967 there were 1,808 wild white-tailed gnus in South Africa. The prospects of this species are now considered favourable.

One of the world's most formidable mammals, second only to the African and Indian elephants in size, is the square-lipped (or white) rhinoceros (*Ceratotherium simum*). This rhino was apparently distributed over a vast area of Africa, but today its two subspecies are rare. Once common throughout a vast area between the Zambezi and Orange rivers, the number of square-lipped rhinoceroses began to decline rapidly at the end of the nineteenth century. They were very vulnerable to their only enemy, man, because they were remarkably easy to approach, behaving almost as if they were tame animals. By the end of the nineteenth century the only survivors of the southern square-lipped rhinoceros (*C. s. simum*) were found in the southeasternmost corner of its former range. When it had almost disappeared from Natal, the Natal Parks Game and Fish Preservation Board began to give it full protection. This organization has done magnificent work in preserving wildlife in general and the white rhino in particular. There were in 1968 some 1,020 square-lipped rhinos in Natal. They all lived in a complex of reserves in Zululand with 717 animals at Umfolozi, 175 in the "Corridor," and a further eighty-nine at Hluhluwe. The Umfolozi population is much in excess of the optimum capacity of the area. About 150 have been reintroduced into other national parks in southern Africa. Since their reintroduction in Rhodesia's national parks the total population for 1969 in this country was eighty-five head. Several hundreds have been sold to zoos, and up to 1971 a total of 730 rhinos had been removed from Umfolozi. The Board is still offering them to conservation authorities, but there are limits to the numbers that can be disposed of in this way. In 1971 the whole population of this race was 2,002 animals.

The very success of its measures has placed the Natal Parks Board in a predicament. It is apparent that the population of the southern race will have to be reduced in order to preserve the strictly limited habitat in the Natal reserves. Unless the relocation of a substantial number of rhinos into suitable areas still available in Botswana are made, there appears to be no alternative but to remove the surplus by any means.

In Botswana the white rhino was once common but is now almost extinct owing to overhunting and habitat destruction.

The two Natal reserves, Umfolozi and Hluhluwe, are situated among forest-covered mountains, deep valleys, wide grasslands, and bushy plains with an abundance of animals. The black rhinoceros as well as the white lives in these reserves. It is interesting to note that these two species while sharing the same habitat do not compete. Part of the explanation of this is that the black rhino is a browser, eating leaves, twigs, and branches of bushes and lower trees, while the square-lipped rhino is a grazer, a grass eater.

Although both species are very similar in structure, the black rhino has a narrow muzzle with a protruding, slightly hooked upper lip, which functions almost as a miniature trunk in seizing leaves and thorny twigs. The square-lipped rhino has on the contrary a wide mouth adapted for grazing. In temperament the black rhino is nervous, suspicious, and ready to charge as soon as disturbed. The square-lipped rhino is just the opposite: quiet, without fear, and willing to let human beings approach at close quarters.

The two African rhinos are an outstanding example of how two closely related species can live side by side without competition because they feed upon different layers of the vegetation. There are other larger herbivores in the same habitat; all of them utilize various parts of the vegetation without destroying either the plants or the soil. The reasons for the square-lipped rhino's rapid decline in Africa are several. It is easy to kill due to its lack of shyness, its enormous body contains large quantities of meat, its skin is useful, and overseas its horns have the reputation of being a powerful aphrodisiac.

There are three true hyenas in Africa. Two of them are endangered. One, the Barbary hyena, has already been discussed. The second is the brown hyena (*Hyaena brunnea*), a species formerly distributed over vast areas of southern Africa, particularly in the dry western parts, from the coasts of the Cape up to southern Angola. In Central and eastern Africa the northern limit was roughly Rhodesia and Transvaal.

The brown hyena's economy was greatly affected by the disap-

pearance of the ungulate herds from the velds of southern Africa.
But it was also persecuted directly by trapping, shooting, and
poisoning by farmers and hunters who claimed that it was a threat
to their livestock. It was exterminated in most of its range and
nowadays occurs in small numbers in scattered localities in the
Cape Province. It is also found in the Umfolozi and Mkuzi game
reserves in Natal, in only one locality in the Orange Free State,
and in the Kruger National Park in Transvaal. It also lives in
South-West Africa, Botswana, Rhodesia, and Angola.

The fact that the brown hyena is not protected outside national
parks and reserves underscores the value of national parks in the
preservation of endangered species. In South Africa the most important and magnificent nature reserve is the Kruger National
Park. Established in 1926 it is, after the Albert National Park in
Zaire, the second oldest in Africa; but as the Sabi Game Reserve,
this area of 5,440,125 acres had been protected as far back as
1898. South Africans were pioneers of conservation in Africa,
perhaps to compensate for the reckless destruction that took place
in their country for two centuries.

There is another rare carnivore, the African cheetah (*Acinonyx
jubatus jubatus*). It belongs to the same species as the Indian
cheetah but is considered to be another race. The species formerly
had an enormous range on two continents. Ecologically it is
adapted to savannas and semiarid plains, but despite the fact that
such habitats cover vast areas of Africa and Asia, the cheetah has
declined in many areas of its original range. The African cheetah
was once a characteristic carnivore in savannas and semideserts in
northern, eastern, and southern Africa; that is, on most of the
continent outside the lowland and montane rain forests. The earliest record of this animal in Africa appears in an Egyptian wall
painting showing Ramses II (1290–24 B.C.) receiving envoys.

The decrease in numbers of the cheetah in Africa is rather
recent. In northern Africa the cheetah still existed during the first
decade of the present century. Today it is no longer found in the
Cape Province and North Africa, and wherever it still occurs in
Africa it is a rather rare animal except in some national parks.
The reasons for the rapid decline of the cheetah are obviously
the transformation of savannas and subdeserts, its diurnal habits,
the disappearance of its prey, and disturbance by man. The African
cheetah is now protected in most areas within its present range.
Since it requires large areas, its future probably lies in the maintenance of larger national parks.

The Tropical Savannas

We now come to animals that have their present main distribution in the tropics, and first of all in savannas. The term savanna, as we have seen, covers a wide spectrum of habitats. The savannas of East Africa rise from sea level to a vast high plateau, about two-thirds of it at levels between four and six thousand feet. The area is traversed by the Great Rift Valley, an enormous fissure creating a depression with many lakes, extensive marshes, and plains and flats that are sometimes flooded. On these East African and some of the Central and West African savannas the ungulates are more varied and numerous than on any other continent. However, the immense herds of only a century ago are gone. Savannas of tropical Africa, more or less untouched by man, support the highest productivity of hoofed mammals in Africa without showing any signs of vegetational or soil deterioration. Onto these tremendously rich lands came man, assuming in his self-assurance that he could do it much better. Despite great fiascoes, man continues to produce failures and destroy lands in Africa, chiefly because he does not listen to those who understand the ecology of the African landscape, the complexity of its energy flow, and the metabolic rate of its organic matter.

The tremendous variety of species and numbers of animals in the large national parks and reserves show the way. Areas like the Gorongoza National Park in Mozambique, the Wankie National Park in Rhodesia, the Kafue National Park in Zambia, the Serengeti National Park in Tanzania, the Masai Mara Game Reserve in Kenya, the Queen Elizabeth National Park in Uganda, and the Albert National Park in Zaire are overwhelming examples of the productivity in areas more or less undisturbed by man and his livestock.

When Africa is thought of as a wildlife country, it is usually the savannas of the eastern and central parts that are meant. That roughly means Mozambique, Rhodesia, Zambia, Tanzania, Kenya, Uganda, eastern Zaire, and parts of Sudan, Ethiopia, and Somalia. But many areas rich in animals are also found in Central and West Africa.

The main factor behind the decimation of wild animals on the tropical savannas is the same as in South Africa. Most open lands of tropical Africa are not suitable for farming in spite of enormous investments and ambitious development schemes. The main menace to wild animals is man's devastation of marginal lands through livestock grazing and attempts at agriculture.

We have already referred to tsetse flies as allies of conservation in Africa. They transmit from immune game to nonimmune cattle the sleeping sickness or nagana caused by a protozoan or tryp-anosome (*Trypanosoma,* several species) that lives in the blood of mammals. This means that the many areas in tropical Africa infested with tsetse flies cannot be utilized by livestock. They therefore remain rich in wild mammals. But cattle carry more diseases than do wild animals; and diseases such as the cattle plague or rinderpest, that introduced cattle have transmitted to the wild animals, have had disastrous effects. The cattle plague, for example, swept over almost the whole continent. Buffaloes and antelopes died in the thousands and became locally exterminated.

There is not even any short-term justification for such destructive pastoralism, as can be shown by what has happened in Kenya. In round figures, cattle farming there yields £ 3,500,000 a year. In 1961 about £ 1,750,000 of this sum came from the approximately four thousand square miles of land cultivated by Europeans, mainly in the highlands. These were clearly regions of optimum production exploited by Europeans only; no Africans had lived there earlier. The other half of the production, mainly hides, came from a region about 183,000 square miles in area which had been exploited by Africans. Thus the average yield for the European cattle region was almost two dollars per acre, while the African region yielded less than thirty cents per acre and at the same time destroyed the land.

It has already been proved that in many regions of tropical Africa the meat production of wild animals on relatively poor land is considerably higher than that of cattle in comparatively good areas. To this must be added the income from tourists. In the fiscal year 1966–67 this income in Kenya alone was about $25,200,000. The expanding rate of Kenya's tourism industry is about 20 percent. In 1968 tourism became Kenya's most important industry, but in 1969–70 the coffee export reconquered this place. In 1968 it employed twenty thousand Kenyans and earned the country more than $44,000,000 in foreign exchange. Under the actual Five Year Development Plan, tourism is expected to provide forty thousand employment opportunities to Kenyans, and to more than double foreign-exchange earnings to $103,600,000 by 1974. In 1970 the figure was $53,249,700, an increase of 14 percent over 1969. It is magnificent animal life in a flourishing landscape, not deserts, half-starved cattle, and dead, rotting cows, that attracts tourists. Thus Kenya's few national parks and game reserves give, without great investments of capital and without destroying the land, greater returns than all the destructive animal husbandry in the country!

A comparison of different areas shows that the capacity of productivity of the ungulates of tropical Africa is far greater than that of livestock. Such a comparison, based on the animal population per square kilometer expressed in tons, is obtained by multiplying the number of each species by the minimum weight of an adult animal. In the Zaire and Uganda national parks, the figure varies between twenty-four and thirty-seven tons, as distributed among ten species, while the figure for cattle on the best natural pastures in Kenya is three to five tons, on the South African veld about eight tons, and on the pampas of the Argentine fourteen tons. On pastures in a high state of costly cultivation with heavy artificial fertilization in Belgium, a yield of up to forty-five tons is occasionally obtained.

Besides their superiority as producers of meat and preservers of land in most of tropical Africa, most species of wild ungulates give proportionately larger amounts of meat in relation to body weight than cattle. The yield of eland antelopes, impalas, Grant gazelles, and Thomson's gazelles, for example, is about 60 percent, while only in exceptional instances do African cattle give 50 percent. On marginal lands wild mammals are much more productive than any domestic animals, and they do not cause any environmental destruction.

Buffaloes, hippopotamuses, rhinoceroses, giraffes, elephants, zebras, and large antelopes of many species provide a rich source of food if utilized wisely. Normally they cause no damage to the vegetation and land in spite of the enormous quantities they eat. Many species increase in size much more rapidly than cattle, are immune to sleeping sickness (nagana), and have none of the other ailments that often attack cattle. They also have a much higher rate of survival, owing to thousands of years of adaptation to their environment. As producers of meat, these wild animals could easily surpass the cattle, qualitatively as well as quantitatively, and even without the help of the tsetse fly. It is easier to "harvest" tame cattle than wild animals, of course, but the cost of hunting, storage, distribution, and sale of wild meat is only a fraction of the enormous investments made yearly, and in vain, to create new grazing for livestock in place of pastures destroyed by the same animals during the previous year.

One may say almost all the large mammals on the dying plains of Africa are endangered by the destruction of habitats. However, we will concentrate only on those species that conservationists are fighting desperately to save. Several of these species have already been commented upon in the section on the South African plains. The species treated here have their center of distribution on the tropical savannas, mostly those of East Africa.

The black rhinoceros (*Diceros bicornis*), briefly mentioned in connection with southern Africa, was formerly distributed over a very large area of Africa. It was common throughout South Africa when the Europeans settled there, but the last one in the Orange Free State was reported killed in 1842, and in the Cape Province a decade later. By the end of the century it was gone in Bechuanaland (today called Botswana). The establishment of reserves in Transvaal and Natal saved this rhino in eastern South Africa. In 1932 less than six black rhinos had survived in the Kruger National Park. In Natal in 1934 there were about eighty-five in the Hluhluwe Game Reserve and a few in the Umfolozi and Mkuzi game reserves. The same year between forty and eighty black rhinos were thought to exist in the Kaokoveld area of South-West Africa. Apparently this species never reached high numbers in that country. In 1966 the population of South-West Africa was estimated to be only ninety, while there were 312 in South Africa, most of them in the Kruger National Park and in the Natal game reserves. North of South Africa the black rhino held out much longer. But it was not until the last thirty years that the reduction reached such proportions that the species became seriously endangered.

In some countries the black rhino was deliberately exterminated because it was considered incompatible with agricultural development schemes. Of course, its aggressive habits made it difficult to tolerate near settlements. Also, much hunting for meat and trophies as well as for tsetse control took place before any protective measures were instituted. Nowadays, much poaching, even in national parks, goes on in this species, because in Asia fabulous sums are paid for its horns, which are regarded as an aphrodisiac.

The total population of the black rhino in 1963 was estimated at 11,000 to 13,500. Tanzania has about 3,500 of the rhinos,

Kenya about 2,500, Rhodesia 740; and lesser numbers are found in Mozambique, Zambia, Uganda, Chad, and Cameroon. In Rhodesia a census in 1968 showed a population between a thousand and fourteen hundred black rhinos, but in 1971 another estimate came to 740 animals. In 1970 the total in Natal was 290.

Though primarily a lowland savanna animal, the black rhino also occurs high up on montane savannas. On Aberdare, for instance, it lives constantly at an altitude above ten thousand feet. This indicates an ecological flexibility in the black rhino that may help to save it from extinction.

The northern square-lipped, or white, rhinoceros (*Ceratotherium simum cottoni*) is a race of the species we discussed in connection with the South African velds. Less than a hundred years ago the northern form was distributed from Sudan in the east to the Lake Chad region in the west, but also in Ubangi-Shari, southwestern Sudan, northeastern Congo, and northwestern Uganda. In the western parts of this range, former French territories, this rhino was so sharply reduced that in 1965 only a few animals were still there, and they may have come from southwestern Sudan, where the species enjoyed strict protection and had at that time apparently increased.

In 1938 the magnificent Garamba National Park was specially created in the Congo to preserve the last one hundred square-lipped rhinos. Twenty-five years later a census revealed a population of about 1,200 animals in the national park. Unfortunately, civil war in the northeastern Congo in 1964–65 upset the long peace of the Garamba wilderness. Many rhinos were shot. Working in this national park in May, 1966, I tried to make a census of the larger mammals both from the ground and from the air. We found only forty-seven white rhinos and estimated, perhaps too optimistically, the population at about one hundred rhinos. This is a reduction of about 1,100 since 1963, a tragic decline for one of the world's rarest mammals. Unfortunately, poaching from the Sudan continued in the Garamba National Park and in 1970–71 the rhino was down to twenty or thirty animals. In the Sudan itself in 1971 there could not be many, if any, white rhinos left. In the West Nile Province of Uganda the population rapidly decreased from about 350 in 1955 to about eighty in 1962. In 1971 there were eighty to a hundred in the Ajai Reserve and one or two in other areas of the same province. In 1961–64, twelve white rhinos were introduced into the Murchison Falls National Park. In 1968 they had increased to eighteen, in 1971 to twenty. This means that the total population of this race now is about 150 animals.

The northern square-lipped rhinoceros is totally protected both inside and outside national parks and game reserves, but as we can see this is not a guarantee of its security.

One of the glories of Angola is the giant sable antelope (*Hippotragus niger variani*). Its limited range is now a part of the Strict Nature Reserve of Luando and the Cangandala Strict Nature Reserve. This antelope is considered a distinct species by some taxonomists but it is more likely a race of the sable antelope of Zaire, East and South Africa. Whatever it is, it is often regarded as the finest of all African antelopes. The males are an intense glossy black with white face markings, underparts, and the inside of the thigh. Their wonderful curved horns, which may reach a length of sixty-four inches, were the prime reason for the decline of the animal, sportsmen hunting it for these trophies. In 1933, when there were less than three hundred animals, the giant sable was put under protection. At first the Africans still trapped it and Europeans shot it indiscriminately, but today the protection seems to be effective. However, the destruction of its habitat by man is an even more serious threat, which is accelerating even in the reserves. The total population was estimated in 1934 at less than three hundred animals, but in 1969 at least 2,500. However, at the end of the 1960's a decline of the species in the reserves had been reported. The reasons are still unknown, but human presence is certainly involved.

The black-faced impala (*Aepyceros melampus petersi*) is a very rare race in Angola (it has recently been claimed to be a distinct species), where the population is estimated at about 650 to seven hundred, and in the Kaokoveld of South-West Africa, where there are between 750 and a thousand individuals.

The largest antelopes in the world are the elands; two species are found in Africa. The western giant eland (*Taurotragus derbianus derbianus*) occurs in West Africa, where it is or was confined to the Ivory Coast, Guinea, Mali, Senegal, and Gambia. It is now reduced to a few hundred individuals and it is doubtful that it will survive because it is an easy target for hunters. In Senegal, where about 180 individuals exist, the protection is efficient. The giant eland is a very valuable natural resource, so it would be wise for the governments concerned to make an effort to save it.

Another race, the Sudani giant eland (*T. d. gigas*) lives in national parks in Cameroon and Chad. It might still exist in the Sudan and northern Uganda. Formerly it also occurred, at least as a straggler, in northeastern Zaire, but it has not been observed there during the last fifteen years.

Another African ungulate with a very limited distribution is Hunter's antelope (*Damaliscus hunteri*). It is confined to a strip of land between the Tana and Juba rivers in Kenya and Somalia behind the coastal rain belt. Curiously, it has extended its range compared to fifty years ago, even though the population was probably under one thousand as of 1962.

Most of the population of this antelope seems to live on the Kenya side of the border; this presents a problem because the government of Kenya plans a 300,000-acre development-and-irrigation project in this area. Conservationists are desperately trying to find a way to save Hunter's antelope from extinction. Some of the animals have been removed to the Tsavo National Park in Kenya, where they have multiplied.

The dibatag (*Ammodorcas clarkei*) is a rare gazelle inhabiting two areas in Somalia, one southeast, the other north of Ogaden in Ethiopia. Formerly it had a much wider range here and in eastern Ethiopia, where it still exists in small numbers. When first described in 1890 this gazelle was more numerous than any other game except Soemmerring's gazelle (*Gazella soemmerringii*). Eight years later dibatags were still plentiful but apparently local in their distribution. In 1905 there were estimated to be about five thousand; today the figure has fallen to between 1,500 and 2,500.

The destruction of habitat through overgrazing by domestic animals is again the chief factor in the decrease. In addition, there is a trade in dibatag skins and this encourages much poaching. If domestic animals could be excluded from certain grasslands and bush in Somalia, this gazelle might be saved and be developed into a valuable natural resource for a country with such poor soil. Also, Soemmering's gazelle has decreased enormously, particularly in the Sudan, where the once spectacular herds have been almost eliminated from the plains of the eastern Blue Nile basin owing to heavy poaching. Small numbers live also in Ethiopia and Somalia.

Though many birds of the African savannas, especially ostriches and bustards, are vulnerable and rare, no species is actually threatened by extinction. If, however, the destruction of habitats and hunting continue, the situation of many birds will become critical.

THE WOODLANDS

There are savanna woodlands and tree savannas, but there are also woodlands that do not fit into any definition of savanna. One may say that woodlands form a transition between savannas and forests. As fire plays an essential role in the ecology of both African savannas and woodlands, the most abundant and characteristic trees of the woodlands are often fire-tolerant species.

We here include in "woodlands" several types of open forests —called *forêt claire* in French—ranging from dry deciduous woods to almost luxuriant ones, sometimes even of high forest type. The term "woodland" is generally used in Africa for habitats having a mantle of trees of one or at most two stories, with crowns that are rather close or even touch each other to form a light canopy through which the sun penetrates. Woodlands are found here and there in the savanna belts of Africa, but chiefly they grow on the elevated plateaus of south-central Africa. The most common type of woodland is the miombo, in which *Brachystegia* and *Isoberlinia* species of trees predominate. In fact, the miombo woodlands constitute the largest single African vegetation type south of the equatorial rain forest. They cover a vast area in Angola, southern Zaire, Tanzania, Malawi, Zambia, Rhodesia, and Mozambique. There are also similar regions north of the equator.

Large parts of the woodlands in tropical Africa are located within the tsetse belt. Several species of these flies are vectors of animal and human trypanosomiasis (nagana and sleeping sickness). This makes many woodlands and savannas unsuitable for cattle raising, which in its turn explains why so much of the woodlands contains a rich wildlife. These woodlands, occupied by a great diversity of large herbivores, are included in the so-called marginal lands because cattle cannot adapt to most of them. But as far as the meat of wild ungulates is concerned, these lands are highly productive. Therefore the woodlands of tropical Africa must be considered a very efficient producer of protein and a most valuable natural resource. Unfortunately, many African woodlands have been changed so drastically by human interference that they are no longer either woodlands or savannas. In all of these woodlands the destructive role of fire is evident, even where man does not cultivate.

The Katanga area of Zaire provides us with good examples of such woodlands. The most common landscape in Katanga is light, open woodland. Katanga might in fact be likened to a vast parkland with numerous species of deciduous trees growing separately, their crowns never meeting. Sun and light can penetrate to the ground and create a dense understory. As always in the tropics, the number of species is enormous. The variety and luxuriousness of the vegetation never fail to arouse wonder. Certain dominant elements can be distinguished in Katanga's *forêt claire.* Among the trees it is most often a species of *Brachystegia,* whereas in the undergrowth it is *Aframomum sanguineum,* a plant that belongs to the ginger family and grows a yard or so tall. Termite hillocks can be seen everywhere, but they are insignificant compared with the gigantic mounds built by termites before this area became woodland. These structures, sometimes twenty-five feet high and thirty feet around the base, are now colonized by plants and trees. It is astonishing that such small animals have been able to erect such mighty structures that have so long defied the action of rain and wind. During an excursion by motorboat on Lake Mwadingusha in 1963—the lake was created in the 1930's by a dam for generating electricity—we hit what we thought was a rock. It turned out to be a termitary that had withstood the action of water for decades. During the warring actions of the United Nations in Katanga, termite hills were frequently used as machine-gun emplacements and gun turrets!

The mighty termitaria tell us that these forests were once quite different. The termites still there show us what the woods once looked like, for the tiny engineers are still active, but only in dense forests (called *muhulu* in Swahili). This dense type of forest is found over a large part of Katanga in patches nearly always surrounded by woods. In many places the light, open forests are the remains of a primeval forest that once covered the whole of Katanga; in other places they are beginning to reconquer lost land. In both types of areas, the termites erect their pyramids at the rate of an inch an hour every night.

What factors give rise to open and dense forests, respectively? The open forest is the result of fire, often as a part of cultivation, while the dense forest is found and expands where man does not clear the woods by fire. The latter type of forest is still the vegetation climax on the plateaus of Katanga at altitudes of 3,300 to 6,200 feet above sea level.

Although, as we have said, the open, parklike forests are now dominant, the dense forests are regaining ground. The forest history of Katanga fits in with what we know of the population history. Originally, the country was sparsely populated by a race of pygmies, Tumandwa, only three feet or so tall, who lived on what they could find in the woods and rivers. They were driven away by taller pygmoids and took refuge on the highest plateaus of Katanga, which are without permanent inhabitants today. There they lived in termitaria. Neither pygmies nor pygmoids burned or cut down the woods on which they depended. Even today their descendants in Katanga and elsewhere in Zaire still live by hunting. This continued to about a hundred years ago, when various Bantu tribes invaded Katanga. They brought "artificial" fires into Katanga, and the open forests spread wider and wider. Only a few decades later the region was explored by white men. Thus man has influenced nature in Katanga for only one hundred years, since the pygmies and pygmoids lived in complete harmony with the dynamics of nature.

The vertebrate fauna of the African woodlands is essentially the same as that of the savannas; many species frequent both habitats. Of those animals found only in the woodlands, none is at the moment among endangered species, but we must remember that many of the threatened savanna mammals and almost all of the browsers have found their last refuge in woodlands and savannas protected by tsetse flies. Moreover, for several mammals the mosaic patches of woodlands surrounded by savannas are essential. That is why the African woodlands are so important for wildlife.

The rapid destruction of the Sokoke Forest on the coast of Kenya, the only remaining larger coastal forest of East Africa, might cause the extermination of no less than five endemic animals, one mammal and four birds, namely the elephant shrew (*Rhynchocyon chrysopygus*), the Sokoke owlet (*Otus ireneae*), the black-headed weaver (*Ploceus golandi*), and local races of the African wood owl (*Ciccaba woodfordi sokokensis*), and of the golden-rumped tinker-bird (*Pogoniulus bilineatus pallidus*). They all occur in the Sokoke Forest only and might disappear with the forest if urgent steps are not taken to stop the deforestation. Moreover, the Zanzibar duiker (*Cephalophus natalensis adersi*) has in the Sokoke Forest its last stronghold on the African mainland,

and on Zanzibar its future is also insecure. This subspecies in Sokoke Forest is very different from other races and might be ranked as a separate species.

THE LOWLAND RAIN FORESTS

Most of Africa's lowland or equatorial rain forests are located in the Zaire drainage basin. They extend from the Albertine Rift Valley in the east to the Atlantic Ocean in the west, and a broad strip continues along the Gulf of Guinea from Ghana to Sierra Leone. Although it has nearly been destroyed, the moist coastal forest of Madagascar may also be included in the lowland-rain-forest category. The gallery forests around rivers and lakes and the coastal mangrove and lagoon forests are also a type of rain forest. As a result of the damage done by man, the rain forests of Africa today cover only one-third of their former area. Nevertheless, about one-third of all the tropical rain forest in the world is in Africa.

In such equatorial forests rain falls for a couple of hours a day, distributed rather evenly over all the months of the year. As in temperate forests or on tropical mountains, trees, shrubs, and herbs form more or less homogeneous plant communities. Hundreds of tree species share the living space, forming a mosaic too complex to analyze. It may eventually be possible to map the distribution of species in this type of forest by studying the composition of the crowns of trees from the air. Such a survey will be necessary if we are ever to learn why no one tree can dominate in these forests.

Besides this mixture of species, the most typical feature of the forests is the stratification. The ground and often the higher tree roots are covered by mosses, fungi, and ferns. Above that comes a layer of shrubs. The third stratum comprises trees of normal height—judged by European standards—mixed with the young offspring of the giants which, 150 feet high, form the top story. Around streams and rivers, the undergrowth is almost impenetrable; in the actual forest the tree trunks are rather far apart, but their crowns are so large that they form a continuous canopy. Between the trunks of these giants are smaller trees whose crowns form a canopy of their own. These tiers in the forest stratify the animal life, too. Mammals, birds, reptiles, and amphibians, not to mention multitudes of insects and other small forms of life, live hidden from the eye of man up in the trees. Although, generally

speaking, we know pretty well what we shall find up there, we
know very little of how these animals live and what their upper
and lower limits are.

All strata of the forest provide shelter for many animals. They
live under and on the ground and in the trunks and crowns of
trees, creating an immense, continuous habitat. Among vertebrates,
not only do bats, monkeys, hyraxes, squirrels, mice, and birds
occur in the highest story of the trees, but also a large number of
snakes, lizards, amphibians, frogs, and toads, and, of course,
insects. And down on and in the dark earth, with its several layers
of decomposed vegetable matter, live an astonishing number of
mammals, reptiles, and batrachians, and even some birds, side by
side with millions of tiny forms of life. Each story has its own
microclimate, and even within the story the conditions vary enormously. The equatorial rain forest is the most complex ecosystem
in the world.

Every year the lowland rain forests in Africa are reduced by
development schemes and shifting cultivation practices. Only a few
animals are, however, in immediate danger of extermination.

The Ituri forest in Zaire is the easternmost part of the lowland-
rain-forest region, and its most famous inhabitant besides the pygmies is the okapi. It lives well hidden in the forest and is seldom
seen, but traces of it are often found. Although it is timid, it does
haunt forests close to roads and villages. Actually it can hide even
better in these secondary forests and finds more food there than
in the less dense undergrowth of the primeval forest. It is not so
scarce as was formerly believed, although pygmies probably kill
more than a thousand okapis each year. The okapi is strictly
protected, it is true, but the hunting habits of the pygmy forest-
dwellers are difficult to control. Okapis fall into pits just as easily
as do bongo antelopes, forest buffaloes, bush pigs, and other animals. There seems, however, little risk of the okapi's becoming
extinct. In fact, it is increasing in numbers and has during the
last fifteen years settled in the transitional rain forest on the western slope of Ruwenzori.

It is in the lowland rain forest of Zaire that many of the more
recent discoveries of mammals have been made. The okapi was
first described here in 1901, a very specialized fish-eating genet
(*Osbornictis piscivorus*) in 1913, a remarkable insectivore, *Sylvi-
sorex congicus,* in the same year, and in 1928 a chimpanzee of its

own, *Pan paniscus.* To these can be added the discovery of the Congo peacock (*Afropavo congensis*) in 1936.

The pygmy chimpanzee (*Pan paniscus*), only occurring in Zaire, is on the official list of rare mammals. At present there is very little in Zaire that constitutes a threat to its existence. If its habitats are not destroyed, and the animal itself is not hunted or collected heavily, there is no reason to fear for its future. It is also important that no introduction of the common chimpanzee is made in the area occupied by the pygmy chimpanzee. However, the common chimpanzee (*P. troglodytes*) is almost all over its range, particularly in West Africa, heavily persecuted for export to research institutions and zoos. Unfortunately, many chimps (mainly mothers) are killed when their babies are captured and many of the latter perish after having been caught. If this heavy population drain continues, the existence of this species will be jeopardized.

The animals of West Africa have been decimated by the destruction of much rain forest and by terrific hunting pressure. Once rich in game, there is today not much left in the strip of high forests in Sierra Leone, Guinea, Liberia, the Ivory Coast, Ghana, and Nigeria. Two mammalian species with restricted distribution occur in this region. The more famous, the pygmy hippopotamus (*Choeropsis liberiensis*), is very rare and has perhaps always been so, occurring only in Sierra Leone, Guinea, Liberia, and the Ivory Coast. However, it is diminishing alarmingly, probably because of hunting. Periodically in 1963–69 we sought this hippopotamus along Liberian streams and rivers, where it had been known to occur, but saw no trace of it except in 1966, when tracks of this hippo were observed close to the Nimba Range. Fortunately, the pygmy hippo breeds fairly well in captivity, a guarantee that it will not become extinct. The Basel Zoological Garden alone had raised forty-four animals by 1972.

Even more rare than the pygmy hippo is a small forest antelope, Jentink's duiker (*Cephalophus jentinki*), known only from a few areas in Liberia and the Ivory Coast. If excessive hunting continues in these areas, Jentink's duiker may become extinct before we have learned anything of its habits. During intensive field work on the Nimba Range in Liberia in 1964–71, we did not find it, but our Mano assistants assured us that it still occurs on the Ivory Coast side of Mount Nimba. Another Mano tribesman reported this in 1955 to the French zoologist P. L. Dekeyser, who recorded specimens in the Klosoke region of Liberia. In 1968 a pair was captured. It was the first male to be seen alive by Europeans. In 1972 a Jentink's duiker was found at Duo in Liberia, about sixty miles south of the Nimba Range. Another rare forest-dweller is the banded duiker (*C. zebra*), occurring in Sierra Leone, Liberia, and the Ivory Coast, where forested habitats are diminishing quickly, menacing animal inhabitants.

Except perhaps for elephants and buffaloes, there is no more spectacular mammal of the lowland rain forests of Africa than the gorilla. There are two subspecies: the lowland gorilla (*Gorilla gorilla gorilla*) and the mountain gorilla (*G. g. beringei*). The former occurs in forests from Nigeria in the west across Cameroon, Spanish Guinea, and Gabon to the Congo (Brazzaville). Up to about fifteen years ago it also existed in the Mayombe high forest of the former Belgian Congo, but the exploitation of this unique coastal forest led to the disappearance of the lowland gorilla. The mountain gorilla lives in eastern Zaire, northern Rwanda, and western Uganda. In general, the lowland gorilla is not considered to be in danger of extermination, but its scarcity, limited distribution, and dependence on dense forests make its future uncertain. (The mountain gorilla is discussed on page 86.) Another West African primate threatened by extermination is the green colobus (*Colobus verus*), distributed from Sierra Leone in the west to Togo in the east. It has been drastically reduced in numbers. The golden potto (*Arctocebus calabarensis*) from Nigeria, Cameroon, and Rio Muni and the needle-clawed galago (*Euoticus elegantulus*) from the coastal rain forests of the Gulf of Guinea and of Fernando Po have restricted ranges and are very rare and endangered. There are also two palm squirrels on the verge of extinction: the African palm squirrel (*Epixerus ebii*) from West Africa and Wilson's palm squirrel (*E. wilsoni*) from Cameroon, Gabon, and Zaire.

The leopard (*Panthera pardus*) occurs in almost the whole of Africa south of the Sahara. It is an extremely adaptable species that could have been discussed in connection with nearly all terrestrial habitats dealt with in this chapter. It thrives on open arid savannas and in dense rain forests, along seashores as well as in montane regions up to an altitude of more than four thousand meters. However, I have an impression, after having worked periodically for twenty years in Africa, that it is in the lowland and montane rain forests that the leopard has its densest populations. This is particularly so in the wild forests of Zaire, but the species shows a remarkable ability also to accept small patches of woods in the heavily cultivated Rwanda and Burundi, where Africa's densest human populations have an enormous impact on the landscape. Yet the leopard is there, though not many people know about it because it has a discreet way of living.

Unfortunately, the leopard has disappeared from many of its former areas in Africa. Local exterminations are known from many countries. There is no doubt that the heavy drain on leopards, chiefly due to illegal hunting, poisoning, trapping, and trade, are beginning to have a serious effect on the African population as a whole. On the other hand, the annual export figures of leopard skins from Africa are quite high, which gives the impression that there are plenty of leopards on this continent. In 1968 and 1969, no fewer than 4,399 and 4,115 leopard skins, respectively, were imported from Africa to the United States alone. Kenya and Ethiopia top the lists of leopard exports in 1968 and 1969 by selling more skins than all other African countries put together. This means that the species is not yet down to a critical level, but if the slaughter continues on the present scale, it is very likely that it will soon be endangered in the whole of its African range.

Among birds, two species, the white-necked rock-fowl (*Picathartes gymnocephalus*) and the grey-necked rock-fowl (*P. oreas*) from West Africa, are very rare. The former occurs from Sierra Leone in the west to Togo in the east and the latter is restricted to Cameroon. Both seem to decline in numbers, especially the grey-necked rock-fowl.

GALLERY FORESTS

Gallery forests, which grow around rivers and sometimes extend far from the banks, form characteristic habitats in many parts of Africa and most of all in tropical areas. In such areas the gallery forests along rivers often develop into tall, luxuriant forests with their own peculiar flora and fauna. Because of heavy forest destruction the gallery forests have often become isolated from surrounding woodlands or forests, trapping, so to speak, several forest animals in them.

There are three rare monkeys which have been narrowly restricted to such river forests. One is the Tana River mangabey (*Cercocebus galeritus galeritus*), which was formerly distributed in the gallery forests of the lower Tana River in Kenya. Cultivation in this region eliminated the forests and forced these animals to withdraw to patches of forests several miles from the right bank of the Tana River. Here they have been subjected to intensive trapping. Several recent expeditions have searched in vain for them along the river. Obviously this monkey (the nominate race of a species distributed in the Zaire forests) is in immediate danger of extinction.

Much the same fate faces the Tana River red colobus (*Colobus badius rufomitratus*), a species discussed in connection with Zanzibar. This subspecies is not so uncommon in its few refuges as the mangabey, but its very restricted distribution makes it vulnerable. About twenty or thirty individuals were seen in 1963 by the Los Angeles County Museum expedition to the Tana River. The subspecies enjoys full protection, but it is the destruction of its habitats that is the problem. A third endangered subspecies of the red colobus is the Uhehe red colobus (*C. b. gordonorum*), which lives in high forests on the lower slopes of the Uzungwe Mountains in Tanzania. Very little is known about this monkey. It is confined to a small area of forest that has been heavily reduced for settlement and cultivation.

Birds are better equipped than mammals to avoid being trapped in isolated forest habitats. Therefore there is no "gallery-forest bird" in Africa that is truly in danger and only one is on the official list of rare birds. This is the white-winged dove (*Streptopelia reichenowi*), living in riverine vegetation in the Juba River valley in Ethiopia and Somalia and along the Uebi Scebeli River in Ethiopia.

THE MOUNTAINS AND VOLCANOES

Tropical rain forests are usually of mixed composition. This is true of African lowland, transition, and montane rain forests, but above these belts the mountains are, in general, clothed by less diverse communities or even dominated by a single community. Formerly almost all the mountains of tropical and subtropical Africa were covered by vegetation. Today a great proportion of them are nude, eroded down to "rock skeleton." Best preserved are the higher vegetation zones of the tropical mountains. The term "tropical" is here used in a geographic sense, because above the montane rain forests the climate is more temperate than tropical. There are mountains all over Africa and in various climatic regions but they are most concentrated in the eastern parts of the continent, from Ethiopia to Natal. Virtually unique habitats exist on these mountains, and the remaining montane forests must be preserved not only for the economic benefit of man but also for the sake of their animal life.

Human activities are a serious menace to mountain rain forests in Africa, the most productive habitat of tropical mountains. Every year more and more montane forests are destroyed, causing the whole ecosystem to break down not only on the mountain slope itself but also in the valleys and on the plains below, mainly because the hydrography of vast regions is upset. The important function of montane forests as watersheds, accumulators, and distributors of water to lowland areas during all seasons is eliminated. Instead, erosion ruins the country.

There is no completely stable natural environment, but in the alpine zones of Africa we have a habitat that comes very close to stability, because it evolves with extreme slowness. The biocommunities of these levels have apparently not changed very much during the last million years, although their vertical ranges have altered in response to pluvial and dry periods. The mountain rain forests are scattered over the higher ranges and volcanoes of Africa—Loma, Nimba, Cameroon, the Ethiopian highlands, Ruwenzori, the eight Virunga volcanoes, Kahuzi, Itombwe, the Cherangani, Mount Elgon, Mount Kenya, Aberdare, Chyulu, Meru, Kilimanjaro, Usambara, Uluguru, and the Crater Highlands in Tanzania, to mention the most important. In eastern Zaire the lowland rain forest turns into mountain rain forest by way of a transitional zone on western Ruwenzori, which makes this region especially interesting in terms of plant and animal geography.

Although they all have plant communities in common, the rain forests on the high mountains of Africa vary in appearance and composition on practically every range. This is because of several factors: climatic, edaphic, and historical. Like the lowland rain forests, the montane rain forests are eternally green. Humidity and rainfall are high, and epiphytes increase in frequency the higher one goes on the forest-covered slopes. But the temperature is the decisive factor in the vertical distribution of the vegetation, and therefore of the fauna.

The mountain flora and fauna are unique in many ways, but several of the mammals found on the savannas and in lowland rain forests are also found high in the mountains. The gorilla is found up to about eleven thousand feet on Karisimbi, and the chimpanzee up to about eight thousand feet on Ruwenzori. The leopard is common up to eleven thousand feet and lives permanently on Ruwenzori at an altitude of about thirteen thousand feet, where the temperature sinks to −5° to −10° C. every night. Elephants and buffaloes in Zaire climb up to ten or eleven thousand feet, and on Aberdare in Kenya we found the black rhinoceros and the waterbuck at about 10,200 feet. Giant forest hogs and bongo antelopes also climb high on the mountains. During an expedition on the northern slopes of Mount Kenya in March, 1966, we were surprised to find herds of zebras, elands, and other antelopes between twelve thousand and 13,500 feet.

During long periods the animals adapted to life on Africa's high mountains were not disturbed by man. The inaccessibility, the cold, damp climate, the density of vegetation were obstacles to man and his livestock. This has now changed. Man penetrates with fire and cattle higher and higher up the mountain slopes, violating the forests and threatening the animals living there.

The Mountain Gorilla

The mountain gorilla (*Gorilla gorilla berengei*), a close relative of the lowland gorilla, is one of the most interesting mammals. In a remote past the two subspecies were presumably united by a continuous distribution across the Zaire equatorial rain forest.

It is really astonishing how persistent man has been in his efforts to exaggerate the frightening aspects of wild animals. They are accused of being ferocious or otherwise dangerous. And so legends have grown and rumours have been given the status of facts even in textbooks. But when these animals are studied scientifically in their natural environments, it is found that many of these charges are wildly exaggerated. Zoological field work has during recent years exonerated one species after another.

One of the last to have been cleared is the gorilla. Since this species is man's closest relative and is in many ways an admirable animal, it has a special interest for man. I have been fortunate to be able to observe several gorillas in the mountain forests of Zaire, to watch them at play and during their siestas, and have lived for months in their habitats. It is impossible not to feel attracted to these animals. The behaviour of gorillas toward one another indicates that they are peaceful animals. Quarrels and fights, either among members of a family or between groups, are exceptional. The males are not rivals for the favours of the females, and the family patriarch allows young males to choose their sexual partners at will.

In its dealing with other animals such as man, the gorilla is a very friendly creature. In the forests on the volcanoes of Zaire, gorillas live as good neighbors with buffaloes, forest duikers, tree hyraxes, and leopards. Once, in a *Hagenia* wood on the slope of Karisimbi, I saw a leopard resting just above a group of at least ten gorillas. They took no notice of each other. Gorillas show the same friendly or simply neutral attitude toward human beings. Talk about their aggressiveness is based on misinterpretation and/or exaggeration by sensation-seeking journalists, authors of travel books, and big-game hunters. There is no proof of a single case of a gorilla attacking a man unless it has been wounded or seriously provoked. The male leader's demonstration of displeasure against a human being is not made until he finds that his herd, after retreating repeatedly, is still threatened or harassed. His display of temper, which lasts for about half a minute, is a violent but peaceful attempt to frighten away the intruder. If this fails repeatedly, he attacks and will fight bravely. This is why ruthless hunters and inexperienced photographers who have ignored such warnings have been attacked by gorillas in Zaire.

Paradoxically, about 75 percent of the mountain gorillas live in the lowland rain forests of eastern Zaire, in about the same environment as their relatives in West Africa. The name "mountain gorilla" is, however, not entirely misleading, for probably the greatest concentrations, four hundred and five hundred individuals, live on the Virunga volcanoes, most of them at an altitude of ten to eleven thousand feet.

It is interesting to observe that mountain gorillas in the lowlands of Kivu about 2,500 feet above sea level prefer to live in secondary forests, rich in ground vegetation, around roads and villages, instead of in the dense forests where the closed canopy excludes light, allowing only meager undergrowth. Like the okapi, the gorilla lives on juicy plants, stalks, and leaves. He also finds these in the primeval mountain rain forests, where light always penetrates to the ground and the ground vegetation therefore is highly developed. Of the different belts of vegetation on the volcanoes, it is the broad-leaved woods of *Hagenia abyssinica* with their dense undergrowth which are the favourite haunts of gorillas. Nowhere in Virunga are these forests so richly developed as on the slopes of the extinct volcanoes Karisimbi and Mikeno. These are the headquarters of the mountain gorillas.

The nomadic life of the gorillas, which is conditioned by their need for food, has many parallels with that of the pygmies in Zaire. The latter are nomadic for the same reason although less mobile than the gorilla, using the same quarters at night for at least a month or more before they move on to new hunting grounds. Many anthropologists consider the forest pygmies of Zaire the most primitive of human beings, but it is perhaps only a coincidence that much of their biology and nomadic life resembles that of the gorilla: both move about in clans, are specialized to forests, live on what the woods yield, climb trees skillfully but prefer to live on the ground, and live in harmony with members of their own and other clans.

The mountain gorillas are not in immediate danger of extermination. But the Africans and their cattle are advancing up toward the montane and bamboo forests. Trees are being felled and the ground grazed and trampled bare. If this is not stopped in time, the mountain gorillas on the Virunga volcanoes are doomed. The threat comes from Rwanda and Uganda to the east. In the west, Zaire respects the fact that the gorilla's domain is in the Albert National Park, oldest of Africa's national parks. The authorities in Kinshasa (Léopoldville) and in Kivu have promised to do their utmost to preserve the living space of the gorillas. Unfortunately, Rwandan tribesmen with cattle moved into the Albert National Park from November, 1967, to June, 1968, destroying large parts of the gorilla habitats. Many gorillas have died from starvation. Constant disturbance causes a heavy mortality and no successful reproduction. In 1968–69 the cattle and the human beings were moved out from the gorilla areas in Zaire, but the situation is less satisfactory in Rwanda.

Hoofed Mountaineers

In the higher mountains of southern Ethiopia south and east of the Rift Valley lives the mountain nyala (*Tragelaphus buxtoni*), an antelope found nowhere else. It occurs here in such mountain ranges as the Chilalo, Gugu, Sahatu, and Mendebo, and possibly also in the Aselta and Arussi mountains. It is found chiefly above 9,500 feet, ranging vertically from high cedar forests (*Juniperus procera*) up to the belts of giant heath (*Erica arborea*) and St.-John's-wort (*Hypericum*).

The nyala population in the Mendebo Mountains alone is estimated at from 1,500 to two thousand, and in the Bale Mountains live about a thousand animals within a reserve, according to an estimate in 1971. It is believed that the whole population still numbers between four and five thousand animals. This is not much for a species that is living in habitats disturbed by man and where it is kept down by illegal shooting.

Unfortunately, one cannot be optimistic at all about another of Ethiopia's animal treasures, the walia ibex (*Capra walie*). This is the southernmost of all latter-day ibexes and, as a Palearctic element in Africa, of great zoogeographic interest. As far as zoologists know, the walia ibex has always had a restricted range in Ethiopia, but it must in the very remote past have been in touch with other ibexes living to the north, where its nearest neighbour is the rare Nubian ibex (*C. ibex nubiana*), which has been seriously reduced in recent years as a result of poaching, not only in Africa but also in the mountains of southwestern Asia, where it has vanished from large parts of its former range.

All reports of the walia ibex originate from the Simien Mountains in northern Ethiopia, where it lives on a fourteen-thousand-foot escarpment on the northern side of the mountains. The number of this ibex in 1969 was estimated to be about 150. This is a dangerously low number, particularly since heavy poaching and habitat destruction go on in Ethiopia despite the fact that a national park was established in 1970 in the Simien Mountains in order to protect the walia. Nevertheless, the killing continued in 1971. During the last few months of 1971, five walia ibexes were killed illegally.

In quite another part of mountainous Africa lives the Cape

mountain zebra (*Equus zebra zebra*). This small zebra once occurred in the mountain ranges of southernmost Africa from Nama-
qualand to the Drakensberg, where it climbed on steep slopes up
to about seven thousand feet. It must have been the first zebra
ever seen by Europeans. Apparently it was not particularly numerous when white men began to settle in the Cape area, because as
early as 1656 it was already being protected by Jan van Riebeek.
By 1937 the Mountain Zebra National Park was established on a
farm in the eastern Cape Province, where there were six zebras.
This herd is now thriving. In 1965 there were fifty-seven animals
in the national park and seventy-five in the whole of South Africa.
In 1971 the former figure had increased to 127 animals and the
latter to 166.

Another race, Hartman's mountain zebra (*E. z. hartmannae*),
inhabits the dry mountains of South-West Africa. Formerly this
zebra had a much wider range, but at present even the occurrence
within South-West Africa is very restricted, and this race is now
rare. The population in 1967 was estimated at about seven thousand, a decline of 3,500 from 1962.

A Vanishing Mountain Fox

The northern Simien fox (*Simenia simensis simensis*) is an
endemic inhabitant of the Simien Mountains and perhaps other
highlands in Shoa of northern Ethiopia. Still in 1963 this fox was
common in the Simien, but after then it was accused without
justification of being a sheep-killer and a relentless persecution
was initiated. In a few years the fox became endangered and is
now down to very low numbers. There are only one or two individuals in the newly established Simien National Park.

Birds

Among the birds some highland species of Africa are considered
very rare, but this may be partly owing to the fact that we do not
know much about them.

This seems to be true of Swiestra's francolin (*Francolinus
swierstrai*) of the Angola highland and the Tadjoura francolin
(*F. ochropectus*), which is recorded only from a nine-square-mile
area of cedar forest on the Plateau du Day in French Somaliland.
Similarly, Prince Ruspoli's touraco (*Tauraco ruspolii*) seems to

be confined to one or two juniper woods in the mountains of southwestern Ethiopia. However, in 1970–71, this rare bird has been observed also in dry *Acacia* scrub, which may indicate that it is less specialized than has hitherto been thought.

One of the Old World's most magnificent birds is the bearded vulture (*Gypaëtus barbatus meridionalis*), which is found in Eritrea, Ethiopia, Uganda, Kenya, Tanzania, Lesotho, and South Africa. The largest populations seem to occur in the high mountains of Ethiopia and Natal. Everywhere in its range this bird is a rarity, and in many areas it is decreasing because of shooting and poisoning. It is protected in many countries, but as long as poison baits are spread indiscriminately for jackals and hyenas this bird will fall victim to this weapon. Another bird of prey on the official list of rare birds is the Teita falcon (*Falco fasciinucha*), which occurs in eastern tropical Africa, chiefly in the highlands. It breeds in "wind holes" in steep cliffs in the gorges of the Zambezi, below the Victoria Falls, between Zambia and Rhodesia. It is everywhere rare, but this is probably owing to natural factors that are still unknown.

Among ornithologists working in Africa, Grauer's green broadbill (*Pseudocalyptomena graueri*) is an almost legendary bird. Although this green broadbill occurs in a very limited area it is not extremely rare. It lives near plantations or in forests in the highlands of eastern Zaire and southwestern Uganda. Grauer's cuckoo shrike (*Coracina graueri*) of the highland forests of eastern Zaire has long been considered rare. However, locally this cuckoo shrike is rather common, for instance in the Lutunguru area west of Lake Edward and on the lower slopes of the Itombwe Mountains above the western shores of Lake Tanganyika, where I saw it on several occasions in 1952. As long as its forest habitats are preserved there are no threats to its survival.

Two races of the dappied bulbul (*Phyllastrephus orostruthus*) are known only from eastern Africa. The nominate race, *P. o. orostruthus,* has been found in forests of the Namuli Mountains in northern Mozambique, while the other subspecies, *P. o. amani,* occurs in the Usambara Mountains in Tanzania. The Teita olive thrush (*Turdus helleri*) also has a very restricted distribution, being confined to patches of relict forests on the Teita Hills and Mount Mbololo in Kenya. The situation is the same with the Kupe Mountain bush shrike (*Telephorus kupeensis*) in Cameroon and the Warsangli linnet (*Warsanglia johannis*) of eastern Somalia.

Finally, two little-known swifts merit mentioning. The scarce swift (*Apus myoptilus*), which occurs in the highlands of eastern Africa from Ethiopia to Rhodesia, is on the official list of rare birds, but hardly deserves such a place. The other species, the Luanda swift (*A. toulsoni*), is known only from Cabinda and Angola, and is dealt with here because its breeding habitat is still unknown.

A Unique Toad and a Unique Tortoise

In the rain forest region of tropical West Africa there are several mountains separated from one another by lowland forests and savannas. One of the most interesting of these equatorial massifs is Mount Nimba, situated on the border between Liberia, Guinea, and the Ivory Coast. It lies some 170 miles from the Atlantic coast and its greatest elevation is 1,752 meters. The isolation of Mount Nimba gives it the character of a great inselberg, and has produced a great number of endemic animal species— about two hundred. Whether this remarkable number is due to the fact that the massif served as a refuge for animals that had a wider distribution during previous pluvial periods, or to the fact that these animals through isolation have evolved from ancestral forms, this massif is very important for speciation studies and research in evolution.

The origin of the savannas of Mount Nimba has been much discussed. Many consider them the remnants of man's burning and clearing and the grazing of livestock. But the visitor gets another impression. Various features of these grasslands, made up mainly of *Andropogon* and *Loudetia,* indicate that they are an ancient type of natural savanna probably representing a vegetational climax in this area. They have produced a great number of unique animal species, including the only endemic vertebrate of Nimba, the toad *Nectophrynoïdes occidentalis.* One race of this toad seems to be adapted to the high savannas of Nimba (not above 3,500 feet), but another not yet described subspecies occurs also in the forest and, what is more remarkable, in the industry landscape of a mining area. However, it is uncertain whether the two races of *Nectophrynoïdes* can survive the far-reaching habitat alterations on Mount Nimba.

This little batrachian is not any ordinary toad. Its nearest relatives, found on the mountains of East Africa, live in trees. Besides this, the female of the species, after a period of gestation lasting eight to nine months, gives birth to living young; they do not pass through a larval stage in water, which is of course very helpful in these mountain savannas. From the evolutionary aspect, this little toad is exceedingly interesting, for many phases of its reproduction are similar to those of mammals; it is an amphibian whose evolution has not followed the paths taken by its kin.

The African pancake tortoise (*Malacochersus tornieri*) lives in mountains of Kenya and Tanzania, where thanks to its flat body it can take refuge in narrow rocky crevices and under stones. When it is disturbed it inflates its body to such a size that it is almost impossible to drag it out from its shelter. Recently an important pet trade has developed, and if this trend continues the existence of this species will be threatened. Its reproduction is very slow, because only one egg is laid at a time. Moreover, a high number of these tortoises are certainly killed or seriously injured when collectors try to pull the inflated tortoises out by force from their rocky holes.

LAKES, MARSHES, AND RIVERS

About two-thirds of the surface of Africa is drained by six great rivers—the Nile, Zaire, Niger, Zambezi, Limpopo, and Orange. Many African rivers flow through vast swamps. Marshes are rather common at altitudes of four thousand to 7,500 feet in the African highlands. They are the remains of former lakes and some of them cover vast areas. The plant communities in them vary with the height above sea level and the length of time they are flooded every year. Many of these marshes are dominated by papyrus (*Cyperus*). Reed grass (*Phragmites communis*) may cover immense areas, and floating islands of both papyrus and cattail are also common. The marshes are often surrounded by palms of the species *Phoenix reclinata,* and the surface of the water may be completely covered by floating bouquets of *Pistia stratiotes,* aquatic plants over which the jaçanas trip daintily.

But it is the animal life in and above the water that is extraordinary in its variety. The fish fauna is usually rich, although varying in abundance depending on the rainy and dry periods. Amphibians and reptiles, including crocodiles, monitors, and snakes, are usually common in the marshes, and many bird species —herons, storks, geese, ducks, waders, crakes, and warblers—

live there seasonally or all the year round. Of the mammals, hippopotamuses are outstanding, as are several species of antelopes.

In many ways, Lake Tanganyika is the most interesting of the great lakes of Africa. It is the longest lake in the world (420 miles) and has an area of 12,700 square miles. It is 2,500 feet above sea level and 4,777 feet deep; only Lake Baikal in Siberia is deeper—and by only 150 feet. When it is remembered that the surrounding mountains attain a height of ten thousand feet, the thought of the creation of this colossal fissure valley staggers the imagination.

The great age of Lake Tanganyika is reflected in its animal life. The degree of specialization of the animals to their environment, the pronounced speciation, and the astonishing number of unique species must be seen as the result of the long periods of time the lake has been isolated and without outlet. For example, the number of species of the family *Cichlidae* alone in Lake Tanganyika is 133, of which 131 are endemic. The various species have evolved during millions of years toward an effective utilization of every existing niche in the lake. This has resulted in an exceptionally high energy flow through various food chains—algae-plankton-fishes—resulting in an immense bioproductivity. Many African lakes show similar features, but for Lake Tanganyika it is remarkable, because below a depth of about four hundred meters there is no oxygen. This means that about two-thirds of the lake is a freshwater desert without life.

In lakes Tanganyika and Nyasa there are several fishes which have extremely narrow ecological niches along the rocky shores. They are so specialized to these pocket areas that they can hardly escape successfully from their habitats. Further reduction of such small populations through disturbance could hurt them permanently.

The disastrous effects that may result from introducing plants from a foreign region can be seen in the Zaire River, where the South American water hyacinth (*Eichhornia crassipes*) appeared in 1954. The species seems to have enjoyed optimum conditions in the Zaire River, the plants becoming larger and tougher than they were in their native South America and reproducing more rapidly. In a short time several rivers in the Zaire basin were covered with a green carpet of floating water hyacinths; the plants prevent fishermen from using their boats and they threaten transport, which in Zaire is based largely on the waterways. Various methods of control have been tried at great cost. In some of the more important stretches of the Zaire system the plants have been more or less brought under control, but they are still invading new watercourses and have also appeared, owing to man, elsewhere in Africa than in the Zaire.

Something similar has occurred in a very brief time in Lake Kariba, an enormous artificial lake in Rhodesia and Zambia created near the end of the 1950's to provide water for a hydroelectric plant. There another introduced aquatic plant, *Salvinia,* is spreading rapidly over the lake and causing much trouble, as it has done in other African lakes where it has been introduced.

Aquatic habitats in Africa have long evolutionary periods behind them in the same way as the terrestrial ones. The recent freshwater communities represent in intact stage a climax and a delicate hydrological-biological balance with a very high productivity, even when measured exclusively from man's point of view. The value of the fisheries in African lakes and rivers as well as many other products from them is immense. They ought to be managed and utilized with utmost care. In a very short time man can upset what it has taken thousands of years to create.

Examples of such disruptions are manifold. Introductions of exotic fish can lead to total and local extinction of indigenous fish. Such a case is a unique monotypic cyprinid, *Barbus quathlambae* (previously erroneously placed in the genus *Labeo*), that has, since the introduction of trout in South Africa prior to 1936, become extinct. No specimens have been collected or observed since 1938. It was the only survivor of a form of cyprinids which must have had a much wider distribution in the past. The same fate probably awaits two other rare and endemic cyprinids, *B. treurensis* and *B. travelyani,* confined to rivers where trouts are established.

Also, pollution by sewage effluent or other oxygen-removing organic substances, or by waste chemical products and pesticides, has certainly in several cases contributed to the decline in numbers of some species, for instance of a popular angling fish, the smallmouth yellowfish (*B. holubi*). It is interesting that the provincial departments of South Africa devote much attention and research to the artificial breeding of important native angling fishes, which are reduced by the impact of introduced species. Is it good economy?

The common carp (*Cyprinus carpio*), exotic for Africa, has become established in many rivers of South Africa, where it is undoubtedly a competitor for living space and food. Also, in rivers that have been stocked with active predators such as trouts (*Salmo trutta, S. gairdneri,* and *Salvelinus fontinalis*) as well as smallmouth and largemouth basses (*Micropterus dolomieui* and *M. salmoides*), populations of small indigenous species have decreased or disappeared. The smaller tributaries are now their temporary sanctuary.

Overexploitation has caused a serious decline in certain species or populations of fish. In some rivers the spawning runs of some species have been reduced to fractions of their former abundance. Particularly mudsuckers (*Labeo*), noted for their migrations up rivers in flood to spawning sites in inundated areas, are vulnerable. During their migrations many thousands of mudsuckers are trapped at various localities along the rivers and a tremendous toll is taken of breeding adults.

Fortunately, relatively few other animals in African waters are threatened by extermination. Among the fishes the blind African cave fish (*Caecobarbus geertsi*) may be mentioned. It occurs in several caves in the neighbourhood of Thysville in western Zaire, where it has been protected. It is, however, extremely vulnerable to disturbance and can easily be wiped out. The case is the same with other blind fish of the genera *Caecomastacembelus, Eilichthys, Phreatichtys, Typhleotris,* and *Uegitglanis,* which are usually cave-dwellers and very specialized as to their habitats.

Micropanchax schoellerei, a formerly very common fish in parts of the lower Nile system, seems to have been exterminated there during the last decade. Recently it has been found in the Lake Chad basin, where it was not previously known.

The Nile crocodile (*Crocodylus niloticus*) is by no means rare in some reserves in Africa, but it has been decimated in most waters, and this killing continues. Locally it has been exterminated over wide areas of Africa. It is true that large old crocodiles seek meat and therefore occasionally kill human beings, but there is no reason to slaughter crocodiles wantonly. They play a useful part in the ecology of freshwater communities, where they help to check fish predators. Where crocodiles have been exterminated, the fishery yield has gone down drastically owing to the predation by unchecked carnivorous fish on fishes useful to man. In many waters, crocodiles prey mainly on barbels, which in their turn feed on fish preying on bilharzia-carrying snails. The result will presumably be an increase of bilharzia, which is one of the most fatal diseases to man in the tropics. On the whole, the crocodile is a good partner to the fisherman and, when wisely managed, of direct economic importance not only for its ecological role but also as a producer of skin and meat. The other two species of African crocodiles, the dwarf crocodile (*Osteolemus tetraspis*) and the slender-snout crocodile (*Crocodylus cataphractus*), have also been depleted throughout their ranges for the same reasons as the Nile crocodile. All three species have been protected in Zaire since 1969 following a suggestion by IUCN.

The most threatened of African freshwater vertebrates is the West African manatee (*Trichechus senegalensis*). Its former range is not known, but at present it occupies coastal lagoons, lakes, and rivers from Senegal to Angola. In some rivers, for instance, the Niger system, it is distributed in upper watercourses several miles from the coast. However, because its meat is prized and has a high commercial value, the manatee is constantly being trapped, speared, or shot and is becoming rarer all the time. The West African manatee is protected by law, but inadequately. This is unfortunate, because this creature feeds on aquatic plants and is a very valuable natural resource. The West Indian manatee (*T. manatus*) feeds largely on the water hyacinth; perhaps its West African relative could do likewise and thus check the spread of this plant in the Zaire River system. It already lives in the estuary of the Zaire River, and may feed on the *Eichhornia* that is constantly floating out to sea, but it is unable to swim in the rapids or scale the numerous falls and cataracts above the estuary.

Some marshes in Africa are inhabited by aquatic antelopes, which are admirably adapted to inundated flood plains and permanently water-covered areas. One of these antelopes is the lechwe (*Kobus leche*), of which three subspecies, the red lechwe (*K. l. leche*), the Kafue lechwe (*K. l. kafuensis*), and the black lechwe (*K. l. smithemani*) have in recent years dropped in numbers to a dangerously low level. The Kafue lechwe, confined to the Kafue Flats in Zambia, has been reduced from about 250,000 animals in 1934 to about 25,000 in the 1960's, but in 1971 its number had increased to about 94,000. This seems to be still quite a number, but the sex ratio of the Kafue herds is for the moment claimed to be six males to every female. The vulnerability of pregnant females seems to increase this disproportion. However, the unusual sex ratio may be a miscalculation due to the congregation of males during certain periods of the year. Unfortunately, the food availability and the range of the Kafue lechwe has been reduced owing to the construction of a dam in the Kafue Gorge. The position of the black lechwe is even more perilous. This sub-species is almost solely restricted to the Bangweulu Swamp in Zambia, where it has decreased, probably because of poaching, from about 150,000 in 1932 to no more than four thousand in 1966. This is tragic, because the vast inundated grasslands bordering the swamps cannot be used for any other purpose or by any other large herbivorous mammal than the black lechwe, which is especially adapted to this kind of habitat. Therefore, this antelope constitutes a natural resource of extreme importance. A normal population of the black lechwe, that is, 150,000 animals, could be cropped and produce about a thousand tons of meat annually. In 1970–71 this subspecies had increased to sixteen to twenty thousand animals. The most threatened of the three races of the lechwe is the red lechwe, of which there are about 1,700 animals. In 1970 there were six to eight hundred in the Kafue National Park, six to eight hundred in the Lukanga-Kafue areas, and about a hundred in Barotseland.

The story of the lechwe antelopes and their habitats in Zambia during the last four decades offers an example of how large populations in Africa are destroyed through human misuse. The Kafue Flats were in the early 1930's not only the habitat of the 250,000 Kafue lechwes but also of thousands of other ungulates such as wildebeest (*Connochaetes taurinus*), hartebeest (*Alcelaphus lichtensteini*), puku (*Kobus vardoni*), reedbuck (*Redunca arundinum*), oribi (*Ourebia ourebi*), roan (*Hippotragus equinus*), sitatunga (*Tragelaphus spekei*), eland (*Taurotragus oryx*), buffalo (*Syncerus caffer*), zebra (*Equus burchelli*), and hippopotamus (*Hippopotamus amphibius*). To this cohort of ungulate species were added other species living in the vicinity of the Kafue Flats, which they entered seasonally or occasionally. No less than eleven other species of ungulates did so. In addition, thirty rodents and shrews made use of the floodplains. Among them were three species of giant and cane rats, which are extremely useful as a protein resource for human beings.

Obviously this extraordinary gathering of herbivores on and around the floodplains of the Kafue Flats was accompanied by an assemblage of carnivores, which added to the richness and productivity of the area. No less than twenty-three species of carnivores were or are living in the area.

The big herds became increasingly slaughtered during the

1930's and 1940's, so in 1952 all species had become much reduced; but still one could see an unbroken line of lechwes, reed-
bucks, oribis, wildebeests, buffaloes, and zebras along the western parts of the Kafue Flats (Bainbridge in 1967).

At the present time herds of lechwes, wildebeests, roans, buffaloes and zebras are found only in limited areas, but still at certain times of the year the concentrations of lechwes are immensely
impressive—for those who have not seen the enormous herds some
decades ago.

The rapid decrease in the ungulate populations of the Kafue
Flats has in a short time eliminated or reduced extremely useful
and valuable animal resources, simply because the slaughtering
exceeded the reproductive capacity of these ungulates despite the
fact that they are very productive.

With wise management and conservation measures the animal
populations of the Kafue Flats and particularly the Kafue lechwe
could be restored provided the habitats do not change drastically.
However, the hydroelectric dam that will permanently flood the
lower part of the Flats and considerably alter the ecology of other
parts constitutes a threat to the animals that may be even more
serious than the human predation. The animals using the floodplains have for millenniums been adapted to the pattern of seasonally varying habitat conditions. The natural water cycles will now
be upset and replaced by irregular and prolonged flood periods.
Therefore, the future of the animals of the Kafue Flats is not
bright. The protein value and the tourist attraction value to Zambia
represented by the mammals and birds of the Kafue Flats—the
most productive habitat in the country—are in the long-term
sense without doubt higher than the electricity value produced by
the Kafue River above the Flats. The mistake has already been
made. Therefore, it is of vital importance that the artificial floods
at the Kafue Flats follow the same pattern in time and space as
the natural flood regime. If this is not done it is likely that the
tremendously rich and spectacular floodplain communities of
mammals in the thousands and birds in the millions will be
gradually destroyed owing to habitat alterations and other disturbances.

The Cameroon clawless otter (*Paraonyx microdon*) is restricted
to rivers and surrounding areas in Cameroon, where it has been
heavily persecuted by man for its valuable pelt. This species is
now seriously endangered.

MADAGASCAR

Biogeographically, Madagascar is almost as peculiar as Australia. The latter area was cut off from Asia more than fifty million years ago, while Madagascar was separated from the African mainland at least twenty million years ago. In both cases the evolution of plants and animals has followed a unique pattern. Eighty-six percent of the plant species of Madagascar are endemic. Also, the fauna of Madagascar is very distinctive, though with affinities as far as vertebrates are concerned mainly with Africa.

Madagascar is tropical and chiefly mountainous. The sea around the island is, in general, deep. The wide Mozambique Channel varies from about five hundred to more than 1,500 fathoms deep. Ecologically Madagascar is a diverse island with such habitats as subdesert brush, open savannas, dry forests, and rain forests. Many of its endemic species are very specialized in terms of certain habitats. Therefore the ravaging of the countryside by "development schemes" and other exploitation has had deplorable results. About 70 percent of Madagascar's natural vegetation and 90 percent of its forests have been destroyed by man, and with them many unique and rare animal species, despite the fact that man has not existed in Madagascar more than 1,400 to two thousand years. Today there are more than ten million zebu cattle in Madagascar, which exploit productive habitats in a very destructive way. Many of the herds roam in a semiwild state, feeding and reproducing freely but without being controlled by predators. Furthermore, between 1930 and 1940 red deer and fallow deer were introduced. They are detrimental to the native vegetation, which has evolved without pressure from ungulate browsing. The main reasons for the rapid disappearance of the Malagasy forests are man-made fires, slashing for pastures, and shifting cultivation. In the past, the plateau forests of Madagascar were eliminated from wide areas around each village in order to detect attacking enemies from neighbouring villages.

Among mammals, four families (one of tenrecs, three of lemurs) are peculiar to Madagascar and as many as seven genera (all lemurs) are endemic. Of other recent vertebrates on Madagascar no class is represented by endemic families, but they do show many peculiarities. The bird fauna is also very distinct. No family exists on Madagascar alone, but considering the whole Malagasy area (which includes Madagascar, the Comoros, Mauritius, Réunion, the Seychelles, and other neighbouring islands) as a faunal region, there are not less than seven recent families and two extinct ones peculiar to this region. Among the 182 species of birds of Madagascar, not less than two-thirds are peculiar to the island; and of the order *Passeriformes* as many as 95 percent, a remarkably high proportion. Among the reptiles there are thirty-two species of chameleons, a greater number than in any other region, and two-thirds of the world's chameleon species. Many of the reptile genera are endemic. This is also true of the amphibians, including about 150 endemic frogs.

Madagascar has already lost many of its unique animals. The largest mammal ever known to have occurred on Madagascar was a pygmy hippopotamus (*Hippopotamus lemerlei*) belonging to another species than the one now existing in West Africa. It was abundant in the Pleistocene epoch and, according to carbon-14 analysis, existed between 780 and 1,180 years ago. It is not improbable that man was implicated in the disappearance of this, the island's greatest meat producer. Two genera of large terrestrial lemuroids (*Palaeopropithecus* with at least one species, *P. ingens,* and *Archaelemur majori*) as well as several arboreal lemuroids (probably fourteen species) became extinct within a few centuries after man's occupation of Madagascar, which, as mentioned above, was a recent event.

However, it is the Malagasy birds which once showed truly spectacular forms. They survived in Madagascar until historical times. Man was surely responsible for wiping out these giant flightless birds, whose large eggs, not to speak of the birds themselves, must have represented an attractive food and tool resource. One of these giants, the great elephant bird (*Aepyornis maximus*), stood nine to ten feet high and probably still existed as late as 1659. The egg was fourteen and one-half inches long and weighed as much as forty-seven pounds.

The Madagascar coucal (*Coua delalandei*) probably met the same fate. It was a member of a genus well represented on Madagascar but this species was restricted to a small island off the east coast. There it was often trapped, until the last one was reported shortly before 1930. Despite large sums offered to local hunters, they could not find a single coucal. The destruction of its habitat probably contributed to the extermination of this magnificent bird.

The Madagascar giant tortoise (*Testudo grandidieri*) was

extinct before the arrival of the Europeans, but was probably exterminated by the first human invaders. Also another gigantic tortoise, *T. abrupta,* became apparently extinct in historic time, but in this case man was probably not involved.

Threatened Mammals of Madagascar

Madagascar is extraordinarily rich in small primates, and almost all of them are in danger of extinction. True lemurs are peculiar to Madagascar; fully twenty species are found on the island. They are mainly nocturnal and arboreal; most of them are cat-sized with well-developed tails and martenlike muzzles. Their food ranges from fruit and insects to herbs. According to a comprehensive study of the *Lemuridae* of Madagascar by the French zoologist J.-J. Petter, the climate is far more important than the vegetation in determining the distribution and dispersal of lemurs. No preference for particular strata in the forest could be found in the various species. But Petter's findings do not affect the fact that forests are essential for these primates.

Lemurs in Madagascar are officially protected by law, but the poaching is extensive and even in the reserves the control is almost nil. It is quite clear that if the destruction of forests goes on at the present rate, most of the lemurs of Madagascar will become extinct in the near future. One species, the hairy-eared mouse lemur (*Cheirogaleus trichotis*), had long been considered extinct. It was known from only a single specimen described in 1875, and was not seen again until 1966. In 1967 it was described as a new genus, *Allocebus.*

One of the rarest lemurs of Madagascar is Coquerel's dwarf lemur (*Microcebus coquereli*). It has been collected or observed at three localities in western Madagascar, but today seems to exist only in one locality near Morondava. Obviously its gradual decrease is due to habitat destructions. The same fate has caused the decline of the fat-tailed dwarf lemur (*Cheirogaleus medius*). Two subspecies (*medius* and *samati*) are threatened, and the eastern one is perhaps already extinct. As late as 1929–31 the squirrel-like fork-marked dwarf lemur (*Phaner furcifer*) was reported as fairly common in an inland area east of Cape St. Vincent and in the rain forest on Mount d'Ambre in the extreme north of the island. It has been found in eight localities representing a wide diversity of habitats. Seven of these areas are in western Madagascar. Today the only reliable reports of this lemur come from widely separated localities.

The weasel lemur (*Lepilemur mustelinus*) is divided into five races, three of them on the official list of endangered animals. The red-tailed lemur (*L. m. ruficaudatus*) now occurs only in six areas along the western forests of Madagascar. Its decline is due not only to the destruction of forests but also to the fact that its meat is highly appreciated. It is also a slow-moving animal and is easily caught. The white-footed weasel lemur (*L . m. leucopus*), now found only in one area in southern Madagascar, lives in a savanna-woodland habitat and seems to be adapted to the remains of a *Didierea* forest, which is unique to Madagascar. The third endangered subspecies is the slender weasel lemur (*L. m. dorsalis*), which appears to occur only in the southern part of an island, Nosy-Bé, off the northwestern coast of Madagascar.

The species *Lemur macaco* is divided into eight subspecies, of which four are regarded as in danger of extermination. Among them are the black lemur (*L. m. macaco*), which is now restricted to only one locality in northwestern Madagascar and two others on islands off the mainland. Up to a hundred years ago the black lemur ranged across ten times the area. Sclater's lemur (*L. m. flavifrons*), today confined to a small area south of the range of the black lemur, is in great danger because the clearing and burning of forest constantly reduces its space of existence. Since its discovery, Sanford's lemur (*L. m. sanfordi*) has been limited to the rain forest of Mount d'Ambre in northernmost Madagascar, which has suffered from burning and cutting and from a plantation near Joffreville. The red-fronted lemur (*L. m. rufus*) was not long ago a common animal across a vast range of western and central Madagascar. Now it occurs in only four areas within its former range.

The two existing races of *Lemur mongoz* are both threatened by the uncontrolled destruction of forest in Madagascar. The mongoose lemur (*L. m. mongoz*) formerly occurred within a broad strip from the west coast into the interior and on some of the Comoro Islands between the African mainland and Madagascar. Its present distribution is limited to two localities on Madagascar but nothing is known of its status on the Comoro Islands. As late as thirty or forty years ago the crowned lemur (*L. m. coronatus*) was very common in dry wooded parts of northern Madagascar and on Mount d'Ambre. The range has now been sharply reduced.

The grey gentle lemur (*Hapalemur griseus griseus*) and the olivaceous gentle lemur (*H. g. olivaceus*) are races of the same species. Both are now rare, but in the recent past their ranges covered most parts of Madagascar. Both are forest-dwellers with a predilection for dense thickets of bamboos. One of the rarest and least-known lemurs is the reed lemur (*Hapalemur simus*). Recent reports to the IUCN indicate that this species prefers a marshy habitat with reeds and that it occurs only on the shores of Lake Alaotra and nearby marshes in northeastern Madagascar. Such a semiaquatic habitat gives it a certain protection, but on the other hand, Lake Alaotra and the surrounding marshes are diminishing in area every year. Moreover, fishermen can capture reed lemurs by shaking the bamboos and reeds until the animals fall.

The largest of the lemurs is the indri (*Indri indri*), which less than seventy years ago was so common that one traveller reported that no one could travel from Tamatave to Antanarivo without often hearing the cries of these animals as he passed through the great forest. The indri has declined because it has been hunted and because the forests of northern Madagascar in which it was found have been seriously reduced. The sifaka (*Propithecus verreauxi*) was three hundred years ago a common animal, venerated by certain tribes and village populations, and therefore protected; but the destruction of forests and the abandonment of tribal taboos have affected the status of this lemur drastically. Five subspecies of the sifaka are recognized. The nominate race, *P. v. verreauxi,* formerly occupied all the southwestern and southern coastal forests of Madagascar. Sifaka populations have been reported from only five areas in recent years. Major's sifaka (*P. v. majori*) is the most endangered of all the five races. Van der Decken's sifaka (*P. v. deckenii*), the crowned sifaka (*P. v. coronatus*) and Coquerel's sifaka (*P. v. coquereli*) range in restricted areas of northwestern Madagascar. Perrier's sifaka (*P. diadema perrieri*) is confined to a small, diminishing forest in northernmost Madagascar. All these lemurs were reported to be "very common" about fifty years ago, but they are now gravely endangered.

Two races of the woolly avahi (*Avahi laniger*), the only species of this genus, live in Madagascar. As late as fifty years ago the western subspecies (*A. l. occidentalis*) was regarded as abundant; the eastern one (*A. l. laniger*) appeared to be less common. Now the western woolly avahi is rare and threatened. As the woolly avahi is strictly arboreal, it is doomed to perish with the reduction of forests. It is also snared by man for food.

Perhaps the most remarkable of all lemurs is the aye-aye (*Daubentonia madagascariensis*), the only member of its family. Formerly it occurred along the coastal rain forests of northeastern Madagascar and in a smaller area on the northwestern coast. Roughly the same distribution pattern was kept until the last decade but much reduced in size and concentrated to three areas isolated from each other. The strictly arboreal aye-aye is, of course, very vulnerable to the destruction of forests, which is threatening it seriously. Its last forest localities were destroyed in 1965, which caused the few remaining animals—only twelve to twenty—to invade plantations. Also, the aye-aye was an object of tribal veneration in Madagascar, but because the animals have been accused of doing damage on coconut plantations, they are now persecuted. In 1966–67, nine individuals were introduced in the island reserve of Nossi Mangabe, where one hopes that they may survive. All together there may still be forty to fifty aye-ayes in Madagascar.

A member of the unique and endemic family of tenrecs (*Limnogale mergulus*) is possibly already extinct. Some years ago it still existed in two areas of Madagascar.

The fossa (*Cryptoprocta ferox*), the largest carnivore of Madagascar and peculiar to the island, is also a vanishing species, chiefly owing to forest destruction.

Also, the Malagasy civet (*Fossa fossa*) from forests along the eastern coast and the falanouc (*Eupleres goudoti*) are endangered because of habitat changes.

Endangered Birds

Obviously the terrific destruction of forests in Madagascar also affects birds, but they can seek new areas more easily than can the threatened arboreal mammals. Nevertheless two species of birds have become extinct in historic time. They are commented upon on page 101.

Several birds are probably extinct or perhaps near extinction. It is likely that a unique species, the small-billed false sunbird (*Neodrepanis hypoxantha*), which seemed to be limited to the forests of northeastern Madagascar, is by now extinct. A recent expedition failed to find it in the restricted area. The Anjouan scops owl (*Otus rutilus capnodes*) may also be extinct because no birds have been observed since 1897, when this owl was collected in large numbers. This collecting for museums went on during 1884–97 and can be the cause of this owl's disappearance. Two other birds may already be extinct owing to the destruction of their forest habitats: Soumagne's owl (*Tyto soumagnei*), a forest bird from northeastern Madagascar that has not been recorded since 1929, and the Madagascar thick-billed cuckoo (*Pachycoccyx audeberti*) from the same area. Near extinction is the Anjouan Island sparrow hawk (*Accipiter francesii pusillus*) which is confined to Anjouan in the Comoros. Only one individual was seen during an expedition in 1958. The Madagascar serpent eagle (*Eutriorchis astur*) is also very rare and has not been observed for a long time. Two vangas, Pollen's vanga (*Xenopirostris polleni*) and van Dam's vanga (*X. damii*), are restricted to small areas of forest north of Fianasantsoa and at Ankarafantsika, where their future is insecure. Another of the threatened birds is the long-tailed ground roller (*Uratelornis chimaera*), which is largely terrestrial and has a weak flight. Such a species is of course particularly vulnerable; moreover, its habitat among bushes of the flat, sandy subdesert is rapidly deteriorating as a result of man's activities. Another endangered bird is the Madagascan teal (*Anas bernieri*), which is now very rare. In 1970 about sixty individuals were found in one lake. As soon as this became known, European sportsmen went there and killed more than 25 percent of the population, which is perhaps the only existing one in Madagascar. The Alaotra grebe (*Podiceps rufolavatus*) is found only in Lake Alaotra. Also low in number are the Moheli green pigeon (*Treron australis griveaudi*) and the Comoro blue pigeon (*Alectroenas sganzini sganzini*), both from the Comoros.

An Endangered Tortoise

One of Madagascar's largest tortoises has become very rare and must now be considered as threatened; it is the angulated tortoise (*Testudo yniphora*). It is restricted to an extremely limited habitat in northwestern Madagascar.

The Revival of a Fossil Fish

The animal of the Madagascar region that has become most famous during the last twenty-five years is a fish, the coelacanth (*Latimeria chalumne*), belonging to a group believed to have become extinct about seventy million years ago. *Latimeria* made its sensational appearance in 1938, when a specimen was caught off the coast of eastern South Africa. Other specimens were later taken in the waters around the Comoro Islands, where this living fossil seems to have its headquarters. It lives at moderate depths and is surrounded by many other fishes. Its biology is still a mystery, and no one has explained why it is the only species of this ancient group that has survived through millions of years. Or is it really the only one? The sea will certainly yield other such secrets in the future. Though we do not know if it is rare or not, *Latimeria* has proved itself unbelievably well able to take care of itself.

BALANCE FOR AFRICA

Man's treatment of the great African heritage, the wonderful, useful, and unique wealth of animal life, during historical time has produced a most discouraging balance sheet. Fourteen species or races of mammals, four of birds, two of reptiles, and one of fish have been exterminated. Of these twenty-one animals, no fewer than thirteen disappeared during the last three centuries. In addition one mammal, six birds, and two reptiles are probably extinct. Ninety-five mammals, forty birds, seven reptiles, two amphibians, and eleven fishes are critically threatened or are so rare that they may easily be wiped out.

The destruction of nature in terms of exterminated animals has been the worst in northern and southern Africa, where ten mammals (five in each region) and one, possibly two, birds in northern Africa and one fish in southern Africa have recently become extinct; while in tropical Africa two birds and in Madagascar also two birds have become extinct during the last three hundred years. In addition, five other birds and two reptiles are now probably extinct in Madagascar, while two reptiles there vanished at an earlier stage but still within historical time. It is true that in tropical Africa, which includes Madagascar, no mammals have been exterminated during these centuries despite drastic environmental changes, although one subspecies (a lemur) is probably now extinct. (The Malagasy pygmy hippopotamus, one of at least four Malagasy mammals extinct in recent time, vanished about 780 years ago. The other three are lemuroids, to which probably eleven other species should be added, but in their case they might have disappeared shortly prior to man's invasion of Madagascar.)

But it must be remembered that tropical Africa is today the last refuge of that great continent's wild animals. And even here no fewer than seventy-seven mammals (forty-seven on the mainland and thirty on Madagascar)—as well as thirty-one birds, six reptiles, two amphibians, and eight fishes—are facing extinction. In northern Africa thirteen mammals and seven birds are endangered, and in southern Africa five mammals, two birds, one reptile, and three fish.

Species and subspecies of vertebrates extinct during historical time, probably extinct, and at present endangered by extinction. (Figures within parentheses show extinction after 1700.)

CLASS	EXTINCT	PROBABLY extinct	ENDANGERED
Mammals	14 (9)	1	95
Birds	4 (3)	6	40
Reptiles	2 (0)	2	7
Amphibians	—	—	2
Fish	1 (1)	—	11
Total	21 (13)	9	155

CHAPTER THREE

Eurasia

The world's largest landmass, Eurasia, spans half the earth. Though usually divided into two continents, Europe and Asia, this immense area is a single physical complex. Its zones of climate range from the arctic to the tropics, and its vegetation ranges from tundra and coniferous forest in the north, through deciduous woodland, steppe, desert, and the Mediterranean maquis scrub in the central and southwestern parts, to tropical jungle and rain forest in the southeastern parts. There is also a tremendous variety of topography: from Lake Baikal, the world's deepest lake, to the Himalayas, the highest mountains. The great taiga is the world's largest forest, extending from the Scandinavian mountains in the west to the Pacific Ocean in the east. Also, the steppes of Eurasia are larger than any other similar vegetational region. And in the southeast one finds the earth's largest archipelago.

This extraordinary range of habitats within one continental block makes Eurasia very rich in animal species evolved over eons. The fact that this largest of continents was connected with Africa and America for long periods has also enriched the Eurasian fauna through animal migrations.

The earliest record of man in Eurasia is from Java and is believed to date back perhaps as much as 595,000 years, according to the Dutch anthropologist G. H. P. von Koenigswald. At that time northern Eurasia had already been affected by the repeated advance and retreat of immense glacial shields. At the height of the last glacial age, the oceans were several hundred feet lower than at the present time. Lands like Indonesia and the Philippines, perhaps also New Guinea and Australia, were not so widely separated as today. At least Indonesia was certainly connected with the mainland and with the Philippines as late as about eighteen thou-

sand years ago. These climatic oscillations, with long warm, interglacial stages between the cold periods, as well as the rise and fall
of the oceans, had a tremendous impact on animal distribution
patterns and migrations, and this is still going on.

The appearance of man in Java half a million years ago must
signify—provided that man's origin took place in distant Africa
and that he had not been able to reach southeastern Asia directly
over the sea—that he had invaded and dispersed across Asia
earlier than the fossil remains indicate. Hence man's presence in
western Asia is of ancient date. He had had much time to influence
and modify his environment. As in Africa, man's activities in
Eurasia has led to a great impoverishment of biocommunities and
species, especially since the process was initiated earlier in Asia
when man evolved more rapidly there. Through human misuse of
land during at least the last three thousand years, and perhaps as
much as ten thousand years, vast Asian areas have been completely
changed. Erosion, started by man, has resulted in incalculable
damage to fertile lands in most areas of temperate, subtropical,
and tropical Asia and in Mediterranean Europe, chiefly in areas
beyond the farthest Pleistocene glaciations. This habitat destruction has done great damage to the fauna.

In general, the Pleistocene ice sheets never reached so far
south in Asia as they did in Europe. This is significant because
there is a much greater resistance to effects of cultivation in
glaciated areas than in those that have never had an ice cover. The
temperate climate has also contributed greatly to the extraordinary
stability and fertility of cultivated areas of formerly glaciated
Eurasia.

The agricultural methods used in large areas of southern
Eurasia, perhaps combined with war and plundering, have over
thousands of years destroyed renewable natural resources. One
can follow this persistent disruption of the balance of nature far
back in history. The oldest civilizations in Asia, whether Chinese
or Indian, go back about twenty-five thousand years, but they do
not become important as destroyers of habitat until much later.
Probably agriculture spread westward from what today is Indonesia, China, and Burma. As early as 10,000 B.C., according to
carbon-14 dating, cave inhabitants in Burma cultivated beans and
chestnuts. About 6500 B.C., seed-crop agriculture was already in
use in Jordan, spreading to the Mediterranean countries and later

on to other areas of Europe, then expanding eastward into Siberia. Apparently early Egyptian agriculture did not influence the Mediterranean countries as much as the Asian patterns.

Such agriculture combined with forest destruction, fire, overgrazing, nomad invasions, and so on resulted in the collapse of the land. The shifting cultivation that has been practiced in tropical Asia since the Stone Age did little damage when populations were small; the forests had time to recover after having been slashed and burned. But in the last few centuries the enormously increased human population has made such agriculture a menace to man himself. Many tropical lands of Asia can no longer withstand the pressure of continuous cultivation. This is also true of the arid subtropical areas of southwestern Asia and Mediterranean Europe, where injurious agricultural methods were combined with the uncontrolled grazing of livestock. In both cases overexploitation cleared the way for erosion of various forms. Today vast areas lie bare, particularly in the homeland of pastoralism—southwestern Asia. Once-flourishing civilizations have in this way been reduced to little more than sandy deserts in the last few thousand years.

Eastern Asia, particularly China, has long been the scene of such land destruction. Once largely covered by forests, China today is only 9 percent forested. Not only have forests been destroyed for the sake of cultivation, but projects to tame great rivers have seriously impaired the fertility of the surrounding plains. Palynological data indicate that five to six thousand years ago the entire Levant was wooded, where today there are mostly deserts. There is no climatic change in this area, but during five thousand years it has been grazed by goats and sheep.

In northern Eurasia, particularly in highly industrialized Europe, natural regions have also been greatly modified. However, temperate zones are, as we have said, less vulnerable than subtropical and tropical areas; therefore, man's reshaping of the earth has been less drastic in the younger, northern areas than in the older, southern ones.

Hunting has also played a role in reducing or exterminating animal species in Eurasia, but it is primarily the destruction or modification of habitats that has wiped out animals or reduced them in number and range, although the hunter is often the one who exterminates directly.

In fact, less than a hundred years ago the steppes, high plateaus, and forests of Asia produced a variety of large mammal species which occurred in numbers that few other areas of the world could match. This wildlife heritage has been ruined in a tremendously short time and this process is still going on to the advantage of nobody. The great assemblages of herbivorous mammals of the plains, swamps, and forests have gone, but there are still people alive who recall the great profusion of wildlife which was a normal situation in the past.

ANIMAL FAMILIES PECULIAR TO EURASIA

In terms of animal life Eurasia is divided in two regions, the Palearctic and the Oriental. The latter includes the tropical part of Asia and extends some degrees north of the tropics, particularly in India. Arabia may be considered a transition zone. Hence, the Palearctic faunal regions cover an immense territory: all of Europe and more than two-thirds of Asia. Nevertheless, the Oriental region is the richest in vertebrate species. This also means that it is in this part of Eurasia that most species are threatened by extinction.

Eurasia does not show the same high number of endemic animal families as does Africa, because the animals moved back and forth across land bridges between the continents. In the Palearctic region most families are widely distributed over many continents and no vertebrate families are peculiar to it.

The Oriental region, embracing continental islands such as Ceylon, Sumatra, Java, Borneo, the Philippines, and Taiwan, has a rather large number of endemic families but not so many as the Ethiopian region in Africa. Mammalian families peculiar to tropical Asia are flying lemurs (*Cynocephalidae*), tree shrews (*Tupaiidae*), tarsiers (*Tarsiidae*), and spiny dormice (*Platacanthomyidae*). Among the birds only one family is exclusively Oriental, namely, the fairy bluebirds and leafbirds (*Irenidae*). Of reptilian families only one, *Lanthanotidae,* with a single species on Borneo, is restricted to Asia. Four fish families are endemic: *Homalopteridae* (loaches), *Pristolepidae, Luciocephalidae,* and *Chaudhuriidae.*

In the following we begin in the arctic and move southward through tundra, various types of forests, steppe, and mountains to the tropics.

THE POLAR REGIONS

The polar lands of Eurasia have long been beyond man's influence and there are still immense expanses of drifting ice and glaciated islands rarely or never visited by man. It is, however, in open water among the shifting wastes of pack ice and on land temporarily without snow that the animals gather. Of course, man's polar activities are usually concentrated in such areas, and the result of encounters there between polar animals and man has often been fatal to the former, especially since man has used aircraft and modern weapons.

One of the mammals whose future is endangered by man is the polar bear (*Thalarctos maritimus*). At least some populations seem to be nomadic, moving on the ice from east to west in a large circumpolar loop which includes Greenland and Baffin Island and in the Old World runs chiefly inside the large islands of arctic Eurasia. Polar bears move south in winter and north in summer, following the food supply—mainly seals—as the ice breaks up and shifts. This movement helps to explain the failure until recently of any country to take responsibility for the welfare of polar-bear populations.

Polar bears have probably always been confined to arctic areas, although from time to time individuals have strayed to Iceland, the Norwegian mainland, Manchuria, and Japan. Intensive hunting did not begin until the early seventeenth century but then increased to such a degree that by 1850 the species had been seriously depleted, particularly in the Spitsbergen area and on Novaya Zemlya. In addition, when most of the arctic whales had been exterminated, man began to hunt the seals, which increased the hunting pressure on the polar bears as well. Soon it became evident that the species was declining in number all over its range, including the New World. Some nations introduced hunting regulations, but these were not sufficiently effective. In Norwegian Spitsbergen there are few regulations. The polar bear is protected in the King Charles Islands and the adjacent waters but in all other parts of the archipelago it may be hunted at any time. The tourist industry has during recent years been offering polar-bear hunts from Norwegian ships. In 1954 the IUCN recommended measures for the protection of polar bears. Two years later the U.S.S.R. introduced total protection of the species, and this has already had beneficial results. In Canada, Alaska, and Greenland only partial protection has been given to these animals. The estimates of the total population are very uncertain, ranging from five to ten thousand. The mean figures of annual kills during 1963–68 are about three hundred in the Norwegian territories, fifty in the U.S.S.R., two hundred and fifty in the U. S., five hundred in Canada, and one hundred and fifty in Greenland—an annual total of about 1,250 bears. In 1968 some 1,250 polar bears were killed. In 1969–70 the Norwegian figures of kills on Spitsbergen alone rose to more than four hundred polar bears, and at least one hundred polar bears were killed illegally in Alaska by "sportsmen" led by unscrupulous guides.

In 1965 at a meeting in Alaska of delegates from the polar-bear nations (Canada, Denmark, Norway, the U. S., and the U.S.S.R.) it was unanimously recommended that all cubs as well as females accompanied by cubs be protected throughout the year, that the bears were an international resource, and that each nation do whatever it could until an international plan could be arranged. However, from Norwegian ships one could still hunt polar bears without restriction. In 1968 and 1970 IUCN organized two other meetings of polar-bear specialists, meetings which finally resulted in somewhat better protection in Norway: an overall annual quota of two hundred bears from the Spitsbergen area, protection of females with cubs, and a ban on capturing cubs. But the shooting from decks of ships or from snow-scooters is still allowed.

Recently another threat to the polar bear has been discovered, namely, that polar bears of the Canadian arctic carry a high concentration of DDT. Because they are at the end of a food chain, this discovery is significant, showing how far the poisoning with toxic chemicals has gone on the earth. The polar bears of the arctic are, in this respect, a parallel to the DDT-contaminated penguins of the Antarctic.

Another polar mammal threatened by extinction is the Atlantic walrus (*Odobenus rosmarus rosmarus*), once common along the coasts of the North Atlantic and the Arctic Ocean southward to the Russian and Norwegian mainland and, in the Western Hemisphere, to the coast of Labrador. Its distribution has been much reduced as a result of the severe exploitation that began in the sixteenth century, but it was not until the introduction of modern firearms and arctic transport that the species was seriously menaced. This animal is an important natural resource, yielding oil, hides, and tusks. It is now protected in Norwegian territories and in Greenland, and there are hunting regulations in Canada and the U.S.S.R. The population of this subspecies is estimated at about twenty-five thousand. The annual mean harvest in Canada is 2,666, of which 90 percent are taken by the Eskimos.

The Pacific walrus (*O. r. divergens*) also is overexploited. About 2,500 to three thousand walruses of this race are caught per year in territorial waters of the U. S. and the U.S.S.R. Russian investigations published in 1969 have shown that this harvest and the normal mortality exceed the annual increment of the population.

Harp seals (*Phoca groenlandica*) occur in the Arctic Ocean and the arctic parts of the North Atlantic in both the Old and New Worlds. The species is migratory and the main sealing grounds are situated in the White Sea, on the pack ice in Norwegian waters, particularly around Jan Mayen, off Labrador and northern Newfoundland, and finally in the Gulf of St. Lawrence. In the beginning of the twentieth century and even as late as 1940 the world population was estimated at about ten million harp seals, which at 1963 had dropped to about three million. It is in the North American area that a reckless destruction of these seals still takes place every year.

In the Atlantic around Jan Mayen, nineteen thousand harp seals were taken in 1961 by the Norwegians and an unknown number by Russian ships. Today the whole population is on the order of about 100,000, excluding pups. That is one-tenth of its 1940 numbers. Of the population off Labrador and Newfoundland, the mean annual harvest during recent years (1965–68) has been about 200,000 seals. In 1966 a preliminary estimate of that year's kill was 195,000 pups and forty thousand adults. This indicated a toll that might have virtually eliminated the year's offspring; about 90 percent of the pups were killed. By 1967 the population was down to about 800,000 seals producing 200,000 to 225,000 young, of which 180,000 were killed in 1967. This is a tremendous overharvesting. The Gulf of St. Lawrence population comprises about one-and-one-half million seals. This seal herd is now under good control by the Canadians. However, the combined populations living off Labrador and Newfoundland and in the Gulf of St. Lawrence have fallen from five million in 1940 to about two million in 1969.

In the White Sea, the number of harp seals gathering on the breeding grounds dropped from about three million animals in 1926 to about one million in 1950 and about 222,000 in recent years. In 1965 all sealing by vessels of this seal in the White Sea was suspended for five years, but local inhabitants took up to twenty thousand pups every year. However, this population is increasing.

The harp seal still exists in large populations, but if the huge slaughter continues off Newfoundland and Labrador, it will not be long before this valuable animal has been exterminated in that part of the Atlantic. Canada itself estimates that the numbers of harp seals killed in this area is three times the number which should be taken if the herd is to maintain its present, already heavily depleted size.

Seal hunting is a brutal, messy business, and public opinion in both the Old and New Worlds has been aroused by the annual massacres and the apparent cruelty of the methods used on the killing grounds off Newfoundland and in the Gulf of St. Lawrence. Recently the Canadian government issued new regulations to reduce unnecessary cruelty in the killing. The same government has also established quota and other restrictions, but there is no protection for the breeding population on international waters. Canada has taken the matter up with the International Commission for North Atlantic Fisheries in an attempt to bring pressure on those fishermen and seal hunters of other countries who up to the present refuse cooperation with regard to controlled harvesting.

Finally, in January, 1970, Canada and Norway agreed to introduce new sealing regulations in the international waters off Labrador and Newfoundland similar to those previously adopted by Canada for the Gulf of St. Lawrence. These regulations ban the killing of baby "whitecoat" seals and limit the harp-seal catch to a level which is consistent with sound conservation practice. However, the control of the new regulations did not seem to be effective, because already during the first two days of the 1970 hunt, twenty-five thousand seals were killed. The quota for 1971 was fixed at 245,000 seals, but this figure seems to indicate overcropping.

Also, hood seals (*Cystophora cristata*) concentrate in partly the same pack-ice areas as the harp seal, and their pups are slaughtered annually.

THE TUNDRA

The open tundra of northern Eurasia is one of the few natural regions that man has not modified. These vast arctic plains of short grass, sedges, mosses, and lichens with a permanently frozen sub-soil, short summers, and dark winters are not hospitable to human beings. This does not mean that man has been unable to occupy the tundra. Men live there, but they have been obliged to accept the hard rules of arctic life, making use of the tundra through domestic reindeer which still utilize this habitat almost as did their wild ancestors.

The interaction between plants and animals of the tundra is to-day essentially what it was before the appearance of man. Tundra mammoths once roamed the Eurasian arctic grasslands. It seems almost unbelievable that such large animals could persist in so poor an environment, but this is no more extraordinary than that musk-oxen still survive on the barren ground of Spitsbergen and Greenland. The musk-oxen do not have even the possibility, available to the mammoths, of migrating seasonally to forests.

Reindeer (*Rangifer tarandus*) are typical animals of the tundra. Almost everywhere on the Eurasian tundra the wild reindeer have been supplanted by domesticated ones. The largest remaining population of wild reindeer in the Old World lives in the Pyasina River basin on the Taimyr peninsula in Siberia, where the number of individuals exceeds a hundred thousand as a result of partial protection.

At the end of the nineteenth century there were about twenty thousand reindeer of Novaya Zemlya; some decades later there were only a few individuals of a local subspecies, *R. t. pearsoni,* left on the northeastern part of the northern island. The main reason for this decline was hunting. The islanders took the meat and skins not only for themselves but also for export. Today hunting is strictly prohibited. Fortunately, this measure was not taken too late to save a natural resource so specially adapted to the harsh environment of these arctic islands. At the present time the population has again reached the same level as it had eighty years ago.

Besides man, the wolf (*Canis lupus*) is the main predator on reindeer. Since time immemorial the wolf and the reindeer have lived side by side on the tundra. Both species were once abundant in Eurasia and North America and there was a close relationship between the two. The wolf controlled the reindeer population, keeping its numbers down, which prevented overgrazing of lichens and in this way also starvation by the reindeer population. Lichens, the staple food of the reindeer, reproduce very slowly. If over-exploited, lichens take several decades to recover. The food chain, consisting of lichens-reindeer-wolves, is an outstanding example of interaction in a tundra habitat where the biocommunities are rather simple.

The wolf has always been persecuted by man and now occurs only in remote areas of arctic tundra or high up in the mountains in the Old and New Worlds. But as a species it is not yet threatened by extinction, thanks to the wide areas still open to it in Siberia, Alaska, and Canada.

CONIFEROUS FORESTS: THE TAIGA

Immense coniferous forests mixed locally with deciduous trees and intermingling with bogs and heaths characterize the Eurasian taiga. Until very recent time this vast forest was virgin country, but it has gradually been conquered by man, generally from the south. Many animal species have been driven away and have re-treated to montane regions or remote parts of the forest. On the other hand, some animals have been favoured by the opening up of the coniferous forests and the replacement of parts of it by a secondary growth of mixed forests or cultivated areas.

The most important population of a forest rcindeer (*Rangifer tarandus fennicus*) occurs in eastern Finland and the western U.S.S.R. In the former country the numbers vary owing to mi-gration, between fifty and two hundred, and there can hardly be many more in Russia. This subspecies, which as late as 1750 ranged over the greater part of the Finnish taiga eastward to the Ural Mountains, became exterminated in Finland between 1880 and 1910, but it returned spontaneously about 1950 after habitat disturbances on the Russian side of the boundary. This forest reindeer is now threatened on both sides of the Finnish-Russian border because of forest destruction. There are still other patchy occurrences in the U.S.S.R. but everywhere this subspecies is de-clining.

Since historic time the peregrine falcon (*Falco peregrinus*) has been distributed over most parts of Eurasia and North America as well as in Africa and Australia. Though it is in no way restricted to the taiga, it has its main range within this habitat. The populations seem to have been very stable until ten or fifteen years ago, when they began to decrease both in Europe and North America. The decline during the past decade has been alarming and is chiefly caused by pesticides. Peregrine victims of chlorinated hydrocarbons and mercury compounds have been found in Great Britain and in Sweden. Many populations of peregrines (*F. p peregrinus*) have been reduced to the verge of extermination. In 1965 fifteen countries of Europe listed the peregrine as the most threatened bird species. Since then the situation has become worse in most countries.

A census in Europe in 1969 resulted in 597 pairs which produced 435 young. Not less than 350 pairs bred in Great Britain, which indicates an increase after pesticides had been banned. In 1971 at least 142 pairs produced large young, so that a total of about three hundred peregrines were reared in Great Britain in 1971. A similar output was estimated for 1970. This is a promising trend after the decline of the British peregrine population, which reached its lowest ebb in 1963–1966. But in many countries the peregrine is now gone. In Finland it has dropped from about a thousand pairs in 1950 to eight in 1970, in Sweden from fifty to sixteen, in Ireland from 160 in 1954 to fourteen in 1970, in France from four hundred to one hundred, in East Germany from 350 to seventy-eight, in Switzerland from thirty-five to one, and so on. In West Germany a 77 percent decline was noted over a fifteen-year period. Many countries not listed here show similar or worse figures of decline. If this rapid disappearance of the peregrines continues, several races of the species will have vanished within one or two decades.

In the bogs of the Asian conifer forests and on the steppes there is a bird, the Siberian white crane (*Grus leucogeranus*), that is almost as famous as the North American whooping crane. Though it is spread over an immense area from the Ural River in the southeast to the coast of the Arctic Ocean in northeastern Siberia, the population was in 1965 believed to be less than two thousand birds. Most of them breed between the Alazeya and Yana rivers. This large snow-white bird winters at the Bharatpur Sanctuary in northwestern India (where sixty were reported a few years ago, but only twelve in 1969–70) and in China, so that it has a very long migration twice a year and is thus exposed to danger in much the same way as the whooping crane. Although it is protected by law over most of its range, it has been much persecuted and disturbed by hunters and apparently maintains its numbers with difficulty.

Temperate Deciduous Forests

Three or four thousand years ago, temperate deciduous forests once covered a vast area from the British Isles and the northern Iberian peninsula in the west across central Europe and eastward in a narrowing strip far into Siberia. Almost the same type of forest existed in China, Manchuria, and Japan. Stone Age men had burned and cut here and there, but it was not until farming spread in central Europe and Asia that the forests began to disappear. Industrialization combined with growing human populations caused the forests to retreat at an ever accelerating rate. With the forests went many of the larger carnivores and also several hoofed animals.

Several mammals belonging to forest regions of Eurasia have vanished forever. They will be dealt with in connection with the various habitats to which they were primarily adapted. One impressive forest species was the aurochs (*Bos primigenius*), ancestor of European domestic cattle. It was a large animal, the bulls weighing up to about a ton. The aurochs roamed wooded areas of Eurasia from the British Isles and Scandinavia in the northwest to the Mediterranean countries in the south and to Siberia and Syria in the east. Destruction of forests, the competition of cattle, and hunting were probably the most important factors leading to the disappearance of this magnificent animal. As early as 1409 only Poland and perhaps Russia seem to have possessed the aurochs. Attempts to preserve the species were made in Poland, and a small herd persisted in the Jaktorowka forest near Warsaw until the beginning of the 1620's. In 1627 the last individual died. Europe had lost one of her most interesting and useful animals.

Many other mammals living in deciduous forests have become very rare. Among the carnivores several species have declined to a dangerously low level. The Spanish lynx (*Lynx lynx pardina*) is one of them. It was formerly distributed over large parts of the Iberian peninsula but habitat destructions, particularly deforestation, and human persecution have restricted it to seven scattered areas, chiefly in the sierras. The habitat best suited to this lynx seems, however, to be the lowlands, and its last stronghold is in the Coto Doñana and the Marismas of southwestern Spain. The population there is estimated at twenty to thirty animals. It is now partially protected. Moreover, the establishment in 1969 of the Coto Doñana National Park increased the possibilities of saving this race, which is by some scientists regarded as a species.

The Korean leopard (*Panthera pardus orientalis*) from the Amur, distributed in Siberia and northern Korea, is like so many of the larger Asian cats threatened by constant persecution. Probably only ten to fifteen individuals remain in the U.S.S.R. The Siberian tiger (*P. tigris altaica*), the largest of all tigers, and formerly found throughout eastern Siberia, Manchuria, and the wooded parts of northern China, today occurs only in the Amur and Ussuri river basins in eastern Siberia and in Manchuria, and in northernmost Korea in beautiful forests of lime, oak, ash, and maple with dense undergrowth. However, in winter these green woodlands become leafless forests with deep snow, a peculiar habitat for a mainly tropical animal such as a tiger. It is believed that there are still between forty and fifty Siberian tigers in Korea, about 130 in the U.S.S.R., not more than about fifty in northern China, and possibly a few in Mongolia. Human persecution and fires that destroyed habitats have reduced the population greatly, but protective measures in the eastern U.S.S.R. have led to an increase both in number and range. The Chinese tiger (*P. t. amoyensis*) is very rare but still distributed in a large part of eastern and central China northward to 38°–40° N. latitude. It is not protected and is heavily hunted. Also very rare is the Chinese Turkestan tiger (*P. t. lecoqi*). It inhabited the woods of the Tarim basin, but hunters using poisoned baits have killed so many that it is near extinction, if not already extinct. The western and the eastern races of the Asiatic wild dog (*Cuon alpinus hesperius* and *C. a. alpinus*) occur in the eastern U.S.S.R. and China, where they have been severely depleted to such an extent that they are now endangered.

This is also the situation of three races of the sika deer (*Cervus nippon*). The North China sika (*C. n. mandarinus*) formerly occurred in large areas of northeastern China, but because of excessive killing it now survives only on deer farms. Also found only on farms is the South China sika (*C. n. kopschi*). The Shansi sika

(*C. n. grassianus*) has long been one of the most mercilessly hunted deer in China and has been brought to the verge of extinction. Its last retreat is the highest forested mountains of West Shansi, but it is uncertain whether it still exists there. Other endangered subspecies of the sika deer are dealt with on pages 162 and 165. Like the sika, several races of the red deer (*C. elaphus*) have been reduced to a dangerously small number: for instance, the Corsican deer (*C. e. corsicanus*) of Corsica (about 140 animals) and Sardinia (about a hundred animals), and the Manchurian wapiti (*C. e. xanthopygus*) of eastern Siberia, Manchuria, and Mongolia.

The Mesopotamian fallow deer (*Dama mesopotamica*), the largest of the fallow-deer group, formerly occurred in northern Africa from the Tunisian border to the Red Sea and in Asia from Syria and Jordan to Iraq and western Iran. It is a deer of woodlands; since most of the forests of this region have disappeared, this deer has vanished everywhere except in a small area along the rivers Dez and Karkheh in southwestern Iran, where in 1971 fewer than thirty survived. Since this area is likely to be deforested, this deer is in imminent danger of extermination. Probably the only hope for it is the transportation of members of the group to protected areas. This was done in 1964–65, when seven deer were captured and shipped to a fenced reserve close to the Caspian Sea, in northeastern Iran. In February, 1971, I visited this reserve, where there were eighteen Mesopotamian deer.

Perhaps the most dramatic history of any animal faced by extinction is that of Père David's deer (*Elaphurus davidianus*). In ancient times this deer had a wide range in China and occurred in Japan as well, but as early as the Shang dynasty (1766–1122 B.C.) it seems to have been exterminated in the wild. Like so many other deer in China, however, it survived in parks. It was in one of these reserves, the imperial hunting park near Peking, that a French missionary, Father David, came upon the last remaining herd. Father David managed to send a number of the animals to European zoos, so that by about 1870 there were small herds at several zoological gardens. This came none too soon, because when floods broke through the imperial walls of the hunting park in 1894, many deer escaped and were killed by the peasants. And in 1900 foreign troops sent to Peking during the Boxer Rebellion killed almost all the deer. The few that remained were sent to the Peking zoo, but by 1921 these, too, were dead.

After the events of 1900, the eleventh Duke of Bedford at Woburn Abbey in England undertook to help the deer by collecting a herd of sixteen animals from European zoos. Today, all survivors derive from this herd. In 1963 there were 405 of these deer in forty-one zoos all over the world, including Peking. Before long this deer may be reintroduced in the wild after more than two thousand years in captivity.

Equally dramatic is the history of the European bison (*Bison bonasus bonasus*), a huge forest-dwelling animal whose disappearance is intimately connected with the retreat of the woods. In historical times it occurred over almost the whole of Europe, ranged eastward to the Lena, and it possibly existed in ancient Assyria, Mesopotamia, and Persia, which at that time were forested. By World War I it had been reduced to one herd of about seven hundred animals in the Bialowieza forest of Poland. Since many of the animals were tame, they became an easy prey for invading troops, who reduced the population to about 150. The last free specimens were shot in Bialowieza in 1921 and in the Caucasus, where another race lived, in 1925. Fortunately, some were preserved in zoos and their numbers were gradually built up again. But after World War II only sixteen had survived in captivity at Bialowieza. They increased, and in 1952 some were released into the wild. After having been gone from the wild for thirty-one years, the European bison once more roams freely in one of Europe's last virgin forests, the Bialowieza. By 1966 the wild herd numbered 112. Altogether in 1969 there were in the world one thousand and sixty-four pure European bisons, of which more than 215 lived in freedom.

In 1965 fifteen European bisons were released in freedom also into the Zverevskoye forest in the Volyn district of the U.S.S.R.

Among the birds, one of the most endangered species is the Korean white stork (*Ciconia ciconia boyciana*). The species was once common in eastern Siberia, Korea, and Japan, but it had dwindled to fourteen birds, according to a count in 1965. No young have matured since 1960. This extremely small population breeds in Korea and Japan. There are also a few birds in China. Also, Tristram's woodpecker (*Dryocopus javanensis richardsi*), a spectacular species found in North Korea, is among the endangered birds. In 1964 the number was estimated at less than ten birds but in 1966 several scores were found on seven localities and in 1969 over forty pairs were estimated.

THE STEPPES

The Eurasian steppes are immense plains covered by a more or less dense herbaceous vegetation, sometimes with bushes but usually with no trees except along rivers. However, there are also what the Russians call forest steppes, a mosaic of deciduous forests and grassy steppes. The greatest grass steppe in the world, it extends in a 2,500-mile-wide belt from the Ukraine eastward to Altai in the heart of Asia and south to Arabia, Iran, and Pakistan. With some mountain interruptions it stretches eastward to northern China.

These steppes were in the past inhabited by wild herds of large mammals, mainly horses and asses, adapted to this special habitat. Much of the European steppe has been cultivated and the large mammals exterminated. On the Asian steppes they have been depleted by hunting. In both areas this has meant a loss of a valuable resource, because many of the steppe mammals represented an important conversion of poor vegetation into meat and proteins.

As late as historic times, the grassy plains and woodlands of southeastern Europe were the haunt of the European lion (*Panthera leo ssp.*). There are unfortunately no remains of this beast, and it is not known whether it was identical to the lion that today roams the savannas of tropical Africa and the Gir forest in Asia. Herodotus reported 2,400 years ago that there were many lions in Thrace and declared that during the march of the Persian king Xerxes through Macedonia (480 B.C.) some of the baggage camels were killed by lions. Later, Aristotle (384–22 B.C.) assigned the same range to the lion, but referred to it as rare. By A.D. 80–100 the lion was considered entirely exterminated in Europe.

We cannot be sure that the lion of ancient Greece was identical to *Panthera leo,* the species we know today, although the latter certainly had a much wider range in the past. Formerly the cave lion (*P. spelaea*) was distributed over large parts of Europe and still existed in the postglacial period; it retreated gradually from Europe and is thought to have become extinct as late as the third century B.C. If the Greek lions were of the species *P. spelaea,* it did not become extinct until about four hundred years later.

The reason for the disappearance of the lion from the European scene must be traced to the unceasing warfare man has carried on against this animal. Neither the climate nor the food supply could have been important factors in the elimination of the lion at that time. Remains of cave lions have been found in the ancient dwelling places of postglacial man in Aurignac and La Madeleine in France. Most probably this lion was identical to the form inhabiting southwestern Asia.

A great part of Europe became steppe after the Ice Age, and herds of wild horses, saiga antelopes, European bison, and other grass-eating animals roamed from one pasture to another. Gradually most of Europe became covered with forest, but southeastern Russia remained steppe, with typical steppe animals surviving there for a long time. As late as the nineteenth century, for example, a wild horse, the tarpan horse (*Equus caballus gmelini*), was still living on the steppes of the Ukraine and Voronezh. Unfortunately, the species has since been exterminated, the last specimen dying in captivity in 1918. Thus the last of the original race of wild horses, once a dominant animal on the plains of Europe, disappeared.

All the wild horses are now extinct except for Przewalski's horse (*Equus przewalski*), but of this species there are more individuals in captivity than in the wild. Prior to 1950 this horse was commonly found in the arid steppes of northernmost Sinkiang in the corner between China, Mongolia, and the U.S.S.R., the surrounding mountain ranges apparently forming a barrier to dispersal southward. At present only three or four herds of not more than seven to eight animals each, all strictly protected, survive in a mountainous semidesert area in southwestern Mongolia near the Chinese frontier. With the introduction of modern firearms, Chinese and Mongolian hunters became a serious threat to the survival of this species. Simultaneously, nomadic tribes with cattle occupied this area and particularly the watering places, forcing Przewalski's wild horse to retreat to less favourable habitats in the mountains. The wild population is estimated at from twenty to thirty animals (eleven were seen in 1966, twenty-seven in 1969), while in 1967 there were 146 in various zoos, which are now cooperating to save the species from extinction. To save the wild population it would be necessary to create a reserve in the present refuge of the species.

In forested river valleys situated between the tundra and the steppelike country of the Amu Darya in Turkmenistan of the U.S.S.R. and close to the border of Afghanistan, lives the Bactrian wapiti or Bokharan deer (*Cervus elaphus bactrianus*). The species seems to prefer forests but often moves to nearby steppe and desert habitats to feed. It has been much persecuted and is also handicapped by the destruction of riverine vegetation, which explains its present very limited distribution. Only about three hundred deer remain, most of them living in reserves. The race is protected throughout its range in the U.S.S.R. The Yarkand stag (*C. e. yarkandensis*) shows a similar distribution pattern within a dry steppe area. It occurs in the Tarim valley of eastern Chinese Turkestan, where it appears to be very rare, but exact information about its status is lacking.

Once Asia's largest bird, the Arabian ostrich (*Struthio camelus syriacus*), a subspecies of the African ostrich, occurred on the arid steppes of Arabia. It was persecuted and became extinct in 1941 (old eggs were found in Saudi Arabia in 1952 and 1953).

The number of great bustards (*Otis tarda*), one of Europe's most spectacular birds, is rapidly decreasing on the cultivated plains and steppes of Europe. There were only 305 birds in Poland in 1963, and it is very rare also in eastern Germany, Austria, Czechoslovakia, Hungary, and the U.S.S.R. In Asia its status is more satisfactory, but owing to its great vulnerability, its future is in danger, particularly in Europe.

DESERTS

Vast areas of Eurasia consist of deserts or semideserts, the latter sometimes shading off into arid steppe. We will treat the semidesert and desert habitats as one, because most of the larger mammals in these poor environments were driven into them from grasslands by man and his livestock. A surprising number of the larger animals have survived in the Asian deserts until recently, when man, equipped with motor vehicles and modern firearms, began to slaughter them recklessly.

Of these deserts—most of them are in Asia—the Arabian, Iranian, Turkestan, Takla Makan, and Gobi are the largest. Some are in lowland areas, others on mountains or high plateaus. Many deserts were formerly grasslands, rich in perennial grasses, but overgrazing has gradually changed them into deserts. If left in peace by man these deserts will gradually change into grasslands, so in a biological sense they are in reality not deserts. One of the largest man-made deserts is in the Middle East, where right in the middle of sandy deserts, monumental ruins bear witness to glorious civilizations once based on fertile lands. The biological capital of countries like Jordan, Syria, and Iraq has probably been continuously mistreated by human beings and their goats for longer periods than any other similar area. The vegetation and the fertile soil have disappeared, the erosion gnaws deeper and deeper, the springs are dried up, and many mammals and birds have been exterminated. And every year the mismanagement accelerates. Soon a stage will be reached when these countries, despite all foreign aid, will not be able to feed their own populations.

The destruction of the natural resources in the Middle East was recently described in Guy Mountfort's *Portrait of a Desert*. If we consider only the larger animals, the inventory of devastation is horrifying. In 1917 Arabian gazelles (*Gazella gazella arabica*) and Arabian dorcas gazelles (*G. dorcas saudiva*), as well as the houbara bustards (*Chlamydotis undulata*), could still be seen almost everywhere. There were also many Arabian oryx and ostrich. In 1959 only about a hundred oryx survived in remote regions of the Rub al Khali; in 1960 and 1961 two parties of poaching sheiks in powerful cars, armed with submachine guns or automatic rifles, slaughtered sixty or seventy of these animals. In 1962 only eleven Arabian oryx were believed to remain in Saudi Arabia. In Jordan the Asiatic lion (*Panthera leo persica*) was exterminated in the early fifteenth century; the roe deer (*Capreolus capreolus*) and the Syrian wild ass (*Equus hemionus*) in 1920, the fallow deer (*Dama dama*) in 1922, the Syrian bear (*Ursus arctos syriacus*) in the 1930's, the ostrich before 1950, and the cheetah probably prior to 1962. The Syrian bear is now exterminated in most of its former range but is still occurring in Iraq, Iran, Turkey, the Caucasus, and Armenia. The Sinai leopard (*Panthera pardus jarvisi*) may be already extinct in Sinai and the Arabian peninsula, its only range of occurrence. Also, the Turkmenian caracal (*Felis caracal michaëlis*) is very rare within a limited range confined to Turkmenistan. About 1955 the two gazelles mentioned above were still so numerous that nobody could imagine that a few years later their survival would be threatened. By 1960 they were declining at an alarming rate as a result of motorized hunting. In the desert these animals are easy to overtake by a vehicle that maintains a speed of thirty miles an hour for a short period. In Israel army officers are credited with having killed one thousand dorcas gazelles in less than five years in the Negev region alone. In 1970–71 the number of the mountain gazelles (*Gazella gazella gazella*) in Israel was estimated at about three thousand and of the dorcas gazelle about one thousand. Gazelles have also been machine-gunned by fighter aircraft in several countries in the Middle East. Such treatment is not a whit better than the slaughter of bison on the American prairies and of various ungulates on the South African veld during the past centuries. At present only some small populations of the two desert gazelles are left, spread over enormous areas. The only figures available are from Israel, where in 1968 the total population of the Arabian gazelle was estimated at about four thousand, while about one thousand of the dorcas gazelle existed, and of the mountain gazelle about three thousand.

Most of the larger desert or semidesert mammals all over Asia have been seriously depleted, which means that an almost unbelievably rich desert meat and protein resource in relation to the thin vegetation has been unwisely eliminated. The Syrian wild ass (*Equus hemionus hemippus*) has probably been extinct since 1927. Fortunately, other races of the wild ass still survive, but they are all endangered and at present cling to a small vestige of their former ranges. The Persian wild ass (*E. h. onager*) occurs in the deserts of northeastern Iran, northwestern Afghanistan, and Turkmenistan, a restricted area compared with its previous range. In Turkmenistan about seven hundred animals live in the Badkhyz Game Reserve. There is also a reserve on an island of the Aral Sea of the U.S.S.R., where in 1966 there were forty-six animals. In Iran the population was estimated at about three hundred in 1960 and the same in 1971. In the Little Rann of Kutch in northwestern India, the Indian wild ass (*E. h. khur*) survived in a population of two to five thousand in 1947, but declined rapidly to 870 animals in 1968. In 1969 an aerial census counted 362 animals and assessed the total number at about four hundred, an alarming decrease. Probably some still live in Baluchistan in West Pakistan and a small herd of twenty to thirty animals has been reported from the Great Rann. The Tibetan wild ass (*E. h. kiang*) from the plateau of Tibet and the Mongolian wild ass (*E. h. hemionus*) in southern Mongolia have not yet been reduced as drastically as the other subspecies: the former is rare but not yet endangered, while the population of the latter in 1965 was estimated to be at least several thousand. The only wild population of the Bactrian camel (*Camelus bactrianus ferus*) is limited to the Gobi and trans-Altai deserts in southern Mongolia and northern China. Whether these camels descend from wild animals or their ancestors returned to the wild stage from domestication is a matter of dispute, but in any case they have now long since been living as pure wild camels. The former distribution of wild camels covered Mongolia and, according to V. G. Heptner (1966), also Kazakhstan, where they are said to have occurred as late as the middle of the nineteenth century. During the 1920's the species could be met everywhere in the Gobi Desert, but during the following decades it declined rapidly. In the 1960's a slight increase in numbers was observed outside the range of nomadic tribes and their livestock. The domesticated camels have a much wider range, occurring in steppes and deserts from Asia Minor and the Crimea in the west to China in the east. Heavy persecution and competition with domesticated animals for pasture and water probably caused the decrease of these camels. The present wild population may be estimated at probably some hundreds, according to information from Dr. A. Dashdorj (in 1964). About forty were seen in 1969.

The Arabian oryx (*Oryx leucoryx*) is perhaps the most valuable food resource produced by the deserts of the Middle East, where it probably once ranged widely. It is a medium-sized antelope living in nomadic herds that follow the rare rains and are able to utilize effectively the meager vegetation that springs up after a rainfall and then dries rapidly under the burning sun.

About 165 years ago this oryx, according to a survey by Lee Talbot (in 1960), occurred in Sinai, lower Palestine, Transjordan, much of Iraq, and virtually all of the Arabian peninsula. Today it is extinct throughout this area except for the southeastern part of the Rub al Khali deserts in Saudi Arabia. This tragic decline is due to excessive hunting by local Bedouin tribesmen, who nowadays carry modern firearms, and also by motorized hunting parties. It was estimated in 1964 that between one and four hundred animals remained, in 1969 less than two hundred. The IUCN and the Fauna Preservation Society have made several efforts to save the Arabian oryx from extinction. The sultan has recently forbidden shooting from vehicles, and this edict seems to be respected. The so-called Operation Oryx established a breeding nucleus of three captured antelopes in the zoological garden of Phoenix, Arizona, where the ecological conditions are rather similar to those in Arabia. Animals from other zoos were brought to Phoenix, so that there are now (1972) thirty Arabian oryxes, including seventeen that were born there. There is also a captive herd of eight oryxes in Los Angeles and thirty animals in Qatar. This latter herd has in 1971 been hit by a serious disease.

The populations of the sand gazelle (*Gazella leptoceros marica*) in central Saudi Arabia have much thinned out and in most areas have entirely disappeared owing to motorized hunting. Again, we have a case of unwise depletion of the few natural resources of a dry region. The same factor lies behind the tremendous decline of the Persian goitered gazelle (*Gazella subguttorosa subguttorosa*) that inhabits Syria, Iraq, Armenia, Iran, Turkmenistan, and Uzbekistan. It has been slaughtered by the thousands and has disappeared from a large part of its former range. In other areas it is now very rare. The population is estimated at about six thousand.

The houbara bustard (*Chlamydotis undulata*), mentioned earlier in this section, is at present, after protection, slowly recovering in Jordan where it was nearly exterminated, but in other areas of southwestern Asia and particularly Pakistan this bird is decreasing drastically owing to overhunting. In 1971 one hunting party alone killed two thousand houbara bustards in Pakistan.

THE MOUNTAINS NORTH OF THE TROPICS

With few exceptions, the mountain chains of temperate Eurasia run from west to east across the continents. Many of them form massive barriers between well-distinguished natural regions; they also serve as huge refuges for plants and animals that have been exterminated elsewhere or driven by advancing cultivation into remote montane areas. These mountainous fauna oases harbour several endangered species. We shall treat them all in this section, despite the fact that montane habitats vary greatly. The number of vertebrate species decreases with the altitude. This in turn affects evolution and speciation due to geographic isolation. In this way many mountains possess species or races that do not occur elsewhere.

The author has visited almost all the mountain ranges of Europe from the Scandinavian mountains in the north to the Pyrenees and those in Sicily, Greece, the Crimea, and the Caucasus in the south, from the British highlands in the west to the Urals in the east. Most free from man-made erosion is the Scandinavian chain. It is still inhabited by the same plants and animals that came there after the last glaciation. Fragments of virgin landscape do, however, also occur on other mountains. They are not only scientific treasures forming a kind of research archive but also very beautiful to look at—the last untouched land in Europe.

In Himalaya there has been a tremendous hunting pressure on the ungulate fauna. No national park and few nature reserves have protected Himalayan wildlife, of which a high number of species is endangered.

The wooded slopes and valley meadows of the Caucasus were the haunts of the Caucasian bison (*Bison bonasus caucasicus*). It will perhaps never be known how long this subspecies had been isolated from its relative, the European bison, which once roamed the forest steppes and woods of lowland Europe. What we know of the Caucasian bison goes back only as far as a hundred years ago. In 1914 there were about five hundred such animals in the Caucasus, but persecution drove them higher and higher up into unsuitable habitats, and by 1925 they were reported to be extinct in the wild. However, some captive specimens that were at least partly of Caucasian ancestry were in 1940 brought to a large enclosure on the northern, forested slopes of the Caucasus. In 1954 a small herd was set free and has since then been strictly protected. In the scientific sense, however, the pure Caucasian bison must be considered extinct.

The various problems in the tricky classification of the wild goats of the genus *Capra* need not concern us here. We will consider the European and Asian true goats in four species: the Iberian ibex (*Capra pyrenaica*), the ibex (*C. ibex*), the wild goat (*C. aegagrus*), and the markhor (*C. falconeri*).

The ibex is now saved in the Alps after long efforts by chiefly the Italians, who managed to restore the almost extinct species and then repopulated various parts of the Alps through reintroductions.

One subspecies of the Iberian ibex is now extinct. The Portuguese ibex (*C. pyrenaica lusitanica*) was still abundant at the end of the eighteenth century, ranging in all the northwestern mountains of the Iberian peninsula. But the hunting pressure was very strong and led to the extinction of this ibex in 1892. Also, the Pyrenean ibex (*C. p. pyrenaica*), once occurring on both sides of the Pyrenees as well as in the Cantabrian chain, was severely persecuted and was believed to have been extinct in the 1910's. But recently about twenty ibexes have been discovered in the Mount Perdido area on the Spanish side of the Pyrenees—the area in which the last specimens were observed half a century ago. In the Pyrenees and other northern Iberian highlands the Pyrenean desman (*Galemys pyrenaicus*), a very rare aquatic mole, is claimed to be decreasing and perhaps threatened, owing to its specialization.

The present population of the Cretan wild goat (*Capra aegagrus cretensis*), living in the White Mountains in Crete and introduced in three Cretan islands and a reserve on the Peloponnesus, does not exceed four hundred animals.

The markhor (*C. falconeri*), which lives in the mountain ranges of Turkestan, Afghanistan, northeastern Iran, West Pakistan, and Kashmir, is also seriously menaced by settlement, domestic grazing herds, and intensive hunting. Particularly, the future of the straight-horned markhor (*C. f. jerdoni*) seems very dark, but the Kashmir race, *C. f. cashmiriensis,* has increased since a cease-fire was agreed on between India and Pakistan after the war in the 1960's, but this trend may in 1971 have come to an end. One hundred and five to one hundred and twenty animals were reported in 1970 in Chitral Gol, a reserve in West Pakistan, but the area is heavily used by livestock. Even more threatened is the Chialtan markhor (*C. f. chialtanensis*) that occurs only in the Chialtan Range and on a few other hills in Baluchistan. The Chialtan Range supports about two hundred animals.

The Arabian tahr (*Hemitragus jayakari*), confined to the mountains of Oman in southeastern Arabia, is locally existing in fair numbers, but the persecution is heavy and it needs urgent protection. Its very restricted range is an indication of its rarity. The golden takin (*Budorcas taxicolor bedfordi*) is limited to an isolated area in the Great White Mountains in southern Shensi in China. In 1934 its number was estimated at two or three hundred. Also, the Szechwan takin (*B. t. tibetana*) in western China is threatened by extinction.

The goral (*Naemorhaedus goral caudatus*) is ranging in the mountains of northern China, Manchuria, Korea, and Amur in Siberia. Excessive hunting has much reduced the population and it is estimated that there are only about four hundred in Amur and about two to three thousand in Korea. There are also several species and subspecies of wild sheep on the list of endangered mammals: the Gobi argali (*Ovis ammon darwini*) in northern China and Mongolia, the Bokharan urial (*O. orientalis bochariensis*) in Turkmenistan, the Punjab urial (*O. o. punjabiensis*) in West Pakistan (about five hundred live in a reserve), the shapu

(*O. o. vignei*) from the Asian steppe highlands south of Iran, and the Cyprian mouflon (*O. o. ophion*). Of the latter one hundred and fifty to two hundred still survived in 1971.

The white-lipped deer (*Cervus albirostris*) is at home on the Tibetan plateau ranging between twelve and sixteen thousand feet. It is intensively hunted, because a concoction made of its flesh, bones, and horn velvet is considered to have the power to heal or rejuvenate, and one made of its blood and heart to give courage. For much the same reason another montane deer, the white stag (*C. elaphus macneilli*), found on the Tibetan plateau at about twelve thousand feet, is threatened by extinction. In this case the antler velvet is believed to have aphrodisiac properties. Also very close to extinction is another mountain deer, the Sikkim stag (*C. e. wallichi*).

The vast Tibetan plateaus were formerly the haunts of the wild yak (*Bos grunniens mutus*). It was found in Ladak, in India, Nepal, Tibet, and Central China, but today it is limited to northeastern Tibet at altitudes up to about eight thousand feet. A few animals still exist in Sikkim. Owing to reckless hunting the species is in great danger of extermination. In these harsh montane semideserts man is again exterminating one of his valuable resources. The same can be said of the Tibetan gazelle (*Procapra picticaudata*) from Kashmir, Tibet, and China, which has been seriously depleted. (The Tibetan wild ass is discussed on page 128.)

Finally, a third mountain deer, the Kashmir stag (*Cervus elaphus hanglu*), is also very seriously menaced. Until 1947 it was regarded as the property of the Maharaja of Kashmir, which gave it adequate protection, but since then this deer has been heavily poached upon and its habitats have been destroyed by domestic livestock. In 1947 the population was estimated at about two thousand, in 1957 at about four hundred, but in 1962 at only 175 to 200. In 1970 there were no more than 140–170 deer in the Dachigam Sanctuary, i.e., in the whole Kashmir, but they were threatened by a farm with about one thousand sheep which compete with the deer within the sanctuary. However, poaching is the main reason for the rapid decline of this deer. A few animals still existed in 1971 in small groups in Himachal Pradesh.

The snub-nosed monkey (*Rhinopithecus roxellanae*) is, strangely enough, a primate that lives for most of the year in snow-covered deciduous forests and bamboo and rhododendron thickets on high mountains in western China and eastern Tibet. All three geographical races (*roxellanae, bieti* and *brelichi*) are very rare and have recently been accorded protection. An even stranger animal is the famous giant panda (*Ailuropoda melanoleuca*), a bearlike creature that probably is a real bear though officially put into another family. It has a very restricted range in high mountains of Szechwan and Kansu in China, where it exists exclusively in the bamboo forests. It is protected and for the moment is not threatened despite its rarity.

A southwestern Asian race of the lynx (*Lynx lynx dinniki*), formerly distributed in Arabia and Israel, is surviving only in northern Iraq, where it is very rare.

Formerly, the Caspian tiger (*Panthera tigris virgata*) had a wide range in western Asia from Transcaucasia to the Ob basin and the Altai. At present its distribution is more limited and it has been exterminated in many areas, but it still occurs in Transcaucasia and northern Iran. However, in Iran the population does not seem to exceed fifteen to twenty animals. Its decline is due to intensive hunting and to burning and habitat destruction by man. In 1968 it was estimated that hardly more than 150 animals were left in existence, and since then this tiger has been exterminated in Afghanistan and Turkestan. In Transcaucasia and partly in Asia Minor, also, the Transcaucasian leopard (*P. pardus tulliana*) is very rare and decreasing. The whole population in Turkey was in 1968 estimated at about twelve animals.

Another rare big cat is the snow leopard (*P. uncia*), distributed in elevated ranges in southern Siberia, Mongolia, China, Tibet, India, West Pakistan, and Afghanistan. In 1967 not more than about four hundred animals were thought to occur in the Himalayas, in 1969 less than 250. The species is declining all over its large range owing to persistent hunting for the valuable fur. The snow leopard is totally protected in India and the U.S.S.R., but skins appear almost every year for sale in Leningrad and Kashmir.

Menzbier's marmot (*Marmota marmota menzbier*), living on high mountain steppes in Tien Shan, is estimated to exist with a few thousand animals. It is protected.

Among birds the Himalaya mountain quail (*Ophrysia superciliosa*) of the northwestern Himalayas has not been seen since 1868. It must now be extinct. The status of the western tragopan (*Tragopan melanocephalus*) is very uncertain. It occurs rarely and locally in the northwestern Himalayas from western Kashmir to the Bhagirathi River in India and near the boundary to West

Pakistan. In 1971 five birds were seen in West Pakistan near the border to Kashmir. Among the other gallinaceous birds living in mountain forests and other highland habitats in Asia and known to be rare and decreasing are the following: the white-eared pheasant (*Crossoptilon crossoptilon*) (three races) of China, Tibet, and Assam; the brown-eared pheasant (*C. mantchuricum*) of China; Hume's pheasant (*Syrmaticus humiae*) (two races) of Burma and China; Elliot's pheasant (*S. ellioti*) of China; cheer pheasant (*Catreus wallichii*) of Nepal and Kashmir; Blyth's tragopan (*Tragopan blythii*) (two races) of India, Burma, and Tibet; Cabot's tragopan (*T. caboti*) of China; the Chinese monal (*Lophophorus huysii*) of China; and Sclater's monal (*L. sclateri*) of China, Tibet, India, and Burma.

LAKES, MARSHES, AND RIVERS

Most lakes of Palearctic Eurasia were produced by the great ice sheets that covered the northern part of these continents for long periods. Northern Europe is therefore much richer in lakes than are the southern parts. A high proportion of the shallow lakes and marshes of northern Europe have been drained for agricultural purposes. Long regarded as a step toward effective land use and prosperity, draining has become a mania. But such drainage schemes have often not been successful. Economically they have failed to produce the expected agricultural harvest, biologically the productivity of the area has been greatly reduced, and hydrologically the surrounding lands have suffered owing to the sinking ground-water level. There may also be an undesirable change in the local climate. These consequences of draining during the last 150 years have resulted from the complete failure to appreciate the intimate relationship between aquatic resources and the long-term productivity of the soil. Hydroelectric systems, including reservoirs with continuously changing volumes, and serious pollution have also affected lakes as well as rivers in Europe, interfering with natural food chains, biotic productivity, and the reproduction of fish and waterfowl, such as the economically important salmon (*Salmo salar*), trout (*S. trutta*), and the Danube salmon (*S. hucho*).

The total annual catch of the salmon, and hence the total population in the sea, appears to have been reduced to about one-tenth of its former exuberance since about 1800, according to statistics, through human interference with the freshwater breeding grounds. The salmon's feeding grounds off Greenland were discovered during the 1960's. In North America the Atlantic salmon is restricted to only eight coastal streams in Maine, where it is endangered, and in Europe the majority of rivers where the salmon once spawned do not offer this fish suitable habitats any longer despite the fact that it asks for so little.

Since 1964 the losses of salmon populations in rivers have been substantially increased by fishing in the Atlantic, where it is estimated that 95 percent of the fish taken are immature. Delegates from eleven countries met in 1969 at the International Commission for Northwest Atlantic Fisheries (ICNAF), where a resolution was passed calling for a high-seas ban on salmon fishing in the Atlantic. Denmark and Germany voted against it. Since then the populations have been further depleted. It is feared that the Atlantic salmon will become extinct before the end of the present century owing to the uncontrolled overharvesting at the salmon's communal feeding ground off Greenland, fishing which depletes stocks of rivers in both Europe and North America. The salmon-catching nets off Greenland also kill sea birds—250,000 guillemots and razorbills are caught each year. At the 1970 meeting of the ICNAF a total ban on high-seas Atlantic salmon fishing was called for again. It was claimed that Danish fishermen were pushing the Atlantic salmon toward extinction and stressed that netting oceanic feeding grounds cancels the fish's return trip to native rivers for spawning. The Danes vetoed the total ban. Negotiations ended in a one-year compromise maintaining the 1971 catch at the 1969 level. This means that an unlimited harvest still goes on or, in other words, destruction by greed and willful stupidity. In the United States the Committee on the Atlantic Salmon Emergency (CASE), together with federal authorities, is fighting for a re-establishment of the Atlantic salmon in several rivers. In 1971 a closed season from July 1 to May 5 for fishing for Atlantic salmon at sea was introduced by the states signatory to the North East Atlantic Fisheries Convention.

With the disappearance or poisoning of many marshes, lakes, and deltas, the habitats of aquatic animals have been greatly reduced and several species are in danger. The rich plant and animal life of one of Eurasia's most interesting bodies of water, Lake Baikal, a unique lake in the world (5,658 feet deep), is threatened by hydroelectric installations and industrial pollution. If the level of the lake is reduced to only ten or fifteen feet, the plants and animals of the littoral zone, where the bulk of the species lives, will be severely damaged. Two of Lake Baikal's economically most important fish, the omul (*Coregonus migratorius*) and the Baikal sturgeon (*Acipenser baeri baikalensis*), were in the 1960's overfished to such an extent that their existence, also imperilled by other environmental disturbances, was threatened. This danger has now been removed and there is a total ban on fishing the Baikal sturgeon, so the population is recovering.

The Balkhash perch (*Perca schrencki*) is endemic to two lakes in central Asia, where it is threatened by the introduction of a predatory fish. Two sturgeons of the Amur River system in the U.S.S.R. have become endangered by overfishing. They are the Amur sturgeon (*Acipenser schrencki*) and the kaluga (*Huso dauricus*). Dams on the Volga River have become a serious menace to the existence of the beloribitsa (*Stenodus leucichtys leucichtys*). Also, the scaleless killifish (*Kosswigichtys asquamatus*), confined to Lake Hazer in Turkey, is threatened by mechanical habitat changes. The ala balik (*Salmo platycephalus*) of the Zamanti River, Anatolia, Turkey, is endangered because of fishing with dynamite. Perhaps already extinct is the cicek (*Acanthorutilus handlirschi*), an endemic fish in Lake Eğridir, Turkey. *Tylognathus klatti* of the same lake and Lake Gölcük is threatened by irrigation.

The otter (*Lutra lutra*) is an aquatic animal that has disappeared from lakes, rivers, and coastal waters in Europe with incredible speed during the last decade. If this trend continues, the species will disappear. Water pollution is a major reason for this decline, but presumably also secondary poisoning by chemicals is involved. Such aquatic organisms as fish quickly absorb poisonous substances. This means that the otters, which prey chiefly on fish, rapidly build up a fatal dosage of poisonous compounds. The otters then die in their dens and are seldom found.

Tropical Asia is much poorer in lakes than is northern Eurasia, but there are many swamps along the watercourses and in the deltas. Because of the disappearance of wetlands, the populations of aquatic vertebrates, mostly birds, are thinning out, but few species are really threatened by extinction. The vast rice fields in southeastern Asia are temporarily an important habitat for many animals.

The swamp deer (*Cervus duvauceli*) in India and Nepal has

rapidly declined owing to cultivation of the marshy grasslands. Although it is completely protected in India, extensive poaching is going on. At present only small, isolated populations remain, estimated to be altogether about three to four thousand, living in Nepal, Assam, West Bengal, and Uttar Pradesh and belonging to the race *C. d. duvauceli*. The most threatened population is the race *C. d. branderi,* which occurs with a few scattered groups in central India, but perhaps the only viable population exists in the Kanha National Park in Madhya Pradesh, where seventy animals were censused in 1969, seventy-one in 1971, and eighty in 1972, a decline from 577 in 1958 and 3,023 in 1938.

The black-necked crane (*Grus nigricollis*) is the fourth threatened Asian crane. It breeds among the lakes of high central Asia, where it is now very rare. Its numbers have dwindled rapidly owing to human persecution.

Man alone was probably responsible for the extermination of the pink-headed duck (*Rhodonessa caryophyllacea*) of northeastern India, where it was never a common bird though it had an extensive but discontinuous range. Hunting pressure wiped out the species. The last known specimens, six birds of which one was shot, were observed at Manroona Lake in 1947.

The population of the white-winged wood duck (*Cairina scutulata*) has dropped by nearly 75 percent in Assam, India, and totals at present 150 to two hundred birds. A few birds occur in two localities in Burma and until 1969 also in the Chittagong Hill tracts of India. These are perhaps the only remaining populations of this species.

The giant ibis (*Thaumatibis gigantea*) of northern Cambodia and southern Laos is another very rare bird with a restricted range in one locality along the Cambodia-Laos border.

A bird which may already be extinct is the Lower Yangtze Kiang crow tit (*Paradoxornis heudei*), that already at the beginning of the twentieth century had a remarkably restricted range in a giant reed-bed area between Nanking and Chinkiang. This region has one of the world's densest human populations and reed-cutting is there a common practice.

The river terrapin (*Batagur baska*) is a useful food resource in southeastern Asia from Bengal to Sumatra. It is rapidly decreasing because of too heavy harvesting of eggs and slaughtering of turtles. The annual egg harvest has decreased by 50 percent.

The China alligator (*Alligator sinensis*) occurs in the Anhwei and Chekiang provinces of temperate China. It has been heavily persecuted and is decreasing. Also, the gavial (*Gavialis gangeticus*) and the marsh crocodile (*Crocodilus palustris*) have been so heavily depleted in southern Asia for trade in skins that their future seems to be jeopardized unless the persecution stops. Even more depleted is the Siamese crocodile (*C. siamensis*), which is probably extinct in the wild state and now only occurs with some specimens in a crocodile farm in Thailand.

The Israel painted frog (*Discoglossus nigriventer*) has been greatly reduced—perhaps even exterminated—by swamp-drainage schemes in the Lake Huleh region of Israel and Syria.

Apparently the freshwater fish fauna of Malaya and Singapore has been depleted much more than hitherto realized. For instance, of fifty-four indigenous species from Singapore, only thirty-five are recorded as surviving at present. Of these fishes eight species are very rare. One of them is the Singapore minnow (*Rasborichtys altior*), peculiar to Singapore Island, where it is limited to one locality only. At least three species known only from Singapore are now extinct: *Mystus elongatus* (not found since before 1855), *Bagarius bagarius* (not found since 1927), and *Mastacembelus armatus* (not found since before 1883). A threatened species in Malaya is the giant cyprinid *Probarbus jullieni,* which is restricted to the Perak and Pahang rivers. *Phallostethus dunckeri* from the Muar River has not been collected since 1904 and is by now probably extinct.

In Malaysia overfishing has greatly reduced the Asian bony-tongue (*Scleropages formosus*), a relict species that was once widespread but now is known in reasonable numbers only in a forest swamp. In Thailand the same factor is depleting a catfish, *Pangasius sanitwongsei,* as well as the giant catfish (*Pangasianodon gigas*) that occurs in the Mekong River basin. Two of Thailand's fishes, *Neostethus siamensis* and *Phenacostethus smithi,* have probably been extinct for one or two decades, probably because of introductions of mosquito fish (*Gambusia affinis*).

THE INLAND SEAS

There are four great inland seas in Eurasia, the Baltic, Caspian, Black, and Mediterranean, each different from the others. The Baltic Sea is brackish, rather shallow, and poor in fish species. The Caspian Sea is the largest lake in the world, but is shrinking

rapidly chiefly because of climatic changes and man's activities in
the Volga River. Its fauna is poor but very varied in origin (there
are 222 endemic species in the Caspian Sea) owing to a fourfold
genesis and former connections with other seas from the Arctic to
the Mediterranean. The Black Sea is at present a satellite of the
Mediterranean. The latter is poor in plankton, and therefore in
aquatic vertebrates, in comparison to the other three inland seas.

An extremely rare gull in the Mediterranean Sea is Audouin's
gull (*Larus audouinii*). It is entirely restricted to this sea, where
it is at present breeding on islands off eastern Spanish Morocco
as well as near Corsica and Cyprus and the northern Sporadhes.
A colony once located off the coast of Syria has vanished. Robbing
of nests by fishermen and egg collectors is thought to have affected
the small population, estimated at about 1,250 birds.

No vertebrate species living in the Black, Caspian, or Baltic
seas are at present in danger of extermination, though the Baltic
populations of the grey seal (*Halichoerus grypus*) and the ringed
seal (*Phoca hispida botnica*) have been greatly reduced in recent
times by the killing of cubs. Moreover, the Baltic Sea is the most
polluted, brackish-water sea in the world. Seals there contain several times as much DDT as they do in the North Sea and Canada.
This might be an even more serious threat to Baltic seals than the
direct killing of them. Very rare indeed is the Saima seal (*P. h.
saimensis*), which as a relict has been isolated in the Saimaa Lake
system in Finland for about eight thousand years. The total population is estimated at two hundred to 250 seals. It has been fully
protected since 1958, but pollution and complaining fishermen
constitute a threat to its existence. During the 1960's the Saima
seal declined rapidly and seems now to be doomed to extinction.

Baltic salmon (*Salmo salar*) populations may in the long run
be reduced by the extensive hydroelectric river regulations in
Sweden that prevent the salmon from reaching their ancestral
riverbeds for spawning. Moreover, this fish is heavily contaminated
with DDT and other toxic chemicals as are many vertebrate species
within the food chain of the Baltic area.

In the Black and Caspian seas and their great river deltas, the
great sturgeon (*Huso huso*), largest in the world of all freshwater
fishes and the prime producer of Russian caviar, has been overexploited to such an extent that, if the trend continues, the future
of this fish is endangered.

THE MEDITERRANEAN COUNTRIES

The Mediterranean countries, once covered by luxuriant forests with a wealth of animal life, are today only a pale shadow of their former glory. During the past three thousand years the soil has been dissipated and eroded as a result of human overexploitation. The climate has scarcely changed, though its effects are no longer what they were when the land was rich in forests.

As we have seen in an earlier section, deer and wild goats of various species, once typical mountain animals in this area, are all very rare, and one subspecies of goat has been exterminated. The mouflon (*Ovis musimon*) of Corsica and Sardinia has been heavily depleted. In Corsica it has decreased from four thousand to less than two hundred in fifty years. (The Cyprian mouflon is dealt with on page 133.)

The Mediterranean monk seal that is discussed under "Africa" (page 42) has some of its last European refuges along Sardinia's coast. (Other marine species of the Mediterranean are commented upon on page 140.)

The Spanish imperial eagle (*Aquila heliaca adalberti*) was once widespread in Morocco and Algeria as well as in Spain, but at present there is a population of only about one hundred birds left in central and southern Spain and possibly a few pairs in adjacent areas of North Africa. The newly established national park in the Coto Doñana in southwestern Spain gives protection to about seven adult pairs, but this is not sufficient to ensure survival.

The Cyprus Island dipper (*Cinclus cinclus olympicus*) was an endemic race that became exterminated in 1939.

THE SAVANNAS AND OPEN SCRUB LANDS

Describing the savannas of Asia—there are none in Europe—we enter the tropics. Asian savannas are chiefly confined to the subtropical parts of India and China. Asian savannas are of several types: rather dry, almost steppelike plains partly covered by shrubs, or somewhat richer grasslands, bushy country, or grassy plains with scattered thin woods.

A large part of the Indo-Ganges plain, ranging across India from the Arabian Sea to the Bay of Bengal, consists or rather consisted of savannas. Much of the former grasslands have been changed into deserts through overgrazing by cattle. As everyone knows, cattle are holy animals among orthodox Hindus. Religious precepts prohibit the killing of cattle and the eating of beef. People in India may go so far as to arrange protest meetings, riots, and hunger strikes when violations occur of these prohibitions concerning cattle.

The taboo on cattle is an ecological tragedy for a population of almost 540 million people. In 1963 there were 226 million cattle in India, about a quarter of the world's cattle population, a large part of it almost completely unproductive. The cattle population of India continues to expand without control. Hence there is a twofold population explosion in India: of human beings and of cattle. Both destroy the renewable natural resources, and with every passing day survival grows more difficult. This vicious cycle can be stopped only by education with the help of religious leaders, effective birth control and the elimination of most of the cattle. Otherwise nature's own remedies against excessive populations— disease, starvation, social violence, and war—may strike at any moment.

The terrific devastation of land in India has had a great effect on the animal life, too. But hunting also has taken a heavy toll of wild animals in India, particularly during the last two centuries when the whole country was used as a happy hunting ground by Asians and Europeans. Between the two World Wars the situation for India's wildlife became a little improved by the establishment of reserves, but after the end of World War II a massacre of wild animals and destruction of habitats started on a giant scale, for "protection of crops" and clearing of forests for growth of agriculture and industry. Since 1955 there has been increasingly widespread destruction of carnivores, particularly tigers, by pesticides. Endrin and Folidol, issued by the Indian Department of Agriculture, have been used indiscriminately and also deliberately for killing wildlife. Uncontrolled trade in pelts and meat is going on.

A third serious threat to wild hoofed animals in southern Asia is disease. Among wild ungulates it is particularly the "wild cattle" (tribe *Bovini*) which are vulnerable to disease. Southern Asia is the home of more species of wild cattle than any other area of the world. No fewer than six wild bovines of ten species live in southern Asia. In some areas in Asia diseases like anthrax, foot-and-mouth disease, and rinderpest, carried by domestic cattle, have been transmitted to wild bovines which, like many other wild ungulates, have little or no resistance to these epidemics. Whole populations have been wiped out in a very short time. Such catastrophes have occurred in a number of countries not only in Asia but also in Africa. As domestic cattle are presently everywhere in India and are widespread in other Asian countries they constitute a deadly threat to their wild cousins. A rinderpest outbreak in Thailand during World War II killed an estimated 80 percent of the wild bovines in the area. In Bandipur, India, rinderpest is believed to have eradicated in 1969 all wild cattle, chiefly gaur (*Bos gaurus*), in the Bandipur Wild Life Sanctuary.

Many mammals in southern Asia have been seriously reduced in numbers and have retreated to remote pockets. This is true of the Assam rabbit (*Caprolagus hispidus*), which is now nearly extinct. It occurred in India from Uttar Pradesh to the base of the Himalayan foothills in Assam. Disappearance of habitats due to cultivation and grazing accounts for its decline. It had not been seen for over ten years when it was found in Assam in 1971. A species that has gone forever is Schomburgk's deer (*Rucervus schomburgki*). It had lived in Thailand on open lands with sparse growth of trees. Cultivation and persecution pushed this deer into thick forests, to which it apparently could not adapt itself. The last observed specimen was shot in 1932.

The Asiatic lion (*Panthera leo persica*) was an animal of open land ranging over almost all of southwestern Asia from the Arabian peninsula and Asia Minor to eastern India. It was probably this lion that roamed the plains of Thessaly in Greece during the fifth century B.C. It still occurred in the 1800's in Turkey, and in 1866 it was described as "not rare in Asia Minor." It ranged widely over the northern half of the Indian peninsula 150 years ago. In Iran this lion seems to have been exterminated during the 1930's—the last occurrence outside of India. It was widespread in India, but human occupation of the land and a tremendous slaughter by the military exterminated it everywhere except in the Gir forest on the Kathiawar peninsula of western India. Since 1884 the Indian lion has been confined to this teak forest and to nearby open thorn scrub and scattered acacias among light stands of grass. The Gir forest is protected to ensure the survival of just the Asiatic lion, but the area is also utilized by more than seven thousand people and ninety thousand domestic animals. The lion population was thought to be rather stable despite the killing of about one hundred annually. In 1936 the population was estimated at

287 lions, in 1955 at 290, in 1963 at 255; but in 1968 only 175 lions occurred there, and in 1970 less than 150. Three Asiatic lions were introduced in the Chandraprabha sanctuary in Uttar Pradesh in 1957; by 1966 they had increased to eleven lions, but in 1969 all of them had been killed.

The Asiatic cheetah (*Acinonyx jubatus venaticus*) had in the past almost the same distribution as the Asiatic lion. It was exterminated in most areas of its former range by persecution and destruction of its habitats. No recent observation of the animal has been made in India except for one area where it was last seen in 1968; in Iran it was near extinction but conservation measures have brought the number of the cheetah to about two hundred; in Arabia it was last reported in 1950; and only a few animals survive in Turkmenistan and perhaps in Afghanistan and Pakistan. It is now protected in Turkmenistan and Iran.

The Baluchistan bear (*Selenarctos thibetanus gedrosianus*), occurring in Pakistan, has been driven from its optimal coniferous forest habitats in the mountains to low, arid hills with thickets of acacias and euphorbias, where it has become very rare, apparently owing to paucity of natural food and to conflicts with man, because it is obliged to raid crops to be able to feed.

The Manipur brow-antlered deer (*Cervus eldii eldii*) is limited to a small sanctuary near Logtak Lake in the Manipur State of India, where there were about a hundred animals in 1960. Formerly it occurred in the scrub of Manipur Valley, but destruction by man caused its decline. The Burmese brow-antlered deer (*C. e. thamin*) was once one of the most abundant deer in Burma, but it was so depleted by killing and habitat destruction that during the 1940's it was near extinction. Sanctuaries were established and the deer was declared completely protected. These measures have resulted in an increase, so that this deer is now out of danger. The population in 1960 was estimated at three thousand. The most endangered race of this species is the Thailand brow-antlered deer (*C. e. siamensis*), of which there now live only a few groups of four or five animals each in northern Thailand. Formerly it was abundant on the open plains and deciduous woods of Thailand, but persecution and loss of suitable habitats have pressed down the number. A herd is maintained in the Vincennes Zoo near Paris, which may save the race from total extinction.

The wild Asiatic buffalo or water buffalo (*Bubalus bubalis*) was once widespread in southern Asia from Nepal, Bhutan, and India eastward to Vietnam and Borneo. In India this species was in the past distributed over the Brahmaputra and Ganges grass plains from Uttar Pradesh to eastern Assam, where it was extremely abundant only seventy years ago. Cultivation of its habitats, firearms, and diseases (particularly rinderpest) transmitted from domestic cattle are some of the factors in the drastic decrease in this species. It is now entirely protected. The total population does not exceed two thousand animals divided on ten different areas in India, Nepal, and Assam. There are also some in national parks in Ceylon. The largest population, about 550, is living in the Kaziranga sanctuary in Assam, and there are perhaps about four hundred in the Manas sanctuary in the same state.

Until recent times the blackbuck (*Antilope cervicapra*) was one of the most common and characteristic of ungulates in India and Pakistan. Herds of ten thousand blackbuck occurred in Punjab. A terrific hunting pressure has during a few decades brought this species to the verge of extinction. It holds on in a few reserves, for example, the Kanha National Park in India, but even there the population is very small. The species has been introduced to game ranches and reserves in the U. S., Mexico, and Argentina, where it has adapted and become numerous. In fact, there are at present more blackbuck in Texas and Argentina than in India and Pakistan. In 1970 a small herd was flown at the expense of the World Wildlife Fund from Texas to West Pakistan for reintroduction in a wildlife reserve.

The great Indian bustard (*Choriotis nigriceps*) formerly ranged over the plains of India, but it is now limited to a small area in northwestern India, and West Pakistan, where it is rare and becoming rarer owing to habitat destruction (cultivation and overgrazing) and heavy hunting despite protection by law. The total number in 1969 was estimated to be 1,260 in India and thirty-nine in West Pakistan. Most birds exist in Rajasthan with about five hundred, in Madhya Pradesh with four hundred, and in Gujarat and Maharashtra with one hundred each.

THE JUNGLE

The term "jungle" is often used to signify either tropical forests or almost impenetrable forests anywhere. In this book we reserve the term for Asian deciduous forests, woodlands, bush thickets, and dense second growths, which are not of rain- or monsoon-forest character. This jungle represents a drier forest type and does not have a continuous closed canopy. Thus, sunlight reaches the lowest story and encourages a thick undergrowth of bushes and low trees. These dense jungles are well represented in tropical Asia, particularly in large areas of India, but also in Ceylon, Burma, Thailand, Laos, Cambodia, North and South Vietnam, and China. The animals are in many cases the same as in the closed, dark rain forest.

All three Asian rhinoceroses are threatened by extinction because of persecution by man. The reputation of the rhino's horn as an aphrodisiac is the main reason for this. The most spectacular of these rhinos is the great Indian rhinoceros (*Rhinoceros unicornis*). Formerly distributed over a vast area of northern Pakistan, India, and Assam, as well as southern Nepal, its ecological flexibility doubtless explains its survival despite constant human pressure of every kind. It has been on continuous retreat to remote areas, although these do not represent the most suitable habitats for it; they have saved the species from extinction and have been declared reserves. The most famous sanctuary is the Kaziranga in Assam, a swampy area with tall, dense "elephant grass" (chiefly *Phragmites karna*). It is often claimed that this type of habitat is the best one for the great Indian rhinoceros, but experiences in other areas indicate that if there is a preferred habitat, it seems to be jungle of the rather dry, mixed forest type and bush with glades and open stretches of grassland. That is why we deal with this animal here.

In 1966 there were between seven and eight hundred rhinos living in eight reserves or sanctuaries in India and Nepal, two in West Bengal, one in Nepal, and five in Assam, of which there were about 360 to four hundred rhinos in the Kaziranga sanctuary and about 155 in Nepal's Chitawan National Park in the Rapti Valley. By 1968 the latter figure had dropped to between eighty and a hundred and in 1971 there were just about sixty. In the early 1950's the number was about eight hundred! This dramatic decline was due to the illegal settlement of several thousand squatters, who destroyed the habitat and drove the rhinos out into swamps and islands of the Rapti River, where poachers killed large numbers. All the other reserves except Jaldapara in India have fewer than forty-five rhinos. The 1971 figure in Kaziranga was about four hundred.

The pygmy hog (*Sus salvanius*) is a jungle species that is nearly extinct. It used to be found in swampy grass jungles below the lower Himalayan foothills in Nepal, Sikkim, Bhutan, and Assam. Nocturnal and as small as a hare, it is difficult to detect. Apparently the reduction in its habitats due to cultivation and grazing gave the species a serious handicap. In 1969 a group of adults and juveniles were observed in Assam between Brahmaputra and Bhutan. In 1971 seventeen pygmy hogs lived in three protected, privately owned areas in Assam.

The black muntjak (*Muntiacus crinifrons*) is one of the rarest deer of the world. It is known only from a limited area in Chekiang, southeastern China, where in 1940 it was represented by "a handful of individuals." Today we know no more of this deer than we did thirty years ago.

The Bengal tiger (*Panthera tigris tigris*) is an inhabitant of Asian jungles as well as of rain forests and mountains. By the end of the nineteenth century it was estimated that probably about forty thousand Bengal tigers roamed the Indo-Pakistan part of Asia. Fifty to sixty years later the number had dropped to two to four thousand owing to excessive shooting, poisoning, habitat destruction, and reduction of prey. An estimated four to five hundred tigers were shot each year in India during the 1960's. This tremendous decline goes on. In 1969 the results of a census of the tiger in India were published. The "total" ranged from 2,724 to 3,700 animals. A conservative estimate of total numbers would be about 2,500 tigers. Of these Madhya Pradesh has six hundred to 1,400, Assam about five hundred, Uttar Pradesh four to five hundred, and Maharashtra 329. Five states have no tigers at all: Haryana, Himachal Pradesh, Jammu, Kashmir, and Punjab. A more recent census in India in 1971 gave an estimate of 1,960 tigers, about 250 in Nepal and about a hundred in Pakistan (most of them live in Bangladesh). If action is not taken to save the Bengal tiger, the world will in the foreseeable future lose this magnificent animal. Fortunately, following recommendations from IUCN, India (all states except Madhya Pradesh) and Pakistan took measures in 1970 strictly to protect the tiger and ban trade in tiger and leopard skins. Nepal and the State of Madhya Pradesh followed this example in 1971.

Also near extinction or perhaps already gone is the Malabar civet (*Viverra megaspila civettina*), which once was common in southwestern India, but during the last decades has decreased to such an extent that there is no recent evidence of its existence.

The golden langur (*Presbytis geei*) of Assam and Bhutan is through limitation of habitat in danger of extinction.

Jerdon's courser (*Cursorius bitorquatus*) was a bird of India's thin jungle forests. It is believed to have been extinct since 1900, when the last bird was collected. Another jungle bird, the forest spotted owlet (*Athene blewitti*) of Central India, vanished from the forest scene in 1872. A very rare, almost unknown bird with limited distribution in India and Sikkim is Rotschild's parakeet (*Psittacula intermedia*).

THE TROPICAL RAIN FOREST

The lowland rain forests of tropical Asia are located in the southeastern parts of the continent. There is also a strip in southwestern India and some other scattered areas that have heavy rainfall. The largest Asian rain-forest region, the tropical Malay archipelago, which politically is located in Indonesia, Sarawak, and Sabah, will be treated in a separate section.

On the Asian mainland it is chiefly Malaya, Thailand, South Vietnam, Cambodia, Burma, and India which are partly covered by rain forests. Of these only the ones on the Malay peninsula are genuine rain forests with all the elements of climax vegetation. Parts of southern China were once covered by tropical rain forests but such forests disappeared long ago. The practice of destroying forest in China is of ancient date. It has reached monumental proportions and is disastrous. Only 9 percent of China's land remains forested. The forests no longer control the rivers, which flood the lowlands with catastrophic results. That is the way nature strikes back when poorly managed.

The remaining tropical rain forests of southeastern Asia are natural refuges for many of the continent's larger mammals, driven away from their original ranges by man's cultivation of the land and persecution. The present dilemma is that the forests are cut down so rapidly that wild animals are stranded in pockets of high forest and jungle with nowhere to go. Lack of food in these limited areas will force them to venture into cultivated regions, and then a clash with human interests is inevitable. This applies particularly to the larger mammals, and especially in Thailand, Malaya, Sumatra, Java, Borneo, and Ceylon. But birds may also fall victim to habitat destruction. This was presumably the case with the Burma race of Jerdon's babbler (*Moupinia altirostris altirostris*), which became extinct in 1941.

A victim of ruthless slaughter, commercialized hunting, and advancing cultivation is the Malayan gaur (*Bos gaurus hubbacki*), a large ungulate constituting an important food resource. Its former range included the Malay peninsula. In the 1930's large herds still grazed by night in open clearings along the forest edge, but forest itself was their refuge. During World War II great numbers of gaurs were killed, and the population has not recovered. Moreover, the Malayan gaur does not seem able to adapt itself to man-made disturbances. The center of the Malayan gaur's present range is the State of Pahang in Malaysia. Small herds, in 1961 estimated at about three hundred animals, live elsewhere in Malaya. In 1963 an estimated number of seven hundred gaurs occurred in the peninsula, but in 1968 this population was believed to have shrunk to less than 350. The future of this splendid mammal seems to be very uncertain unless it is given strict protection in reserves.

Another of southeastern Asia's large bovids is the almost fabulous kouprey (*Bos sauveli*), a magnificent animal, discovered by science as late as 1937. Prior to the twentieth-century wars in Indochina, the kouprey existed in Thailand, Cambodia, and Vietnam with probably about two thousand individuals. During the 1940's and 1950's it disappeared from Thailand, but still in 1955 it was found in Vietnam. In 1952 the population in Cambodia was estimated at two to five hundred individuals, but later estimates arrived at 650–850. At the end of the 1960's the species was restricted to the forests of northern Cambodia, where it grazes in clearings and glades. During the 1960's it was found in only two separate areas on each side of the Mekong River. The 1960's estimates of these two populations vary from five hundred to a thousand animals, but in 1969 there were hardly more than a hundred animals. They are protected by law, but their number is declining. No koupreys exist in captivity. A plan for raising this species was worked out by IUCN and the U. S. National Academy of Sciences in co-operation with the Cambodian government, but before it could be executed, Cambodia was invaded in 1970 by Communist troops and war broke out over the whole country. Before the fighting started, the kouprey population was split in three areas. One of these was a reserve in northeastern Cambodia which probably had between twenty and thirty koupreys. This area has been a headquarters for Vietcong military activities, so there is little hope that any koupreys are left there. The second place was a famous reserve with not more than twenty animals. This area has been overrun by the military and there is little hope for survival of the koupreys. The most important concentration of this animal was in the famous reserve of Kolilen Promtet, near Stung Treng in northern Cambodia. In June, 1970, this area also became invaded by Vietcong, who were undoubtedly shooting koupreys. The total population was in June, 1970, estimated at less than seventy animals. It is indeed tragic if fighting between human beings should result in the extermination of a unique mammal, which represents a great protein-resource value and a genetic heritage of exceptional importance, besides being scientifically of great interest.

One of the rarest ungulates of tropical Asia's forests is Fea's muntjac (*Muntiacus feae*), which is known only from some regions in Burma and Thailand. The Indo-Chinese lar gibbon (*Hylobates lar pileatus*) in Thailand, Cambodia, and Laos was in 1968 reported to be heavily persecuted and in danger of extinction. But smaller mammals have also been greatly reduced by forest destruction and human persecution. Among them is the douc langur (*Pygathrix nemaeus*) from Annam, Laos, and Vietnam, Oweston's banded civet (*Chrotogale owstoni*) from Tonkin, Laos, and Vietnam, and the otter civet (*Cynogale bennetti*) from Vietnam, Malaya, Sumatra, and Borneo. Similarly, a small bird, Rueck's blue flycatcher (*Muscicapa ruecki*), is known only from two localities.

TROPICAL MOUNTAINS OF THE MAINLAND

Most of the Asian mountains south of the Himalayas are located in southeast Asia. On the mainland there are high mountains in southwestern India and throughout southeastern Asia, including southern China. Burma in particular has range after range of rugged mountains with virgin cloud forests. Some of these mountains have been denuded of forests and lie bare, exposed to erosion. Others are still clothed in forests of various types from high jungle and montane rain forests to alpine associations.

Flying eastward over India, Burma, and Thailand, one is struck by the variety of natural areas, from deserts to rain forests. Thanks to moist monsoon winds, forests thrive on the hills and mountains, and shrubs and grass on the open plains. Despite the fact that the melting snow and glaciers of surrounding mountains produce large quantities of water, these countries could hardly have survived without the monsoons.

Monsoon forests lose their leaves with a marked seasonality and therefore differ from true rain forests. The distribution of monsoon forests in mainland and insular Asia corresponds to the pattern of seasonal monsoon winds (bringing rainfall and moisture) and high summer temperatures.

The monsoon forests of tropical Asia are among the most important habitats left for wildlife. Unfortunately, they are disappearing rapidly. Owing to heavy population pressure, cultivation, and grazing, as well as improper use of land, many monsoon montane forests have been destroyed and have given way to the results of erosion. Serious landslides are common on devastated mountain slopes, violent floods are an annual occurrence, and the water table in valleys and plains is sinking. The deforestation of these mountains thus releases formidable challenges not only to agriculturists, foresters, and soil conservationists but also to whole populations.

Four mammals and three gallinaceous birds are at present threatened on the tropical mountains of the Asian highland. The lion-tailed macaque (*Macaca silenus*) is limited to mountain ranges of the Western Ghats of southwestern India, where destruction of indigenous evergreen forests for replacement with exotic trees has caused disastrous effects on this endemic primate. In 1963 the population was estimated at less than a thousand. Since then the situation has become more precarious owing to habitat devastation, hunting pressure, and capturing for zoos. In 1970 there were seventy-nine lion-tailed macaques in U. S. zoological gardens, but under present conditions their birth rate does not equal the death rate. The disastrous deforestations are, however, the prime cause of the dramatic decline of this species. Similarly, the Nilgiri langur (*Presbytis johni*) has for the same reasons been reduced to a point that cannot be very far from no return.

The Nilgiri tahr (*Hemitragus hylocrius*) is at present also confined to the mountains of the Western Ghats. Presumably it had a much wider range in the past, because it has relatives in the Himalayas and Arabia. Excessive hunting is believed to be the cause of the substantial reduction of the species. There are now

four sanctuaries for this tahr in the Nilgiri hills, where the population is estimated at 420 animals; about six hundred other tahrs live
in other parts of the same mountain range according to an estimate
of 1970. The red goral (*Nemorhaedus cranbrooki*) from mountains in northeastern Assam and northern Burma has a very limited
distribution. Its lack of shyness makes it vulnerable. Two gallinaceous birds are almost extinct: the imperial pheasant (*Lophura
imperialis*) is restricted to a few areas in Vietnam and Laos, and
Edward's pheasant (*L. edwardsi*) to some mountains in central
Annam and Vietnam. The latter has not been observed in the wild
since 1923, the former not for some years. Both species are beautiful, the cocks in metallic dark-blue feathers with red chins and
legs. Also a passerine bird, the rufous-headed robin (*Erithacus
ruficeps*) belongs to the very rare birds. It is only known from two
areas, the Cameron Highlands in Malaya and the Tsinling Mountains in China.

THE BIG ISLANDS AND ARCHIPELAGOES

Off southeastern and eastern Asia, archipelagoes and islands
form a gigantic link of large and small land fragments. Some of
them are continental islands, others of oceanic origin. The former
category includes islands which are continental remnants and are
usually inhabited by mammals and amphibians having affinities with
animal life on nearby continents. Oceanic islands are born in the
ocean as a result of volcanic eruptions or by the work of marine
organisms. These islands consist of volcanic rocks or coral limestone. Most often terrestrial mammals and amphibians are lacking
on such oceanic islands.

In this section we shall deal with the threatened animals on
large islands and archipelagoes like Ceylon, Sumatra, Java, Bali,
Borneo, Celebes, the Philippines, Taiwan, Japan, and Sakhalin.

Ceylon

Ceylon is an island with two climates, a very humid one in the
southwestern part and a very dry one in the northeast. The southwestern monsoon sweeps the southwest with moisture and nourishes
it with a high precipitation, but almost all the rainfall is released
in southwestern Ceylon, because the oceanic winds are stopped by
a mountain barrier rising to more than five thousand feet in the
southern interior of Ceylon.

More than 2,500 years of cultivation have deprived Ceylon of almost all its virgin vegetation. However, much of the island was still covered by more or less dense forests up to the 1850's. During the last hundred years these forests have been cut down to make way for plantations. This threatens many of Ceylon's animals with extinction, though the establishment of national parks and reserves has saved them at least temporarily.

It is, of course, difficult for a large herbivore like the Ceylon elephant (*Elephas maximus ceylanicus*) to exist on an island that has a large human population and where suitable habitats are constantly being reduced. The Ceylon elephant is a subspecies peculiar to Ceylon, and owing to its long isolation has acquired characteristics that distinguish it from its ancestor, the Indian elephant (*E. m. maximus*). Between 1831 and 1900 about ten thousand elephants were shot for sport. Ceylon's present population of wild elephants in 1969 was estimated at about 2,500 animals. Formerly this race occurred all over Ceylon and at all elevations, but nowadays it is limited to a few areas. Three national parks give refuge to this elephant but they are not quite suitable habitats during the dry period. This elephant is also protected from hunting and capture. The problem, however, is the climination of habitats by agricultural development, which makes the remaining natural areas too small for the elephants, particularly as they are seasonal wanderers. Only the most urgent conservation measures can save this elephant. There are plans to enlarge the national parks to include jungle corridors and areas used by the animals as traditional migration routes between the habitats they need for feeding during the various seasons of the year.

The rarest bird of Ceylon is the red-faced malkoha (*Phaenicophaeus pyrrhocephalus*), a cuckoo peculiar to the island, after having been seemingly exterminated on the mainland. In Ceylon it is decreasing rapidly owing to forest destruction, but during two visits to Ceylon in 1966 I learned that the species had moved into more cultivated habitats, thus showing an ecological elasticity.

Sumatra

Sumatra lies close to the Asian mainland and in nature differs only slightly from the nearby Malay peninsula. The other islands of Indonesia are similar to Sumatra. They are, of course, all tropical, with diverse habitats, large forests, and high mountains.

The islands of the Indo-Australian archipelago are at present separated from each other and the Asian mainland by shallow water, but during the Pleistocene and probably until early historic time they were all connected to the mainland. Tropical rain forests are characteristic features in Indonesia and were originally the major biome. A rapid population increase and subsequent spreading of agriculture and shifting cultivation has reduced the forest area of Indonesia during the last hundred years, but before the forests were opened to timber companies in 1966 the human impact had not been very serious. In 1972 concessions of ten million hectares have been issued to foreign companies and a further eight million are under negotiation. Altogether there are hardly more than twenty-four million hectares of productive forests in Indonesia. Obviously such a reckless exploitation constitutes a great threat to forest animals and to water and soil resources.

Sumatra has more terrestrial mammals than Java and Borneo. The tapir and the serow are, for example, on Sumatra but not on Java and Borneo. The Indian elephant was probably introduced on Borneo, whereas it is spontaneous on Sumatra. Sumatra is also richer in bats than the other islands. This richness in mammals is probably an effect of the past and present proximity to the Asian mainland. However, there are some mammals that no longer exist anywhere else or whose largest populations are on this large tropical island. One of them is the short-eared rabbit (*Nesolagus netscheri*), which has been found only in two areas of montane rain forests in Sumatra. A more spectacular animal is the Sumatran rhinoceros (*Didermocerus sumatrensis*), which in the 1850's was distributed over almost all of southeastern Asia from Assam, India, Bangladesh, southern China, and North Vietnam in the north to Malaya, Sumatra, and Borneo in the south. Today this rhino is limited to a few localities in Burma, Thailand, Cambodia, Malaya, Sumatra, and in Sabah on Borneo. Again, it is chiefly the magical value of the rhino's horn that explains the tremendous decline within a century. The price of the horn in 1963 was about one thousand dollars, or about 210 dollars an inch. Almost every part of the Sumatran rhino's body is in addition believed to have healing power and even religious importance. Thus it is obvious that protective measures must include the strictest patrol of sanctuaries. In 1963 the population of the Sumatran rhino was between one hundred and 170 animals; in 1968 it was thought to be 150 animals. They are divided in several separate areas of which five are situated in Burma, some in Malaysia, two in Sumatra, and one in Sabah. Between thirty-five and forty-six rhinos were estimated in Burma in 1960, and fifty-eight in Sumatra in 1970, where the Loeser Reserve and Riau harbour this number and are the last strongholds. In 1965 ten Sumatra rhinos were definitely known to occur in Malaya, with a probable total of thirty; but in 1968–70 only about twenty known animals occurred in six different localities. In Sabah the number was in 1970 fewer than one hundred.

The Sumatran serow (*Capricornis sumatraensis sumatraensis*), a relative of the chamois, has been much persecuted in most parts of its former range. It now occurs only in almost inaccessible volcanic regions. It is protected by law, but this seems to have little effect: It is still hunted persistently.

The local race of the Sumatran tiger (*Panthera tigris sumatrae*) has become increasingly rare and is now endangered owing to human persecution and cultivation. It still occurs in northern Sumatra and in the southwestern mountains, where it is thought that "a few hundreds" may still exist. The pig-tailed langur (*Simias concolor*) and the dwarf gibbon (*Hylobates klossii*) are both restricted to three islands of the Mentawai group off the west coast of Sumatra, where habitat destruction is a threat to these rare species.

Java

Owing to soil cultivation and a staggering increase in population from three or four million people in 1800 to sixty-one million in 1961, there is not much left of virgin nature in Java. However, the equatorial monsoon climate, thirty-two active volcanoes spreading ash rich in mineral nutrients, and fertile soil carried by flooding rivers help to keep Java's vegetation healthy. A fourth factor, most unusual in a densely populated tropical area, also helps: the scarcity of goats in large areas and the destruction they cause.

Some of the volcanoes and mountain ranges in Java are covered by beautiful rain forests harbouring rich animal life. The one remaining lowland rain forest in Java, located on the westernmost tip of the island, the Udjung Kulon peninsula, has been a reserve since 1921. This sanctuary also harbours many rare mammals, the most outstanding of them the Javan rhinoceros (*Rhinoceros sondaicus*), the rarest of the world's five species of rhinos. Only twenty-one to twenty-eight individuals live in this reserve according to a census in 1970; it is uncertain whether any survive elsewhere in Asia except for the Loeser Reserve in Sumatra and perhaps Tenasserim on the boundary between Thailand and Burma, where a few may remain. During the 1850's the Javan rhinoceros ranged over most areas of southeastern Asia, from eastern India and southern China southward to Sumatra and Java. In Sumatra it became exterminated during the 1940's except in Loeser. The smallness of the remaining population makes this species very vulnerable. The IUCN and the World Wildlife Fund have in cooperation with the Indonesian government worked hard for eight years to save the Javan rhino at Udjung Kulon. Evidences in 1969–70 have indicated that the species is increasing slowly in this area.

The banteng (*Bibos javanicus*) was once a common wild ox in the forests of Burma, Thailand, the Malay peninsula, Java, and Borneo, but destruction of habitats for cultivation as well as heavy poaching have caused a steady decline in numbers in most parts of its range. It is not known whether the mainland race (*B. j. birmanicus*) still survives. About two hundred pure-bred bantengs of the subspecies *B. j. javanicus* occur at present in the Udjung Kulon peninsula; the same number are found in Baluran National Park and almost one hundred in the Tjikepuk reserve in eastern Java. Other bantengs in Java are hybrids crossbred with cattle. Little is known about *B. j. lowi,* the banteng on Borneo, and it may still occur in goodly numbers.

The Bartiri Forest Reserve of eastern Java is the last refuge of the Javan tiger (*Panthera tigris sondaica*), once numerous in Java but probably the island's rarest animal today. In 1972 only five were thought to be left. The tigers in Udjung Kulon and Baluran reserves were exterminated during the 1960's.

On Bawean, north of Java, there lives the Bawean deer (*Hyelaphus kuhlii*), a species peculiar to this island. It was almost exterminated by hunters during World War II but has since recovered. It lives exclusively in hilly and mountainous areas, and in 1965 the population was estimated at "several thousands." This figure is certainly too optimistic. In fact, this deer is again menaced by deforestation and the attitude of the local people, who consider it a nuisance because of the damage it does to plantations.

On Christmas Island, south of Java, three mammals have been exterminated: the Christmas Island shrew (*Crocidura fuliginosa trichura*), Maclear's rat (*Rattus macleari*), and the bulldog rat (*R. nativitatis*). All became extinct about 1904, probably because of some introduced disease. Abbott's booby (*Sula abbotti*) became extinct by about 1936 on Assumption Island but survives in declining numbers on Christmas Island. Man was responsible for its disappearance from the former island, but on Christmas Island, its only remaining locality, it is protected. From one thousand to 1,500 birds in 1941, the species had decreased to about two hundred pairs in 1967. Dangerously decreasing is the Christmas Island goshawk (*Accipiter fasciatus natalis*) that is also confined to this island. It was reported to be common all over the island in 1947, but in 1963–64 its numbers had dropped to about twelve.

Bali

Bali had a tiger, *Panthera tigris balica,* that has recently become extinct. Up to World War I the Bali tiger was rather common, but by 1963 there were no more than three or four left and they were on a reserve in western Bali. When I visited Bali in December, 1965, I found no sign of this tiger anywhere, but I was assured that the tiger still occurred within the reserve. However, none were sighted in the period 1963–71 and it is almost certain that this subspecies is now extinct. Bali is also the haunt of the rare Rotschild's starling (*Leucopsar rotschildi*). It is a remarkably beautiful bird, entirely white except for the black tips of the wings and tail and the steel-blue bill, chins, and legs.

Lesser Sunda Islands

The world's largest lizard, the Komodo lizard (*Varanus komodoensis*), has its home on four of the Lesser Sunda Islands, Komodo, Padar, Rintja, and the westernmost part of Flores. This large reptile, measuring up to twelve feet, has seriously decreased in numbers since the 1930's. Twenty years ago there were still between a thousand and 1,100 individuals on the four islands. Most of them live on Komodo. The reason for the decline is that hunters kill the Komodo lizard's prey. The staple food of the lizard is carrion, but carrion is common only where there is an abundance of prey. The populations of the Komodo lizard have dwindled to a dangerously low level. In May, 1966, Komodo Island was proclaimed a strict nature reserve.

Borneo

Borneo, a huge island that straddles the equator and is exposed to the monsoon winds, has immense rain forests in both its lowlands and mountains. The latter are very high; in fact, Borneo's Kinabalu, which raises its cloud-covered peak to 13,455 feet, is the highest in the whole Asian archipelago.

Although the light of the sun scarcely penetrates the dense canopy of Borneo's rain forest, the heat warms the damp air and soil in the half-darkness below the trees' upper stories. The interior of this vast hothouse is the home of one of the world's most seriously menaced mammals, the orangutan (*Pongo pygmaeus*). This species has declined drastically and at an accelerating rate during the present century. Tragic and shameful pressure has been put on this ape by hunting and trading, and to this is added the destruction of its habitats for the sake of timber. An orang mother must usually be killed before the young are captured, and the mortality of captured young is exceptionally high, probably owing to mistreatment. The orangs are sold to animal dealers and for laboratory use: it should be added that members of the International Union of Directors of Zoological Gardens refuse to buy illegally captured orangs.

Three-quarters of the orangutan population are probably confined to Borneo, where the population in 1965 was estimated at about 2,500 animals. In Sumatra, according to one estimate, there were about one thousand orangs in 1963, but this figure seems to be too optimistic, especially for an area where the species has been mercilessly persecuted. In 1971 the total number of living orangutans was estimated at under five thousand, of which more than five hundred were being held in zoological gardens and research stations. Regulations concerning exportation and importation of orangs seemed to have had little effect. Despite energetic measures by local authorities, IUCN, and other institutions the trade in orangutans continues and the traditional catching of babies goes on. In Sumatra alone about 250 animals are probably lost each year due to this misuse. In addition about 75 percent of the orangutan forests in Sumatra may vanish within the next decade, and the ape has no way to retreat to other areas. It is urgent that strictly protected reserves be set aside for this primate both in Borneo and in Sumatra. A recent threat in Sumatra is extensive timber exploitation by American firms in the best remaining orangutan forests.

The Bornean striped ground squirrel (*Lariscus hosei*) frequents the banks of jungle streams, which are the first to be destroyed when man penetrates up the rivers. It has become very rare. Another mammal that is peculiar to the mountains of Borneo is Hose's palm civet (*Diplogale hosei*).

The Malaysian peacock pheasant (*Polyplectron malacense schliermacheri*), a bird of dense forests, is very rare and probably constantly hunted in Borneo, where it is endemic.

Celebes

Celebes is another large forest island of the Indonesian archipelago and proportionately even more mountainous than Borneo. Its most famous mammal is the anoa (*Anoa depressicornis*), a dwarf buffalo that in the past was distributed over the whole of the island. One lowland race (*A. d. depressicornis*) lived on the plains along the coastal areas and on several nearby islands, while two montane races, Quarles' anoa (*A. d. quarlesi*) and the mountain anoa (*A. d. fergusoni*), were restricted to the highlands. Because of uncontrolled hunting and spreading cultivation, the species abandoned the lowlands and gradually retreated to remote, dense forest areas in the interior. It is believed to have declined seriously. At present the lowland race still occurs in swampy forests of northern Celebes, while the mountain races seem to be limited to the peak of Bonthain, the Toradja Highlands, and probably the central mountains of Celebes. Before World War II some reserves and game regulations for the anoa were established but today they exist only on paper. The military wantonly slaughter the anoa with machine guns.

The black ape (*Cynopithecus niger*), confined to Celebes and Aru Island, has become very rare and is now listed among endangered species.

Even more scarce is the maleo (*Macrocephalon maleo*), a gallinaceous bird that, owing to hunters, is now found in only a few localities in the northern and southeastern peninsulas of Celebes. Also very rare is Platen's Celebes rail (*Aramidopsis plateni*), known only from a few areas on Celebes. A most mysterious bird, Salvadori's parrot (*Tanygnathus heterurus*), is known only from a single specimen and has not been observed since the one was collected before 1912. It is not even known whether the bird originated in Celebes or in New Guinea. Still another rare bird, the Kalabat Volcano nightjar (*Eurostropodus diabolicus*), occurs, as far as we know, only on this volcano.

The Philippines

The 7,107 islands of the Philippines are a continuation northward of the Indonesian archipelago. The natural resources of the Philippines have been terribly devastated, particularly during and after World War II. Only a few decades ago the forests of the Philippines were the home of an abundant wildlife. During the last half-century the total forest area of the islands has been reduced by half, more than 80 percent of this reduction occurring in the last twenty years. Most of the destroyed forests have been completely wasted by slashing and burning for shifting cultivation, which is of no lasting benefit to anyone.

All of this destruction must, of course, be seen in the light of a gigantic population increase—more than one million persons a year. This means a terrific increase in hunting pressure and disregard for game laws and wildlife reserves. The fauna is suffering accordingly.

One of the most endangered animals in the Philippines is the monkey-eating eagle (*Pithecophaga jefferyi*), largest eagle in the world (wingspan over eight feet). In 1963–64 an investigation indicated that there were about one hundred monkey-eating eagles in the Philippines. Because it is a spectacular bird, it is illegally exported to zoos and is considered an outstanding hunting trophy. It is therefore in grave danger of becoming extinct. It became totally protected in 1970. Formerly the monkey-eating eagle was found on Mindanao, Samar, Leyte, and Luzon, but today it is confined to Mindanao, where in 1969 only about forty birds remained. Most of them live in Mount Apo National Park, but this does not mean that they can easily be found there. During a visit to Mount Apo National Park on Mindanao in 1966, I found it difficult to get guides because they feared the tribes living on the mountain. I was told that head-hunting tribes in the mountains discourage hunters and collectors. Thus, in this case a mountain tribe seems to be an ally of the conservationists, but on the other hand, it destroys forest habitats by burning.

The Mindanao gymnure (*Podogymnura truei*) is a hedgehog

restricted to Mindanao, where it occurs only on Mount Apo and two other mountains. It is threatened by habitat destruction.

The giant scops owl (*Otus gurneyi*) has a limited range on Mindanao and on the island of Marinduque. Disturbance of its habitat seems to have reduced the small population.

The island of Cebu has lost much of its original habitats and therefore many of its endemic birds. The Cebu amethyst-brown fruit dove (*Phapitreron amethystina frontalis*) was wiped out by 1892; while the Cebu hanging parakeet (*Loriculus philippensis chrysonotus*), the Cebu barred graybird (*Coracina striata cebuensis*), the Cebu black graybird (*C. caerulescens altera*), the Cebu slaty-crowned bulbul (*Hypsipetes siquijorensis monticola*), the four-colored flowerpecker (*Diacaeum quadricolor*), the Cebu orange-breasted flowerpecker (*D. trigonostigma pallidius*), the Cebu Everett's white-eye (*Zosterops everetti everetti*), and the dark-throated oriole (*Oriolus xanthonotus assimilis*) were last seen in 1906 by a collecting expedition. Another expedition in 1947 found no sign of them. Apparently these forest birds all fell victim to deforestation. Other birds face the same fate. Of them the Cebu black shama (*Copsychus niger cebuensis*), not seen since 1956, will probably be the next to be marked "Gone."

The Palawan peacock pheasant (*Polyplectron emphanum*) is restricted to this island whose name it bears, where it has decreased seriously during the last decade.

The most famous mammal of the Philippines and one of the world's rarest is the tamarau (*Anoa mindorensis*), a small buffalo on Mindoro. Formerly it was also found in the lowlands but at present it is limited to bamboo thickets in the highlands. One can only guess how many tamaraus still survive. It is clear that the population is very small and that its habitats are rapidly diminishing. A reserve has been set aside on the Mount Iglit Plateau for about fifty tamaraus, but this area is insufficient for long-term protection of this species. In 1968 only about twenty animals were confirmed surviving on Iglit, but in 1971, thirty-two animals were reported. There are two other isolated populations on Mindoro. A total of perhaps a hundred tamaraus was in 1968 estimated for the three sectors. In 1971 they were censused to 108. Hunting of tamaraus is prohibited, but there is no enforcement of the law. The tamarau is even hunted by helicopter. In 1968 seventeen animals were killed in one such hunt alone. The future of the little buffalo seems to be somber indeed.

A threatened bird of Mindoro mountain forests is the Mindoro imperial pigeon (*Ducula mindorensis*). The very rare ashy ground thrush (*Zoothera cinerea*) is also threatened, but this species occurs also on Luzon. Among the extremely rare endemic birds on Luzon is Koch's pitta (*Pitta kochi*), which is localized to mountain forests.

The tremendous habitat destructions in the Philippines have led to the threat of extinction also to a reptile. The sailfin lizard (*Hydrosaurus pustulatus*) is a victim of this negative development.

Gulaphallus mirabilis, a fish from Luzon, where it is restricted to one creek, is perhaps extinct. It was not observed during the 1960's.

Taiwan (Formosa)

Taiwan or Formosa, about ninety miles off China's coast, once had a rich diversity of habitats, but the human population explosion has led to a severe destruction of forests and other habitats. As a result the Formosan sika (*Cervus nippon taiouanus*) has declined to the point of extinction. This deer prefers lowland forests and seems to have difficulty in adapting to the montane forests to which it is driven by persecution. No protection has been given to this sika. It may, however, survive in captivity, because there are several captive herds. The Formosan muntjac (*Muntiacus reevesi micrurus*), the Formosan serow (*Capricornis crispus swinhoei*), the Formosan black bear (*Selenarctos thibetanus formosanus*), the Formosan yellow-throated marten (*Martes flavigula chrysospila*), and the Formosan clouded leopard (*Neofelis nebulosa brachyurus*) are all decreasing and threatened for the same reasons as the Formosan sika.

Two pheasants of the mountain forests of Taiwan, Swinhoe's pheasant (*Lophura swinhoii*) and the mikado pheasant (*Syrmaticus mikado*), are extremely rare and seem to have decreased to a precariously low level. However, in July, 1969, no fewer than 106 Swinhoe's pheasants and eight mikado pheasants were on display for sale in shops at the Sun Moon Lake on Taiwan. Apparently both species are captured in hundreds each year. In 1959 two pairs of the former species were sent to the Ornamental Pheasant Trust in Great Britain, where they produced more than 150 birds. In 1967 thirty and in 1968 twelve of these pheasants were released in Taiwan. The mikado pheasant is also breeding in captivity. Probably the rarest and most threatened bird on Taiwan is the endemic yellow tit (*Parus holsti*), which is also captured for sale.

Japan

Japan comprises islands—Kyūshū, Shikoku, Honshū, and Hokkaidō, to mention the four largest—that have long been densely populated. The country's remarkable industrial development has inevitably hurt its natural habitats. However, the Japanese are pioneers in conservation in eastern Asia and this has saved much of Japan's fauna.

The Japanese islands are centered in the temperate zone but the southern extremity reaches the subtropics. They are affected by the monsoons and are characterized by humidity, high rainfall, and warm temperatures, all of which produce a rich vegetation. The great number of high volcanoes and mountains add a subarctic zone to this spectrum of climates and give rise to a wide range of habitats. As much as 80 percent of Japan is filled by mountains, of which the highest, the world-famous Fuji, is 12,289 feet.

One of the animal victims of Japan's advancing economy is the Japanese wolf (*Canis hodophilax*). It lived on Honshū, where it was much persecuted because it preyed on cattle. The last of these small wolves seem to have been killed in 1904 or 1905. A threatened mammal of the deciduous forests is the Amani hare (*Pentalagus furnessi*). It occurs exclusively on the two islands off Kyūshū in southernmost Japan. The only species in its genus, it is of great scientific interest. Since 1921 it has been completely protected. The population is estimated at five to nine hundred animals. The Japanese serow (*Capricornis crispus crispus*), estimated to number about two to three thousand animals, is distributed in Honshū, Shikoku, and Kyūshū. Uncontrolled deforestation has sharply reduced the habitats suitable for it despite the total protection of the serow itself. However, it finds refuge in some national parks.

The Japanese race of the California sea lion (*Zalophus californianus japonicus*) was confined to the Sea of Japan, more than five thousand miles from the nearest colonies in California. Formerly it occurred on Kyūshū, Shikoku, and on islands around Honshū. As late as 1951, fifty or sixty of these sea lions lived around Takeshima, a rocky islet in the open sea between Japan and Korea, but after 1950 the island was occupied by soldiers and the animals have never been seen again. Presumably this race is now extinct.

Among the birds, a few are gone forever, while some are menaced and face extinction. The crested shelduck (*Tadorna cristata*) disappeared in 1916. Three specimens exist in collections, one from near Vladivostok, the other two from Korea. Presumably it was familiar in Japan, since it was drawn by Japanese artists during the nineteenth century. Possibly it bred in eastern Siberia and migrated to Korea and Japan.

The Ryūkyū Island kingfisher (*Halcyon miyakoensis*) has not been seen since a specimen was collected on Miyako Island in 1887.

Extremely rare is the Japanese petrel (*Pterodroma leucoptera longirostris*). Only ten specimens are known, all taken along the Japanese coasts, but the bird's breeding place and status are unknown.

Also at a dangerously low point is the number of the Japanese crested ibis (*Nipponia nippon*): In 1964 there were eleven adults and four young in Japan. In 1965 there was a total of twelve birds only, in 1966 nine, in 1968 ten, and in 1970 again nine. Up to about eighty years ago this species was common in Japan and also occurred in Korea, China, and Manchuria. Now all the known birds breed in two reserves in Japan. In Korea it has not bred since World War II. It is possible that some ibises still exist in northern China and Manchuria. Also very rare is the Japanese crane (*Grus japonensis*), once widely distributed but today found only in two areas in Hokkaidō and a few localities in Manchuria and China. It numbered 171 birds in Japan in 1969 and two hundred to three hundred in the U.S.S.R.; but in 1964 some 1,800 to 2,200 Japanese cranes wintered in Korea alone, so there is probably a population also in northern China. Another crane whose population is dwindling critically is the hooded crane (*G. monacha*): there were 1,564 birds in Japan in 1965 and a small breeding group on the Amur River in eastern Siberia.

Blakiston's fish owl (*Bubo blakistoni blakistoni*), a very large and impressive bird, is restricted to a small area on Hokkaidō and on Kunashir Island of the southern Kuril Islands. The Japanese ancient murrelet (*Synthliboramphus antiquus wumizusume*), a marine bird, is much reduced in number. It breeds on the Izu Islands and other islands between Kyūshū and Korea.

The Ryūkyū wood pigeon (*Colomba jouyi*) was exterminated on Okinawa during the present century. It is now found only on some islets of the Ryūkyū Islands. The Okinawa woodpecker (*Sapheopipo noguchii*) is found only in the remaining virgin montane forests of Okinawa, where certain areas have been set aside for the protection of the species. Its numbers do not amount to more than about a hundred individuals. The Ryūkyū spring rat (*Tokudaia osimensis muenninki*) is a rodent disappearing from the Okinawa and Amanio islands, where it is seriously endangered. Of the Ryūkyū sika (*Cervus nippon keramae*) only about thirty individuals remain on Yakabi Island, Japan.

Finally, the Sakhalin reindeer (*Rangifer tarandus setoni*) of Sakhalin Island is rare, but exact numbers are unknown.

The Japanese giant salamander (*Megalobatrachus japonicus japonicus*) is the largest of recent salamanders and confined to limited areas of Honshū and Kyūshū, where it has greatly decreased. The decline is due to overfishing (for food and medicine), destruction of habitats, and poisoning of aquatic organisms serving as food for this salamander. As early as 1927 and again in 1952 protection measures were taken. Captures are not allowed, but this is not enough if the species' environment is destroyed.

In Japan the following fishes are endangered by extermination:

Tokyo bitterling (*Tanakia tanago*). Restricted to an area near Tokyo. The urbanization of the habitat is the cause of decline.

Ayumodoki (*Hymenophysa curta*). Restricted to Lake Biwa and a few rivers.

Nekogigi (*Coreobagrus ichikawai*). Confined to a few rivers in Honshū.

THE COASTS

Since the arctic regions are excluded as they have already been dealt with, we will here consider only the coasts of the Atlantic, the Pacific, and Indian oceans with exception for the great islands and archipelagoes already treated.

One of the most remarkable animals that has ever existed was the giant sea cow (*Hydrodamalis stelleri*). When in 1741 the Russian, Danish-born navigator Vitus Bering was shipwrecked on the island that today bears his name, he discovered three mammals: the sea otter, the fur seal, and the giant sea cow. It was fortunate for science that Bering was accompanied by a German zoologist, G. W. Steller, for he was the only zoologist who saw this extraordinary animal in life, and he wrote an extensive report on it.

This mammal was a true giant, attaining a length of twenty-five to thirty feet and a weight of up to four tons. As all other living sirenians are tropical, it was a surprise to the scientific world that such an animal could survive so far north. Many zoologists were inclined to attribute Steller's account to imagination, but in 1883 a number of skeletons collected at Bering Island confirmed Steller's data.

At the time of its discovery the giant sea cow was fairly common along the coasts of Bering and Copper islands off the east coast of Kamchatka. Being very similar to dugongs and manatees in structure and habits, the giant sea cow was very vulnerable to human persecution. The animal represented an enormous supply of meat, and man soon began to slaughter it. During the intensive hunting of sea otters and fur seals in the Aleutians in the eighteenth century, sea cows were killed in high numbers. By 1768, only twenty-seven years after its discovery, the species had been exterminated.

In 1965 Russian sailors created a sensation with a report that a small number of giant sea cows still survived, but an analysis of the report by a Russian mammalogist, V. G. Heptner, concluded that the sailors had actually seen female narwhals.

The ribbon seal (*Histriophoca fasciata*) has a wide range off the coasts of northern Asia and Alaska. It occurs from northern Hokkaidō, Sakhalin, Kamchatka, the Kuril Islands, and the Commander Islands to the Bering, Chukchi, and East Siberian seas. Along the west coast of North America it ranges from Point Barrow to Bristol Bay and the Pribilof Islands. At present this seal is rarely seen and only small numbers are killed. There are said to be between five and twenty thousands animals, a vague figure that seems too optimistic. A bounty is still offered on the fish-preying species in Alaska; such a reward should be abolished. The Kuril harbour seal (*Phoca kurilensis*) is confined to Hokkaidō and the Kuril Islands. The population is estimated at two thousand to 2,500.

Bering Island has functioned as a death trap for various animals. Two birds of the island, the spectacular cormorant (*Phalacrocorax perspicillatus*) and the Bering Island Canada goose (*Branta canadensis asiatica*), have been wiped out by man. The cormorant was almost flightless and therefore an easy prey for merciless hunting. It was exterminated by about 1852. The goose was the only Old World race of the large North American species. On Bering Island the last specimen was killed about 1900, and on the Kuril Islands, 1911.

Plume hunters of the nineteenth century almost brought the Chinese egret (*Egretta eulophotes*) to extinction. Since then human persecution has continued, and the species' future causes concern. In 1962 two Chinese egrets were collected and two observed on the Korean coast of the Yellow Sea. There are still some in China, but breeding has not been confirmed. In Hong Kong up to ten pairs bred during the period 1959–62; thereafter only two pairs continued to breed until 1969, but in 1970 there were three pairs.

Another shameful episode was the extermination of the great auk (*Pinguinus impennis*), the largest species of its family. This flightless bird occurred on islands in the North Atlantic such as the Orkneys, St. Kilda, the Faeroes, islands near Iceland, and Funk Island off Newfoundland. It probably also nested on the mainland. This auk was discovered in 1534 and almost immediately the persecution began. Hecatombs of great auks were slaughtered by ships' crews who drove them into stone pens where they were killed, or directly to the ships, where they were cooked to extract the oily substances. Many ships also used the fat birds as fuel under pots in which other auks were being cooked. Finally, the nestlings were used as bait in fishing, and eggs were collected for food. When the species became rare, museums and private collections hurried to get their share of specimens and eggs. The last two birds were killed on Eldey Island off Iceland in 1844.

A unique case of extinction due to the evacuation of human beings from an island is shown by the St. Kilda house mouse (*Mus musculus muralis*). This endemic race had evolved at Hirta, one of the St. Kilda Islands, west of the Hebrides, where it was dependent on man's presence. After human beings evacuated Hirta in 1930, the St. Kilda house mouse died out.

About seventy pairs of one subspecies (*Troglodytes troglodytes hirtensis*) of the wren (*T. troglodytes*) is restricted to the St. Kilda islands, and about forty to fifty pairs of another race (*T. t. fridariensis*) to Fair Isle south of the Shetland Islands. These very small flocks are probably adjusted to the local conditions on the islands, but any interference with them might prove fatal.

Narcondam Island in the Bay of Bengal is the home of the Narcondam hornbill (*Aceros narcondami*), whose population seems to be very small and in need of protection.

The estuarine crocodile (*Crocodylus porosus*) has a wide distribution in coastal areas of southeastern Asia, New Guinea, Australia, and Oceania. Nevertheless, it has become rare and endangered owing to overkilling for leather.

BALANCE FOR EUROPE AND ASIA

It is not surprising that animal life in Eurasia has suffered most in the Asian tropics, since man has occupied those areas for a longer period and they are more vulnerable to mismanagement and abuse than the temperate and arctic regions. Vast Asia is, of course, much richer in animal species than is small Europe, but the ultimate factor behind the reduction of animal species and populations in Asia is the immense human population in the southern parts of the continent. Thus, while Europe has seen six mammals (of which two also occurred in Asia) and one bird exterminated in historic time, in Asia ten mammals (of which two also lived in Europe), twenty-one birds, and at least nine fishes have been wiped out. In addition, there are eight vertebrates—three mammals and five fish—which are probably extinct, all in Asia. Of threatened or extremely rare species and subspecies, there are sixteen mammals, four birds, and one fish in Europe, but no fewer than 125 mammals, fifty-six birds, eight reptiles, two amphibians, and at least twenty-one fishes in Asia. To these figures should be added animals (two mammals and two birds) that are endangered in both Europe and Asia, as well as several Asiatic birds about whom information is not available but whose status is possibly precarious. Of these endangered species in Eurasia, five mammals occur also in North America and one in Africa, and of the birds two species live also in Africa.

In dividing the balance figure between the Palearctic and tropical Eurasia, the number of extinctions is higher in the tropics but the number of endangered animals is higher in the Palearctic. The Eurasian balance is worse than that for Africa and North America.

What is most disturbing is that many large mammals are among the species seriously menaced in Asia. They include the orangutan, three rhinoceroses, the Ceylon elephant, and several unique ungulates, an animal heritage from the past that we should do our utmost to preserve and hand on to our descendants.

Species and subspecies of vertebrates extinct during historic time, probably extinct, and at present endangered by extinction. (Figures within parentheses show extinctions after 1700.) Species and subspecies occurring or having occurred in both Europe and Asia are listed under Eurasia.

CLASS	EXTINCT				PROBABLY EXTINCT				ENDANGERED			
	EUROPE	EURASIA	ASIA	TOTAL	EUROPE	EURASIA	ASIA	TOTAL	EUROPE	EURASIA	ASIA	TOTAL
Mammals	4 (3)	2 (1)	8 (8)	14 (12)	–	–	3	3	16	2	125	143
Birds	1 (1)	–	21 (21)	22 (22)	–	–	–	–	4	2	56	62
Reptiles	–	–	–	–	–	–	–	–	–	–	8	8
Amphibians	–	–	–	–	–	–	–	–	–	–	2	2
Fish	–	–	9 (9)	9 (9)	–	–	5	5	1	–	21	22
Total	5 (4)	2 (1)	38 (38)	45 (43)	–	–	8	8	21	4	212	237

CHAPTER FOUR

North America

Little more than a century ago, herds of bison thundered across the North American prairies and flocks of passenger pigeons swept across the sky, almost covering it from horizon to horizon. Vast virgin forests, both coniferous and deciduous, stretched across the continent from the tundras of the north to the subtropical glades of Florida. Thousands of lakes, marshes, and rivers drained the country, channelling and accumulating the water on its long journey from the mighty mountains down to the oceans. Everywhere there was an abundance of wildlife.

The first men in North America, the American Indians, arrived late in a geological sense. They treated the land and waters, the vegetation and the animals, with great care, without leaving any environmental wounds. With the arrival of the white man this harmony came to an end. North America has in three centuries been the scene of a tremendous and rapid alteration of the natural environment, and consequently of the destruction of animal life. During the short period of the European settlement, a tragically long series of animals has become extinct. The white man swept over the continent, attacking almost everything: grass, trees, animals, and the aborigines who had lived in harmony with the environment for eleven to twelve thousand years. With their technological means, the Europeans destroyed more of the renewable natural resources than they built up.

Despite all this, there remains much unspoiled country, a great diversity of natural habitats, and a wealth of animal life in North America. This gives hope for the future of nature on this continent, especially since the conservation movement is more developed and stronger in the United States and Canada than anywhere else in the world. In particular, the United States government and especially its Department of the Interior are certainly more con-servation-minded and have done more for the preservation of nature than any other government. This positive attitude is mani-fest in many ways: legislation, national parks, and nature reserves; wildlife management, outdoor recreation, and education. The United States has in fact achieved such magnificent results in the field of nature conservation that one may say that this great coun-try has tried wholeheartedly to repair in a few decades what it had destroyed in a few centuries.

Once this has been said, one must immediately add that the situation is still critical. North America today is witnessing an almost unbelievable increase in the destructive exploitation of living nature. Habitats are changed and animals retreat or vanish. The struggle between exploiters and conservationists is violent and bitter. Some people still do not seem to realize that conservation of nature and a sound land use are of great value to themselves. As the population expands, it will constantly become more im-portant to make efficient and beneficial use of natural resources.

The physical features and the major biotic regions of North America are almost a mirror of those of Palearctic Eurasia. At the northern tip of the continent are the polar areas, succeeded to the south by tundras, coniferous forests, deciduous woodlands, grass prairies, deserts, chaparral, and subtropics. Cutting through these natural regions from north to south in western North Amer-ica is an enormous mountain chain which divides midway into two separate ranges. As in Eurasia, vast Pleistocene ice sheets advanced southward from the polar regions, reaching beyond the Great Lakes and thus covering at their maximum more than one-half of North America. Curiously, parts of Alaska escaped glacia-tion.

Man is young in North America, having been there, as far as we know, only during the last thirteen thousand years, which is the earliest unanimously accepted time for the presence of man in North America. In the beginning he certainly modified locally the environment in one way or another, although without catastrophic results for the natural balance. It is true that a large number of mammals—not less than forty-one species—and two reptiles have become extinct in North America, in prehistoric times during the last fifteen thousand years and prior to the arrival of Europeans, but it is uncertain if man was involved in this disaster. However, according to the palynologist Paul S. Martin, it now appears by

carbon-14 dating that all major instances of the extinction of
mammals in North America occurred within less than one thousand years of the arrival of the so-called fluted-point hunters,
whose culture disappeared with the fauna. One must agree with
Martin that these events seem to indict man as an even more
colossal exterminator than we previously believed. On the other
hand, the fact that these human hunters disappeared simultaneously with the other mammals may indicate that the same factors
were responsible for eliminating both. The facts are quite certain
that the present natural regions of North America have been
greatly influenced by man, and that this process has taken place
in the last three hundred years alone.

ANIMAL FAMILIES PECULIAR TO NORTH AMERICA

North America is in zoogeographical terminology the Nearctic
region. Both include Greenland, Canada, the United States, and
Mexico.

North America has received animal migrants from both Eurasia
and South America. Terrestrial animal elements from the west
invaded North America using a land bridge across the Bering
Straits, while South American animals had access to North America across the Isthmus of Panama.

Consequently, North America has few animal families which
are peculiar to the continent. Among the endemic fish families are
the bowfins (*Amiidae*), with only one existing species, *Amia
calva,* mooneyes (*Hiodontidae*), cave fishes of the family *Am-
blyopsidae,* the family *Goodeidae* in Mexico, trout perches (*Per-
copsidae*), pirate perches (*Aphredoderidae*), with one species,
and freshwater basses (*Centrarchidae*).

In spite of its richness in amphibians, North America has no
endemic family of this class, but among the reptiles there are two
families which are exclusively North American, the annielids
(*Annielidae*) in California and the gila monsters (*Helodermati-
dae*). Not a single bird family is endemic. There are only two
endemic mammal families: pronghorns (*Antilocapridae*) and se-
wellels (*Aplotondidae,* a rodent), both with only one species.

THE POLAR REGIONS

Because North America includes Greenland, the largest island
in the world, the American arctic comprises a much larger island
area than does arctic Eurasia.

The polar regions are an icebound and snow-covered region in which the natural communities are very simple, relatively poor in species, but rich in individuals. In North America the pack ice lies close to the northern shores of the continent. Anyone who has visited such places as Alaska's Point Barrow in summer will remember the strange effect of a warm sun shining down on a narrow stretch of open water between the mainland and the polar pack ice. This is quite different from the conditions prevailing in arctic northwestern Eurasia in summer. Most of Greenland is permanently covered by thick ice.

Of North American polar mammals, except whales, only the polar bear, the Atlantic walrus, and the harp seal—as we said in the chapter on arctic Eurasia (pages 112–116)—may be considered in danger if the present human predation continues. It is particularly the North American population of the harp seal, breeding on the ice off Labrador and northern Newfoundland, that is threatened by the present sealing industry. Other populations of North American arctic or subarctic seals, for example, the hood seal, have also been depleted but not yet to a dangerously low level. It is to be hoped that international agreements between countries that have polar territories or that sail in polar waters will protect these marine animals as a renewable natural resource.

THE TUNDRA

The arctic Barren Grounds of the North American tundra stretch in a broad belt across the continent, from western Alaska to eastern Canada and the coast of Greenland. Relatively few species of plants and animals have adapted themselves to such arctic conditions as short summers, extreme cold, and a scarcity or even a lack of moisture. The present habitats of the tundra are climax communities, corresponding to a maximal bioproductivity of the arctic. Lichens form an essential part of the tundra life system, serving as a basis for the existence of the caribou (*Rangifer tarandus*), which in its turn is the staple winter food of the wolf (*Canis lupus*). In his ignorance man has destroyed vast areas of lichen tundras by fire. Since it takes about fifty years for lichens to recover and to recolonize a burned area, this is a catastrophe for the herds of caribou. They starve to death or are weakened and die from diseases that normally would not be fatal to them. Moreover, the increased competition for food among the caribou herds results in overgrazing, which also leads to a shortage of food and sooner or later a population crash of the caribou. So intimate is the relationship between plant and animal communities. At the end of the 1930's three million Barren Ground caribou were estimated in parts of its range in Canada. In the 1948–49 the first aerial survey of Barren Ground caribou in northern Manitoba, Saskatchewan, Alberta, and the Northwest Territories in Canada yielded only 670,000 caribou and in 1955 the species was down to 278,900; but in 1967–68 it had increased to 385,500. This is still an alarmingly low figure.

The tundra is still little exploited by man. The first men here, Eskimos, were caribou hunters, entirely dependent on the herds for food and clothing. Modern civilization has had its effect on the tundra, even though settlements and cultivation are very little developed. In the immense wilderness of Alaska, for example, the caribou was exterminated in the southern and western parts, the musk-ox (*Ovibos moschatus*) in the northern areas; and various species of river salmon were menaced by industrial overfishing. Fortunately, a public reaction against this plundering set in. The animal populations of Alaska have now been restored, and the state can base a considerable part of its economy on its living natural resources. The reintroduced musk-ox, which have inhabited Nunivak Island off Alaska since 1935, in 1971 numbered about 750.

In other parts of the American North, animal species have vanished for ever. The breeding range and habitat of the Labrador duck (*Camptorhynchus labradorius*) are unknown, but it is supposed that the only eggs that have been collected have come from Labrador. Whether the bird was confined to tundras or forests is, of course, unknown. It was already rare at the beginning of the nineteenth century, and the last known specimen was shot in 1875. Cooper's sandpiper (*Calidris cooperi*) became extinct in 1833.

One may hope that another bird with an unknown breeding area, the Tule white-fronted goose (*Anser albifrons gambelli*), will not go the same way. It breeds somewhere in Yukon of the western Canadian arctic and winters in small numbers in a restricted area in the Sacramento Valley, California. Since this is probably the entire population, the bird is extremely rare.

Even rarer or perhaps already extinct is the Eskimo curlew (*Numenius borealis*). Its breeding grounds unknown, but they were somewhere in the barren tundras of Canada north of the Arctic Circle and possibly also in Alaska. It migrated southward to Labrador, whence it started its nonstop flight over the Atlantic Ocean and the Caribbean Sea to South America; it wintered and, we hope, still winters in Patagonia. The spring flight followed a more western route, because there are records indicating a flyway passing over Yucatan, Texas, and west of the Great Lakes to northwestern Canada. Hence, it flew twice a year across the two Americas.

Excessive shooting during the migration in eastern Canada and New England is thought to account for the tragic decline of the Eskimo curlew. In 1863 over seven thousand birds were killed in one day on Nantucket Island. As late as the period between 1856 and 1875, immense flocks used to rest in Texas, but by 1905 only three birds were seen there. Hecatombs of these curlews were shot as they migrated across the United States. Hunters sent wagonloads of birds back from the shooting grounds. These birds were very easy to kill, because they fed close together and were trustful of human beings. In 1929 A. C. Bent, in his famous *Life Histories of North American Shore Birds,* declared of the curlew: "It is now but a memory of the past." However, in 1932 a bird was taken in Newfoundland, and a week later four were seen on Long Island. Other sight records followed at long intervals: in 1945, 1946, 1950, 1959, 1960, 1962, 1963, and 1970 on the coast of Texas and Louisiana as well as on the Atlantic coast. Some of these are doubtful, but in 1964 one Eskimo curlew was shot in Barbados. The shooting was tragic, but it was at least proof that the species still survived.

The Hudsonian godwit (*Limosa haemastica*) has a migration pattern like that of the Eskimo curlew. Also a bird of the tundra, it was formerly abundant but is now greatly reduced in numbers. Its breeding range is in the Northwest Territories of Canada and it winters in southern South America. When it was still abundant, it was a regular passage migrant in Alaska, but after 1907 it was not recorded there for forty-four years. Once it had been protected by law over much of its range, the species began to increase slowly in numbers. Since 1951 it has again been observed in Alaska and breeding records have been established in the Anchorage-Kenai area. In 1964 some 640 birds were counted on migration near Anchorage, and in Missouri a flock of about 370 individuals was observed in 1956—data indicating that this bird may now be considered out of danger.

The Greenland white-tailed eagle (*Haliaeetus albicilla groen-*

landicus) is restricted to southwest Greenland, where the population was established at about fifty pairs in 1969.

THE CONIFER FORESTS

A flight over North American coniferous forests or a walk through a spruce and muskeg area reveals how strikingly similar this country is to the Eurasian taiga. From the air the general pattern of forests and bogs, lakes and rivers, is the same, and in a walk on the ground one can find a surprisingly high number of organisms, both plants and animals, which are of exactly the same species in North America and in Eurasia. Thus the two biocommunities as a whole are very much alike. However, the North American regions are much richer in species than are parallel latitudes in the Old World.

There is one type of coniferous forest on the northwestern coast of North America that is not found in Eurasia: a temperate rain forest dominated by conifers. This extraordinary habitat is produced by a combination of maritime moist climate, mild temperature, high rainfall, and the huge mass of organic matter accumulated and produced by the forest itself. This impressive forest has a rich animal life. There are a few other coniferous forests in North America that are unique, such as the sequoia forests in California, but they are rather poor in animals.

During the last few centuries North America has witnessed the most violent exploitation of forests that has ever been seen. We are still so close to these drastic alterations that we can hardly appreciate their full significance. The rapid decrease of forests and the habitat changes in them have had serious effects not only on the wildlife but also on entire ecosystems. Many species of forest mammals and birds have been wiped out or are on the verge of extinction. Fortunately, an increasing public as well as official governmental consciousness of the value of unspoiled habitats, rich in wildlife, has done much to ameliorate the situation in Canada and the United States during the last three decades.

The coniferous forests of North America extend across Alaska and Canada and parts of the northern United States. Many animal species in this area have become extinct. In early colonial days the eastern wapiti (*Cervus canadensis canadensis*) ranged from southern Quebec to the edge of the plains and south to northern Alabama. Everywhere it was a common animal, but was always much hunted. Gradually it declined all over its range and was at last exterminated. In New York State the last one was killed in 1834, and in Pennsylvania in 1877. The eastern wapiti held on till much later in the western parts of its range, where the human pressure was less severe. It still existed in Wisconsin in 1892, and it was found in Minnesota north of Lake Superior as late as 1885.

Apparently this wapiti is now extinct, at least in the wild. It is also doubtful if there is any pure eastern wapiti in captivity. No elks now in the eastern states seem to represent native stocks. Many introductions have been made of elks from the West.

The Columbia white-tailed deer (*Odocoileus virginianus leucurus*) was once distributed in the northwest from the Columbia River in the north to southern Oregon. As late as 1875 this deer was abundant in the Willamette Valley, but when settlers occupied and cultivated the valley floor, the deer disappeared. In 1939 the Oregon population was estimated at only 211 animals. There is now a white-tailed deer refuge in Douglas County, Oregon. Remnant populations also occur on two islands in Washington and Oregon. The number of the total population is estimated at three to four hundred animals.

The dramatic and tragic history of the bison (*Bison bison bison*) of the Great Plains is well known, but few people seem to know that there was also a wood bison (*B. b. athabascae*) in North America. This northern race of the species also had a wide range. It extended throughout the coniferous forests and mountains from the Canadian Northwest Territories to Alberta and south to Colorado.

When the plains bison had become almost extinct through wanton exploitation, man turned to the wood bison. It could not withstand the tremendous persecution, and the number dwindled rapidly. The wood bison was practically extinct south of Peace River by 1875, and by 1891 only about three hundred animals remained in an area south of the Great Slave Lake. In 1903-4 only twenty-four individuals were observed, and three years later, thirty-three. In 1922 the Canadian government set aside a reserve, the Wood Buffalo National Park, which included the entire habitat of the remaining herd. By 1929 the wood bison had increased to about fifteen hundred, but at that time a serious mistake was made in the introduction into the reserve of no less than 6,673 plains bison. As might have been expected, the two subspecies interbred freely and the wood bison disappeared as a pure breed.

Fortunately, a small herd of two hundred pure wood bison was discovered in the northwestern part of the Wood Buffalo National Park, where they were isolated by swamps, but by 1965 only about one hundred were left. In 1963 eighteen wood bison were transplanted to Fort Providence north of the Mackenzie River to establish an independent herd; two years later they had increased to twenty-four. In 1965 forty-three wood bison were captured, destined for Elk Island National Park in the aspen parkland of Alberta.

Another large mammal that was thought to be threatened by overhunting and is now protected within a reserve is the glacier bear of Alaska and British Columbia. This is apparently only a color phase of the black bear (*Ursus americanus*), though it has been described as a race, *emmonsii*. The population is estimated at about five hundred.

The eastern cougar (*Felis concolor couguar*) became in colonial days almost extinct in its range that extended from New Brunswick in Canada westward to the Plains and southward to Georgia and Alabama, where it presumably overlapped or rather merged with the Florida cougar (*F. c. coryi,* cf. page 197). Habitat destruction, disappearance of deer, and heavy persecution led to near-extinction of the eastern cougar at the end of the nineteenth century. Apparently a remnant of the population managed to survive in Ontario. Landscape recovery after the settler period and increase of deer helped the cougar to come back in Canada. At present it occurs discontinuously from Nova Scotia in the east to Alberta in the west. However, the population is very thin, probably fewer than a hundred.

The Kaibab squirrel (*Sciurus kaibabensis*) is a rare and beautiful rodent whose present range lies entirely within the ponderosa pine forests of the Kaibab Plateau of Arizona. Though this is outside the coniferous-forest region of North America, we deal with this squirrel here because it is adapted exclusively to conifers. Only 10 percent of the range of the Kaibab squirrel lies within the Grand Canyon National Park, which is inviolate, while 90 percent is in the Kaibab National Forest, which is open to hunting by the Arizona Game and Fish Department. In 1964 the population of this squirrel was estimated at about one thousand animals. It was at its highest during the 1930's and is now, according to the federal Fish and Wildlife Service, "at its lowest ebb in a half century."

Another rodent of conifer forests that is said to be threatened by habitat changes is the yellow-cheeked vole (*Microtus xanthognathus*) from Canada. The spotted bat (*Euderma maculatum*) from the southwestern United States and probably northwestern Mexico has a limited distribution and seems to be restricted to the yellow-pine and piñon belt, where it is rare.

As in Europe the peregrine falcon has disappeared from large parts of North America during the last few decades, chiefly because of the lethal effects of pesticides. The North American peregrine (*Falco peregrinus anatum*) is now on the official list of U. S. endangered wildlife. It is not breeding any longer in North America except in Alaska and arctic Canada. In the latter country there were less than thirty pairs in 1970. Only a decade ago the peregrine ranged from Alaska and Canada to Baja California, Arizona, and Texas—an alarming decrease.

No governmental agency or conservation organization in the world has ever made such tremendous efforts to save an endangered bird as have the United States and Canada in the case of the whooping crane (*Grus americana*). This magnificent bird, now well-known in North America through the publicity its plight has received, formerly bred in isolated marshes and bogs from southern Mackenzie and Great Slave Lake region in Canada, south to Alberta, Manitoba, North Dakota, and Iowa. There also was a breeding population on the coast of Louisiana. Its winter quarters were located along the coast of the Gulf of Mexico from Florida to Mexico. Shooting and disturbances in breeding and wintering grounds almost wiped out the whooping crane and limited its breeding area to only one region, which fortunately is within a reserve, the Wood Buffalo National Park in the southern Mackenzie District of Canada, where a very small population has its last stronghold. From this area the whooping cranes migrate southward to Texas and Louisiana, also where they are protected.

Fortunately, during the last few years the whole population of whooping cranes has spent the winter in the Aransas National Wildlife Refuge in Texas, established just for these cranes. This provides an opportunity to take a census of the birds each year. When the record-keeping began in 1938, there were only fourteen birds. After years of fluctuating, the population reached a height of thirty-eight in 1961. The following year disaster struck—six birds were lost and no young birds were born. But in the fall of

1964 the cranes brought ten young back to Aransas, making a total of forty-two birds. In 1965 the figure was forty-four, the highest since the inventories were initiated, but one bird was apparently lost in 1966, when only forty-three returned to their winter quarters. In 1967 forty-seven birds returned to Aransas, in 1968 fifty, and in 1969 fifty-six. Exactly fifty-six birds—forty-eight adults and eight young—returned to the Canadian breeding grounds in 1970. In the fall of 1970 fifty-seven cranes (fifty-one adults and six young birds) came back to Aransas. So the trend is upward, but fifty-six whooping cranes (besides twenty-three in captivity) is still a precarious total for the survival of a long-distance migrant.

A bird requiring an extremely specialized habitat is Kirtland's warbler (*Dendroica kirtlandii*), which occurs within a small area of Michigan (where the population in 1961 was less than one thousand birds) and winters in the Bahamas. Even before man, fire was an aspect of nature, and Kirtland's warbler is one of the creatures dependent on fire. It nests only in thickets of jack pines not less than six and not more than twenty years old, a habitat that from time immemorial has been produced only by forest fires. In addition, the soil must be dry and porous, and the ground cover under the pines must be sufficiently high to conceal the nest and yet not too high. A stand of growing trees satisfies these warblers for only ten to fifteen years; they then move to another area where the trees are smaller.

The Kirtland's warbler is protected by law and, in addition, the United States Forest Service and Michigan State Conservation Department have set up special areas for the bird in the Huron National Forest. Here controlled burning, timber harvesting, and planting schemes produce exactly the habitat required by this bird—a truly remarkable instance of a government's capacity for humane action. It gives one hope for the future of wildlife when the mightiest nation in the world does so much to preserve a tiny bird.

Another warbler, the golden-cheeked warbler (*D. chrysoparia*), seems to have a similarly specialized habitat, because it occurs only in a small part of the Edwards Plateau, the part covered with cedars (*Juniperus ashei*), in south-central Texas. But the population is small and is declining as a result of bush eradication, in spite of the fact that the bird is protected by law.

A jet-airport project in New Jersey is a threat to the habitat of the pine-barrens tree frog (*Hyla andersoni*), which also in its restricted ranges in North Carolina and Georgia is near extinction.

THE MOUNTAINS

Like a gigantic barrier, a great mountain system runs along western North America, the highest peaks exceeding eighteen thousand feet. The most important of these chains are the Rocky Mountains. On the lower slopes there are grasslands and deciduous forests, which give way at higher altitudes to coniferous forests and gradually to alpine plants. As on other continents, mountains have become the last refuge for many animals, but unfortunately the mountains are far from safe. Several of these species have already been exterminated, and others are endangered.

The constant human warfare against the grizzly bear (*Ursus arctos horribilis*) in North America has led to the breaking up of its almost continuous range from the eastern edge of the Great Plains westward to the Pacific, and from the arctic coast of Alaska in the north to Mexico in the south. The grizzly was in particular an inhabitant of the entire extent of the Rocky Mountains in the United States. Nowadays the grizzly bear has vanished from much of its former range. It survives in large wilderness areas in Alaska and Canada as well as in some national parks and reserves in the United States. There is also a small population in Mexico. All these populations are isolated and with a few exceptions are in danger of extinction.

The North American brown bears have been divided into numerous species and subspecies. This is an example of taxonomic hairsplitting that confuses more than it helps. Many features indicate that all the North American brown bears belong to a single but very variable species which is wide-ranging and represents two stocks. Presumably both took part in the invasion of North America and later evolved through isolation in time and space to various races. Therefore in this book we will deal with grizzlies and brown bears as one species, *U. arctos* (the same as the Old World brown bear), but with four subspecies: the grizzly (*U. a. horribilis*), the Barren Ground grizzly (*U. a. andersoni*), the big brown bear of Alaska and British Columbia (*U. a. middendorffi*), and the Mexican grizzly bear (*U. a. nelsoni*).

No fewer than twelve species (in the old classification) and four subspecies of grizzlies (brown bears) have become extinct in North America. The populations were distributed over a great variety of habitats, indicating that it was an animal of a very wide ecological range. Today, greatly reduced in number except locally in Alaska, Canada, and some U. S. national parks, the grizzly bear is restricted to mountains and uplands above the timber line. In the United States it seems to be making its last stand in the Glacier and Yellowstone national parks in Montana, Wyoming, and Idaho, where seven to eight hundred survive, but there is also a handful (about ten individuals) in Washington. In Alaska there are about twelve thousand brown bears, in the Yukon Territory ten thousand, in British Columbia 6,800, in the Northwest Territory five to a thousand, and in Alberta about eight hundred, according to estimates by McT. Cowan (in 1972).

The total population of the grizzly and other brown bears in North America is, according to McT. Cowan's estimate, 26,000 to 31,000, of which approximately 1,300 bears are killed annually, chiefly in Alaska, where the mean annual kill in 1961–64 was seven hundred. No less than 33 percent of the Alaskan brown bears are killed illegally. In British Columbia about four hundred were killed each year during the period 1964–69. In the U. S. about sixty bears constitute the mean annual kill, of which forty are taken outside national-park areas in Montana.

These figures seem to reflect a viable population. In fact, a comparison with a census made in 1964 (by Cahalane) indicates that the North American population maintains its level. Nevertheless, there are local reductions due to pasturing livestock on alpine ranges and to overhunting.

Nowhere, except for the national parks in Canada and the U. S. as well as in the Northwest Territory of Canada and the states of Idaho and Washington, is the grizzly protected and can be considered really safe. In several provinces of Canada and in Alaska they may be shot, and in Mexico they are often killed by poison. Most endangered at present are the grizzly populations on the Canadian Barren Grounds—the relict plains grizzly in the Swan Hills area of Alberta—and in Mexico, where a small population of *U. a. nelsoni* survives. The latter was thought to be extinct in 1962, but a tiny group, estimated at between thirty and forty bears, was discovered in the Sierra del Nido of central Chihuahua in Mexico in 1967. A few years later this population was exterminated by poisoning. In 1969 another group was detected in

Sierra Madre, where the population seems to be fair-sized, but its survival is nevertheless problematic.

Grizzlies are indeed impressive animals. I remember an unforgettable summer evening at sunset in the Yellowstone National Park, where we could count thirty-two adult grizzly bears gathered in a valley. Not far from them bison and wapitis grazed and browsed quietly—thanks to their protected environment.

Merriam's elk (*Cervus merriami*) was a large deer living in the mountains of California, New Mexico, and Arizona. Competition with cattle and reduction by hunting led to its extermination in about 1906.

In arid mountains of California and Baja California in Mexico lives the peninsular bighorn (*Ovis canadensis cremnobates*), now rare owing to overhunting. In 1966 there were about nine hundred animals in the U. S., and in 1964 about five hundred in Mexico.

Two species of volelike rodents, the coast spruce mouse (*Phenacomys albipes*) and the dusky tree mouse (*P. silvicola*) from coastal mountains in the western United States, are reported to be threatened.

One of the world's "rarest, most spectacular, and most scientifically valuable birds"—to quote Carl W. Buchheister, former president of the National Audubon Society—is at present found only in California. It is the California condor (*Gymnogyps californianus*), the largest soaring bird of North America, which once ranged from the Columbia River to Mexico and Texas. At present it is limited to the coastal mountains of Santa Barbara and Ventura counties in southern California. Persecution brought a tremendous decrease in its range and numbers. At present the California condor is protected by law and there is a nesting sanctuary in the Los Padres National Forest in Sierra Madre. However, these safeguards do not prevent people from shooting these magnificent birds, poisoning them, or disturbing them on their breeding grounds. Moreover, a plan to build a road across the condor refuge and to develop it into a recreation area is a further threat to this unique species. These plans are, however, being vigorously fought by an array of public and private conservation agencies. In 1965 the results of a two-year field study showed a decline of the species in twelve years from sixty to about forty individuals, or about 30 percent, most of the decline due to illegal shooting. Thus it is a result of direct persecution by man that the California condor is so near extinction. In October, 1966, fifty-one condors were enumerated, and in 1969 fifty-three. In 1971 the U. S. government refused oil- and gas-drilling rights to an oil company in order to protect the nesting area of the California condor.

A plethodontid salamander (*Plethodon richmondi shenandoah*), living on three isolated talus slopes of Hawksbill Mountain, Shenandoah National Park, Virginia, is faced with potential extinction due to the erosion of soil into its talus habitat, followed by subsequent encroachment of another plethodontid salamander *P. cinereus,* and due to the paucity of isolated pockets of soil which are the centers of its distribution. This is an example of potential extinction through competition between two related species.

THE PRAIRIES AND THE PLAINS

Natural grasslands called prairies once covered a broad belt of North America. The term "prairie" implies tall grass, in general, but it is most often applied to the North American grasslands. Not much of the ancient prairie remains today. It has been cultivated, settled, industrialized—violently changed to uniform fields, where few wild animals can exist.

When the pack trains, covered wagons, and broad-hatted men on horseback as late as 1846—according to Francis Parkman's account of his travels—started across the prairie, the bison, mule deer, elk, and pronghorn antelopes barely lifted their heads to look at the newcomers. Men shamelessly took advantage of this trust to massacre the animals. Soon the animals learned to flee from destroying man, but they could not escape modern weapons. At first they were killed for fun or food or hides, later because they were considered vital for the existence of the Indians, and still later because it was claimed they were serious competitors with domestic sheep and cattle.

In crossing the prairie on the high plateaus of the Rockies of Montana, Idaho, and Washington, the present-day railway traveller sees nothing else for long hours but vast grasslands without sign of human or animal life. These prairies are still to a large extent a wilderness, but they lack entirely what once made them actively alive: millions of bison utilizing the grass, and Indians utilizing the bison. Was it really necessary to exterminate them both? It is true that efforts are now being made to restore some of the bison. In 1962 I saw two bison on those immense plains. In this almost endless landscape the two animals were a pathetic memorial of past grandeur. The two stragglers had undoubtedly wandered southward to their ancient pastures from the National Bison Range in northwestern Montana.

The tragic story of the American bison (*Bison bison*) has been told so many times that it is not necessary to give a detailed account of it here. The plains or prairie bison have been divided into several races, but they seem to be rather imperfectly known and their exact ranges remain undefined. The northern race, the wood bison, however, still exists and is a subspecies clearly distinguishable from the prairie bison. If the latter should be divided into several races, probably only three would be recognized, the nominate *B. b. bison;* a western subspecies, the Oregon bison (*B. b. oregonus*), and the eastern bison (*B. b. pennsylvanicus*). What was considered pure populations of these presumed races no longer exist. The eastern bison was extinct by 1825, the western one by the 1850's.

When the white man penetrated into the interior of North America, the prairie bison occurred as far east as western New York State, Pennsylvania, West Virginia, Tennessee, and North and South Carolina. Its center of distribution was the Great Plains, both in lowlands and highlands, west of the Rockies, and north to southeastern Oregon. In the south it ranged to northern Alabama, southern Texas, and northeastern Mexico. Hence, it had an immense range and constituted a tremendous natural resource, converting prairie grass into tons of meat and hides.

The enormous herds utilized the prairies without destroying them. They made seasonal migrations on a scale rarely seen in terrestrial mammals. At the time of the white man's arrival in North America, the bison were the largest aggregation of land animals on that continent and perhaps in the world. Only the herds of ungulates that once roamed the savannas of Africa can compare with them in numbers. All those who saw the herds agreed that they were almost unbelievable in their size and in the thunder of their hoofs. A traveller to the Rocky Mountains wrote in 1832: "As far as my eye could reach, the country seemed absolutely blackened by innumerable herds." He estimated the herd at about four million animals covering an area ten miles in length and eight miles in width. The historian Francis Parkman, who like John James Audubon foresaw the doom of the bison, reported that these huge, dark beasts at certain seasons literally turned the prairies into seas of black life.

It is generally believed that the Indians had hunted bison for centuries before the European settlers streamed westward. In reality it was at a rather late stage that the Indians began to base their economy on the bison. Hunting bison on foot was certainly not productive. Most cultures of the few tribes inhabiting the prairies were based on cultivation of maize, beans, and squash, but already at that time bison provided much material needed by the Indians. When horses became available to the Indians of the prairies during the seventeenth and eighteenth centuries, quite a new culture developed. Indian tribes from the mountains converged on the prairies, making use of horses, and quickly changed their economy so that it became based on the bison. Because of the horse the Indians could pursue the bison effectively, but their hunting was still without any negative effect on the population of the bison.

When the Europeans started to push westward over the plains at the beginning of the nineteenth century, the slaughter of bison commenced. But it was not until the construction of the Union Pacific Railroad in the 1860's that the herds began to be annihilated. Professional hunters moved in and millions of beasts were killed. Many deplored this wanton destruction, but any measure to stop or regulate the carnage was opposed by politicians, who saw in the destruction a way to get rid of the Indians. Idaho attempted in the 1870's to protect the bison as well as other hoofed animals. A law giving protection to the bison was passed in Congress, but President Grant never signed it, and the massacres continued.

Despite this, a herd numbering several million bison was reported as late as 1871. However, from then on the number dwindled rapidly. Between 1870 and 1875 at least two and a half million bison were killed every year. In 1883 the last important herd, about ten thousand animals, was destroyed. Only stray groups remained in remote areas. One group in Colorado was destroyed by taxidermists in 1897. In 1899 a census put the number of plains bison at 541. In Canada there were only a few. In Wyoming the species was first protected in 1890; in 1908 the National Bison Range in Montana was established; and later other reserves were set aside in the United States, Canada, and Alaska. Bison have also been reintroduced in national parks.

The bison was thus saved from extinction at the very last moment. Since then it has increased steadily. In 1951 there were about 8,875 bison in the United States and about 13,900 in Canada, including both plains and wood bison as well as hybrids and zoo captives. In 1967 there were about 23,000 bison in North America. Recently twenty bison were released on the plains of the new half-million-acre Mawdesley Wildlife Management Area in Manitoba.

The pronghorn (*Antilocapra americana*) also formerly occurred in large herds on the American plains and was said to be as numerous as the bison. It is the only survivor in North America of the antelope family and has evolved exclusively on that continent. Thus, it is a unique species. It ranged from Alberta in the north to the Pacific slopes in the west and the Mexican plateaus in the south, frequenting prairies, sagebrush plains, deserts, and tablelands. This species was also hunted senselessly and by 1910 only small scattered groups remained. Like the bison, the pronghorns escaped extinction at the last minute. Protection saved them, and they have since recovered in Wyoming and Montana, but those in the black hills and tablelands of the northern Great Basin, the peninsula of Baja California, Arizona, the Sonora region, and the plains of northern Mexico have decreased seriously. Particularly endangered are the two subspecies: the Sonoran population, considered to represent a peculiar subspecies, *A. a. sonoriensis,* and the lower California pronghorn, *A. a. peninsularis.*

The Utah prairie dog (*Cynomys parvidens*) is the least common of all species of prairie dogs. This rodent is restricted to south-central Utah. In 1935–36 it was found to occur in nine counties, but a survey in 1962 showed that its range had decreased to only five counties, with a population of only 2,775 animals in nine prairie-dog towns. The reason for this decline seems to be its vulnerability to poisons. Instructions have now been issued to prohibit control measures by poison of the Utah prairie dog. In 1968 the population was estimated at possibly six thousand animals.

However, the black-tailed prairie dog (*C. ludovicianus*), that not long ago occurred in enormous colonies on the plains and foothills from Saskatchewan and North Dakota to Arizona, Texas, and Mexico, is also now restricted to remaining short-grass regions, where it continues to be depleted. Only colonies in reserves may survive. Several other species, like the black-footed ferret and the burrowing owl, are disfavoured by the disappearance of the black-tailed prairie dog. Most threatened is the subspecies *C. l. arizonensis.*

The range of the northern kit fox (*Vulpes velox hebes*)

formerly covered the plains of western Canada and the United States south of Colorado, the Dakotas, and Iowa, but at present this race is confined only to the Cypress Hills of southwestern Saskatchewan, where it has not been observed since 1964. The settlement of the plains brought trapping, poisoning, and capturing by dogs in its wake, which reduced this fox almost to extinction. It still has no legal protection.

The black-footed ferret (*Mustela nigripes*) may be the rarest mammal in the United States today. This large weasel is a denizen of prairie-dog towns, that provide it with prey and den sites. Thus, its former range coincided with that of the prairie dog, that is, the Great Plains from Alberta to Texas, as well as up to about 10,500 feet in the Rocky Mountains. Destruction of the prairie dogs by poisoning and the elimination of the prairie-dog burrows, as well as of original grasslands, have presumably helped to bring the black-footed ferret to the verge of extinction. The preservation of the prairie dog would seem to be the best remedy for the decline of the ferrets.

At present the black-footed ferret is found only in parts of the plains country from Montana and North Dakota south to New Mexico and Texas, but it is everywhere extremely rare. From 1955 to 1964, fifty-five sight records of the species were reported, mostly from South Dakota. The combined efforts of the United States Fish and Wildlife Service and the National Park Service to save this species may be too late.

Not all prairie animals have been saved from extinction even at the last moment. The heath hen (*Tympanuchus cupido cupido*), distributed in the eastern United States from Massachusetts to the Potomac River in Washington, D.C., has vanished from the scene. Heath hens and prairie chickens were once found in great numbers on the grassy prairies and along the edges of forests. Cultivation of land and intensive shooting greatly reduced these birds. From 1830 on it was restricted to the island of Martha's Vineyard, Massachusetts, but in 1932 it became extinct.

Fortunately, there still are two other races of this extremely interesting and beautiful species living in North America—the greater prairie chicken (*T. c. pinnatus*) and Attwater's prairie chicken (*T. c. attwateri*). The former is at present confined to remaining prairie habitats and other suitable places from central southern Canada to northeastern Oklahoma, but it is everywhere very rare and in most areas decreasing. Despite the vanishing prairies, the greater prairie chicken may perhaps be saved. Wisconsin has shown the way. Through intensive research and magnificent conservation work, two scientists of the Wisconsin Conservation Department, Frederick and Frances Hamerstrom, have succeeded in turning the decrease of the greater prairie chicken into a local increase. It is primarily a question of food. Originally the prairie supplied the birds with food throughout the year. The fields cultivated by man lack the most important food plants of the prairie chicken. It is necessary to promote a sufficiently extensive growth of such plants to feed this excellent game bird. It is now protected, and when its population has increased sufficiently it may serve once again as a game bird.

The prairie chicken is interesting in other ways. It is almost a legendary bird. Its courtship display in spring, when the cocks boom and dance in front of the hens, is spectacular and has greatly influenced Indian dances, costumes, and music. The prairie chicken symbolizes the American prairies of the past as much as does the bison. The restoration efforts of the Hamerstroms should be gratefully acknowledged.

The southern race of the prairie chicken is extremely rare. Formerly ranging over the prairies of Texas and Louisiana, it is now localized to a few areas in southeastern Texas. Plowing of the prairies, predation by cats, and hunting pressure have reduced the population by 99 percent and its range by 93 percent within the past hundred years. In 1937 some eight to nine thousand prairie chickens remained, in 1963 there were about 1,300 birds, but today their number is estimated at less than nine hundred. The southern prairie chicken is also protected by law, but this is not enough as long as its habitats are altered. A project to establish a strict reserve for this bird in Texas has recently been established.

The masked bobwhite (*Colinus virginianus ridgwayi*) seems always to have been limited to grasslands between southern Arizona and northwestern Mexico. Grazing and trampling of the grass by cattle destroyed its habitat to such an extent that it is at present restricted to a few localities in Sonora Mexico. It is protected in Arizona, and its habitats are being restored in preparation for a plan to reintroduce the bird.

The Florida sandhill crane (*Grus canadensis pratensis*) is a bird of prairies, cultivated fields, meadows, marshes, and tundras. Hence, it has a wide ecological range, which makes it less vulnerable than its cousin, the whooping crane. Shooting and egg collecting led to a pronounced decline in its numbers and a reduction in its range. At present it is found locally west of Pascagoula, Mississippi, in Baldwin County, Alabama, the Okefenokee Swamp in Georgia, and several parts of Florida. In 1949 the population was estimated at 2,650 birds, but in 1964 there were only about 600 sandhill cranes. They are now fully protected by law and are increasing locally.

The Deciduous Forests

The broad-leaved deciduous forests of North America are found chiefly in the eastern United States. They consist of mixed hardwood species, for example, as in Michigan, beech (*Fagus grandifolia*) and sugar maple (*Acer saccharum*). In Canada there is a vast belt of aspen woodland. The deciduous forests have been drastically modified by man—much more than the coniferous forests. About 40 percent of the United States mainland was originally covered by virgin forest. In 1600 these forests were intact except for some local tree removal in the northeastern states and in Virginia. Today primeval forests cover no more than about 5 percent. Probably only one-tenth of 1 percent of deciduous forests represents areas from which no trees have been removed. This means a tremendous reduction of animal habitats and the extirpation of many species.

The gray or timber wolf (*Canis lupus*) has, forced by man, made an enormous retreat in North America during the last hundred years, but it still occurs in fair numbers in Alaska and Canada. A local race of the Great Plains, the plains wolf (*C. l. nubilus*) was exterminated in 1926. There are still about eight hundred gray wolves in Montana, Wisconsin, Minnesota, and Michigan, while the population in Alaska and Canada is estimated at about twenty thousand. This means that the wolf is still out of immediate danger of extinction. Quite different, however, is the situation for its relative, the red wolf (*C. niger*), a woodland species that at present exists with fifty to seventy-five animals in Texas, and perhaps Louisiana and Arkansas, where it is seriously endangered by human persecution and changing environmental conditions. This species has never had as wide a distribution as its gray cousin. The Texas race, *C. n. rufus,* has retreated to prairie marshes along the coast, while another race, *C. n. gregoryi,* may still occur in ranch areas of Louisiana and Arkansas. The Florida race, *C. n. floridanus,* is apparently exterminated.

The fox squirrel (*Sciurus niger*) is an animal of open wood-

lands such as oaks mixed with pines. Two of its geographical races
have declined during the present century. One is the eastern fox
squirrel (*S. n. vulpinus*), which formerly occurred in the eastern
states from Connecticut to Virginia. At present it is confined to
southern Pennsylvania, Maryland, and west and northern Virginia.
The reason for the decrease is the disappearance of primeval
forests of old timber, which this squirrel prefers, and the pressure
of hunters, because it is in great demand for food. If adequate
measures are not taken, the eastern fox squirrel seems destined to
disappear. Even rarer is the Delmarva Peninsula fox squirrel (*S.
n. cinereus*), which once spread over southeastern Pennsylvania,
Delaware, and eastern Maryland, but today is found only in six
of Maryland's coastal counties, chiefly in Dorchester, where the
population in 1964 was estimated to be in the lower thousands.
Its decline was due to overhunting and habitat alteration by cultivation, logging, forest fires, and construction. Though a small
population lives in the Blackwater National Wildlife Refuge, it
now seems to be near extinction.

The Indian bat (*Myotis sodalis*) from the eastern United States
is, like the latter fox squirrel, on the official U. S. list of endangered
species.

Perhaps the passenger pigeon (*Ectopistes migratorius*) was the
most famous bird of North America's deciduous forests. Prior to
the permanent settlement by man, the breeding area covered a vast
area from the Great Plains in the west to the Atlantic coast, and
from Manitoba and Quebec in the north to the Appalachians and
northern Mississippi in the south.

Much has been written about this pigeon. There is no doubt
that the seemingly fantastic accounts of flocks darkening the sky
or of their weight breaking great branches from trees where they
perched are reliable. The well-known ornithologist Alexander
Wilson estimated 2,230,272,000 birds in a flock he saw in 1832.
Audubon witnessed an immense flock passing over him for hours
on end in such a concentration that the sunlight was almost blotted
out and the sky in all directions as far as the eye could see was
filled with flying pigeons. He calculated that there were well over
one billion. A. W. Schorger found as many as 136 million pigeons
in a concentrated nesting area in Wisconsin as late as 1871.

When the European settlers pushed westward they hunted
passenger pigeons mercilessly, but it was not until professional
hunters began to earn their livelihood by killing pigeons that this

species started to decrease. The annual slaughter of tens of millions in the 1860's and 1870's was more than the bird could endure. In the 1880's it became evident that the species was doomed if the hunting remained unregulated. Nobody seems to have heeded the warning signs, and in the 1890's the species faded out as a wild bird. The last wild specimen was taken in Wisconsin in 1899 and various sight records were made up to 1907. However, the last individual of the species died in the Cincinnati Zoo in 1914. In less than fifty years man had wiped out one of the most valuable birds of North America.

The Carolina parakeet (*Conuropsis carolinensis carolinensis*) and the Louisiana parakeet (*C. c. ludovicianus*) were two races of the same species occurring in deciduous forests from southern Virginia south through Florida and west to Texas, Oklahoma, and Nebraska. It showed a preference for deep cyprus swamp forests, but this feature did not save the parakeets. They were shot indiscriminately and large numbers were taken captive. Probably the destruction of habitats, though to a lesser degree, was also involved in the extermination. By the end of the nineteenth century the birds had been exterminated everywhere except in the Florida swamp forests. The last specimen was collected in Florida in 1901, and a flock of thirteen birds was seen at Lake Okeechobee in 1904. The Louisiana parakeet became extinct about 1912, the Carolina parakeet about 1920.

A mysterious bird, Townsend's finch (*Spiza townsendi*), once occurred in the woods of Pennsylvania and perhaps elsewhere. It is known only from the type specimen that was taken in 1833 and named by Audubon. Since then it has never been seen. Its peculiarities cannot be accounted for by hybridism or individual variation.

It is uncertain if the ivory-billed woodpecker (*Campephilus principalis principalis*), one of North America's most impressive birds and its largest woodpecker, will survive. In historical time it ranged in riverine and swampy forests from the Carolinas, Georgia, and Florida westward to Texas, and in the Mississippi Valley north to Illinois, where it was dependent on dying and dead trees. Destruction of habitats deprived this species of food and suitable nesting sites. Shooting also reduced the numbers of this magnificent bird. It is now protected by law, but such measures are probably too late. In 1950 two ivory-billed woodpeckers were seen in Florida, and in 1960, six. Probably the species still exists in northern Florida and western Louisiana and on the coast of central Texas. In 1967 an ornithologist of the Fish and Wildlife Service claimed having seen it in the big thicket country of eastern Texas. He estimated the population at between five and ten pairs.

CHAPARRAL AND BRUSHLAND

California has a Mediterranean climate and its coastal hills and mountains have a Mediterranean vegetation, chiefly dry brush scattered with evergreen trees and bushes. This vegetation is called chaparral and is equivalent to the Italian macchia and the French maquis. Chaparral burns easily, almost exploding into flame, and fires have probably long played an important role in forming this type of habitat. In California the chaparral can probably be considered a climax area, an end-product of climate, fire, and soil, and perhaps of some browsers.

California's chaparral is a good country for deer. The area even has a subspecies of its own, the Tule elk (*Cervus elaphus nannodes*), which formerly ranged over a part of northern California but is now restricted to the Owens Valley, where an aerial count in 1965 showed at least 308 elks. In deference to agricultural interests, it has been agreed not to let this herd exceed three hundred animals, which was the population size in 1970. There are two other herds of Tule elk in California, but one (one hundred to 145 deer) is not a pure breed and the other (forty-five) is half-tame and lives within a fenced area. The reason for the decline of this species was heavy pressure by market hunters during the gold rush between 1850 and 1872, when it was almost exterminated. It is now probably safe from extinction. A wildlife refuge for the Tule elk was authorized in 1967.

The big-eared kangaroo rat (*Dipodomys elephantinus*) seems to have a restricted distribution, perhaps of relict character, in central California. Alteration of its habitat on chaparral slopes seems to endanger the existence of this species. Another threatened kangaroo rat is the Texas kangaroo rat (*D. elator*) living in mesquite country in Clay County, Texas. A third species, the Morro Bay kangaroo rat (*D. heermanni morroensis*), is threatened by habitat destruction and predation by cats.

THE SEMIARID LANDS AND DESERTS

Western North America has a variety of deserts, ranging from the Great Basin Desert in the north to the Mohave, Painted,

Colorado, Yuma, and Arizona deserts farther south, and the
Sonora and Chihuahua deserts in the far south. In these deserts
lifeless zones are uncommon. The vegetation may be relatively
abundant, chiefly composed of creosote bushes and cacti, and such
deserts may even serve as a refuge for certain animals. The semiarid regions, a kind of transitional zone, are colonized mostly by
sagebrush and other drought-resisting, low-growing shrubs.

To these arid areas some animals have adapted themselves by
evolving specialized characters. The long-eared kit fox (*Vulpes
macrotis*) of the sandy deserts is such a species. It is divided into
various races, all of which are rapidly decreasing in numbers and
range. One of them, *V. m. macrotis,* is already extinct. This race
formerly ranged in southern California, chiefly in the so-called
Lower Sonoran life zone. It was extensively hunted for its fur and
large numbers were trapped. But it was also killed by poison during campaigns against coyotes. The last long-eared kit fox of this
race was trapped in the San Jacinto plain in 1903. At present it
is the San Joaquin kit fox (*V. m. mutica*) that struggles for its
existence.

The desert vole (*Microtus californicus scirpensis*) was long one
of the rarest desert mammals of North America. It was restricted
to two tiny localities in the Inyo County of southern California,
where it became extinct in 1917.

The black legless lizard (*Anniella pulchra nigra*) is doomed to
disappear in California because of habitat destruction unless a
reserve is set aside for this interesting reptile. The blunt-nosed
leopard lizard (*Crotaphytus wislizeni silus*) from brushy deserts
in California is on the verge of being totally exterminated by habitat changes due to cultivation. This is also the case with the San
Francisco garter snake (*Thamnophis sirtalis tetrataenia*). Other
vanishing reptiles from California are the giant garter snake (*T.
couchi gigas*) and the two-striped garter snake (*T. elegans ham-
mondi*), which are sensitive to environmental modifications.

The only native North American tortoises (four species) are
confined to the southern parts of the United States and northern
Mexico where they are all threatened owing to illegal collecting,
trading, and exploitation as pets despite the fact these tortoises
usually do not withstand living outside their native habitat. The
desert tortoise (*Gopherus agassizi*) is protected in Arizona, California and Nevada; the gopher tortoise (*G. polyphemus*) in Mississippi; Berlandier's tortoise (*G. berlandieri*) in Texas; and bolson

tortoise (*G. flavomarginatus*) in Mexico. Such protection of law does not seem to be sufficient, because of ineffective surveillance of the pet trade.

THE FLORIDA EVERGLADES AND KEYS

The immense marshes of the Everglades at the southern tip of Florida have no parallel in the world. From vast Lake Okeechobee and the Big Cypress Swamp the water spreads out over the lowland to a width of from fifty to seventy miles before it reaches salt water and forms immense grass swamps of brackish water. Gradually, toward the coast, the salinity increases and mangrove forest dominates.

The Everglades is the largest subtropical wilderness area in North America, a complex type of landscape with a tremendous range in vegetation and animal life. It is a combination of land and water, where every inch of altitude above the sea level determines how long an area will be flooded by fresh, brackish, or salt water, which in turn determines the formation of various habitats.

For animals the subtropical wilderness of Florida's Everglades with its saw-grass glades, its tree hammocks, swamp-cypress forests, fire-dependent pine woods, and dense mangrove belt is a last refuge. Therefore, it is a tragedy that despite a total protection by law the plants and animals of this national park are threatened because water flowing from north of the park has too long been diverted by man-made canals and levees chiefly for commercial use. This diversion of water disrupts the hydrologic cycle and the ecosystem of southern Florida, destroys the natural habitats of the Everglades National Park, and will considerably reduce shrimp and other fisheries off the Florida coast which are of great economic value. The swamplands and water holes in the Everglades, so important for wildlife, have begun drying up. Wintering and spring-nesting birds cannot feed, alligators have no place to swim, and fishes die in the thousands when the water in their isolated pools evaporates. If this diversion of water from Lake Okeechobee continues, the Everglades will be drained and the American people will lose one of the most interesting national parks on the continent.

In addition to this threat to the unique Everglades, local interests in Miami began in the late 1960's to build a jet airport including a pilot-training strip on the edge of the Everglades National Park and high above the receding waters of the Big Cypress

Swamp. The latter was threatened by draining and filling. This plan would be the *coup de grâce* to what is perhaps the most extraordinary natural region of North America. The training airstrip was built, a tragic shortsightedness. Fortunately, after years of discussions and battles to save the Everglades National Park, the federal authorities could persuade the local ones to move the proposed South Florida Jetport elsewhere than in the Everglades and to close down the existing pilot-training strip. However, it is up to the federal government to provide another airport site and training runway at no cost to Dade County. This means federal expenses on the order of thirteen million dollars for correcting an inexcusable environmental mistake by both federal and local authorities. So far the new airport site has not been found. At present oil-drilling crews are exploring the Everglades to try to find still another reason to destroy this unique synthesis of water and land. It was a serious mistake when in 1947 the Big Cypress watershed was not included within the boundaries of the Everglades National Park.

But still the destiny of the Everglades National Park is uncertain. Until the Army Corps of Engineers (which, curiously enough, in the U. S. is equipped with the power to decide over water systems) agrees to route an adequate supply of water through the National Park, the remarkable and irreplaceable Everglades will remain in peril.

Another chapter in the long fight for saving the Everglades National Park was written when Congress passed and the President signed (in June, 1970) a law that seems finally to spell out a guarantee that the water requirements of the Everglades National Park will be met. It remains to be seen, however, how and when the Army Corps of Engineers and Florida politicians will implement the new law, which is embedded in a flood-control act.

Another important step forward in the preservation of the Everglades was announced on February 8, 1972, by the President of the United States in his message to Congress, where he stated: "After careful review of the environmental significance of the Big Cypress Swamp in Florida, particularly of the need for water from this source to maintain the unique ecology of Everglades National Park, I directed the Secretary of the Interior to prepare legislation to create the Big Cypress National Fresh Water Reserve. This legislation, which has now been submitted to the Congress, will empower the Federal Government to acquire the requisite legal interest in 547,000 acres of Big Cypress."

The cougar (*Felis concolor*), the largest North American cat, has many names—mountain lion, panther, puma—a fact which indicates that it formerly was a rather common animal over a large range. In North America it is now confined to Canada and the western parts of the U. S. The only occurrence east of the Mississippi River is in the Everglades National Park, where the species is represented by the Florida cougar (*F. c. coryi*). As late as the end of the last century, this race was still common throughout the Florida peninsula as well as in adjacent areas of Georgia, Alabama, and Louisiana. But constant persecution led to a general decrease in numbers and local extermination until it was gone everywhere except in the Everglades National Park. In 1964 the population there was estimated at less than one hundred animals. In that year the Canadian zoologist Leslie Tuck and I had the fortune to catch a glimpse of a puma in the bushes near the shore of Cape Sable. Its tracks revealed that it was a young cougar.

Extending for 125 miles in a chain of islands southward from Florida into the Gulf of Mexico are the Florida Keys. Key West is halfway between Florida and Cuba. The climate is subtropical but the flora and fauna are much influenced by the proximity of the tropics.

The most famous land mammal of the Keys is the Florida Key deer (*Odocoileus virginianus clavium*), the smallest of American deer. Even before historic time it was confined to the Keys, occupying most of the lower keys. Wanton hunting, habitat destruction by real-estate developers, fires, and hurricanes brought down the number to about thirty by 1949. Protection by law, the establishment of the Key Deer Wildlife Refuge on Big Pine Key, and effective propaganda helped restore the population of the "toy deer" to about 575 in 1970, which means that it more than doubled its size in the period 1965–69.

The Florida manatee (*Trichechus manatus latirostris*) is geographically isolated from its cousin, the West Indian manatee (*T. m. manatus*). At the time Ponce de León rounded Florida, the manatee was common around the Gulf states, particularly in Florida. It was found even in Virginia, but these were probably stragglers. This phlegmatic marine browser of submerged plants became an easy target for hunters who shot for fun or for food.

Rapidly the number of the Florida manatee dwindled. A few persist in Florida, where they are legally protected. In spite of field work during three expeditions along the coasts and the labyrinthine mangrove archipelagoes of southern Florida, I have seldom seen this manatee.

The Everglade kite (*Rostrhamus sociabilis plumbeus*) has in historical time survived on the peninsula of Florida, but ruthless shooting and egg collecting along with the drainage of marshes and disturbance of the nests by man have brought this endemic race near extinction. Not long ago this subspecies of a widely distributed tropical bird of prey ranged the freshwater marshes throughout peninsular Florida. It is believed that the specialized food habits of this kite—it feeds on a single species of freshwater snail (*Pomacea paludosa*)—have been the main factor in its catastrophic decrease. Although the range of the snail has been much reduced by drainage, it seems unlikely that there should not be a sufficient supply for such a small population as the Everglade kite.

Since the 1950's the main range of this bird has been the Lake Okeechobee region, where about a dozen individuals are usually found. When I visited the area in 1964–65, the warden reported that two pairs had nested there in 1964, and in the same year fifteen kites were located in the Loxahatchee National Wildlife Refuge in Palm Beach County, but in 1965 only ten birds were counted. In 1967 the total minimum population was estimated at fifty. In 1968 ten nests produced at least seventeen young. The Everglade kite is of course protected by law. In 1971 the situation was roughly the same.

The bald eagle (*Haliaeetus leucocephalus leucocephalus*), the national bird of the United States, is still found in various parts of the continent, but more of these eagles nest in Florida than in any other state except Alaska, where a northern race occurs. In 1964–65 I participated with Dr. William B. Robertson of the National Park Service in some aerial counts of bald eagles in southern Florida and got impressive records of the extraordinary density of nesting birds there. Moreover, when working with herons in the swamps and on the keys of the Everglades, I was constantly surrounded by these magnificent eagles, wonderful in their chestnut and white plumage.

But this situation does not hold for these eagles elsewhere in the United States. They breed from northern California, Arizona, Kentucky, and Virginia south to Baja California and the southern

Gulf coast of Mexico; formerly they also appeared in Nevada, Nebraska, and Iowa. All over its range, except Florida, this eagle has diminished despite full protection by law. Many ancient sites have been abandoned. Reproduction shows a trend to decrease, adults frequently failing to nest. In 1963 only 41 percent of more than four hundred controlled pairs from the whole continent nested successfully. In 1970 of thirty known nests in Maine eleven eaglets were produced in eight nests, while twenty-two nests failed completely. Unhatched eggs contained about 23 parts per million of DDT. In 1971 even the formerly stable population in central Florida may have been suffering. Possibly contamination by pesticides discharged in coastal and fresh waters is affecting the reproduction capacity of the bald eagle much as it has its cousin in the Old World, the white-tailed eagle (*H. albicilla*) and other birds of prey. Disturbance of habitat and the nests is probably also involved in the decline. Moreover, direct persecution also plays a role. In Wyoming more than five hundred golden and bald eagles were slaughtered between September, 1970, and August, 1971, despite the fact that it has been against federal law to kill bald eagles since 1940. The birds were slaughtered from helicopters and airplanes, hired by Wyoming ranchers "obsessed with the neanderthal notion that eagles are a serious threat to livestock," as it was testified before a U. S. Senate subcommittee.

The Florida sandhill crane (*Grus canadensis pratensis*) is dealt with on pages 189–190.

Two extremely rare sparrows are restricted to two limited areas in Florida. The dusky seaside sparrow (*Ammospiza nigrescens*) is confined to some small salt marshes near Cape Kennedy. It is likely that security regulations in the rocket-firing area have improved the possibilities of survival for this bird, because it is now less disturbed. About one thousand individuals were reported in 1968 as total population. Thus, man's attempts to reach the moon may prove beneficial for a little passerine. The Cape Sable sparrow (*A. mirabilis*) was found in the coastal prairie along the shores of Cape Sable in the Everglades National Park in 1918. In 1928 it was also recorded in the Big Cypress Swamp. However, hurricanes and fires have changed the habitat at Cape Sable drastically, and the species was not observed there any longer. I searched for it in vain in 1964–65. In 1970, 35 years after its supposed destruction, eleven individuals, adults as well as juveniles, of this sparrow were found at Cape Sable.

During the 1860's the number of alligators (*Alligator mississippiensis*) in Florida was estimated at about three million, but nowadays it is believed to be down to less than a hundred thousand. And during recent years the drought combined with the reduction in the natural flow from Lake Okeechobee has become a serious threat to this freshwater reptile. Moreover, hide-hunting poachers were reported to have killed no less than fifty thousand alligators in 1964 alone. The species is distributed from North Carolina to southern Florida and westward into Texas, but the bulk of the population is in the Everglades National Park. Recent studies in the Everglades National Park suggest that the alligator population has been reduced by 98 percent since 1960. It was in 1969 down to about twenty thousand individuals. The U. S. Department of the Interior has recently placed the alligator on a list of endangered American animals. Like other crocodiles, the alligator is valuable in the maintenance of a suitable environment for food and game fish. It is protected all over its range within the United States, but destruction and losses of habitats, heavy poaching, and killing because of unmotivated fear are the main reasons for the rapid decline of this harmless but useful reptile.

MEXICO

Mexico is a mixture of temperate, subtropical, and tropical climates resulting from both its extension across the Tropic of Cancer and a considerable variation in height. Only about 30 percent is tropical; about 70 percent supports vegetation characteristic of northern temperate regions. A country with a high ecological diversity, Mexico has deserts, chaparral, scrublands, mesquite grasslands, savannas, coniferous forests (chiefly on high peaks of the cordilleras and sierras), temperate deciduous forests, tropical acacia forests, tropical deciduous forests, rain forests, montane rain forests, and alpine meadows. Mexican animals of the coasts and marine islands will be treated in a later section.

Because of its location, Mexico has long served as a bridge for animals between North and South America. As a result the country has a rich fauna of species representing Nearctic and Neotropical elements. But for a long time man's thoughtless abuse of the land over vast areas has greatly changed Mexican vegetation and consequently entire biocommunities. Agriculture, grazing of livestock, clearing of forests, and draining of lakes have so altered the face of Mexico that the conquistadors would not recognize the country. The alterations have impoverished both habitats and wildlife, causing the erosion and destruction of productive land. Against this background is an exploding human population, one that has doubled in the past fifty years.

The Mexicans seem to believe that predator control represents a positive wildlife management, and they therefore kill carnivores and birds of prey very energetically. This is a serious mistake. Besides its direct economic yield, wildlife with its attraction for tourists and its implications for commerce may in many areas be a higher and more productive form of land use than the activities of agriculture, forestry, and livestock production. Proper wildlife management could play a vital role in the rural economy of Mexico.

The slender-billed grackle (*Cassidix palustris*) has long been confined to some marshes near Mexico City, where it has been scarce. As it has not been observed for about fifty years, it must be considered to be extinct.

The volcano rabbit (*Romerolagus diazi*) has an extremely limited range in pine grasslands on the upper-middle slopes of three volcanoes in central Mexico. It has been much reduced in numbers by encroaching agriculture, burning, and shooting, and it is now threatened by extermination. The rabbit is protected by law and is not used as food by man, but it is illegally shot for target practice. Scientifically it is unique, the only species of its genus.

The Mexican prairie dog (*Cynomys mexicanus*) is a species of mountain ranges and valleys of central Mexico, but the encroachment of wheat fields has made this rodent very rare. It is protected by law, but since its habitat is drastically changed, its prospects for survival are for the moment rather dark.

The Mexican duck (*Anas diazi*) is one of the rarest vertebrates in Mexico. Its distribution center is located in lakes and ponds in the uplands of the volcanic cordillera; an aerial census in 1952 found 4,700 birds there. Since then the species has continued to decrease, probably owing to the drainage of suitable marshes. There are also about a hundred to 150 birds in southern New Mexico and about twenty birds in Texas and Arizona.

The horned guan (*Oreophasis derbianus*) lives only in scattered areas in high mountain forests of the Sierra Madre in the Chiapas State of Mexico and in the nearby border country of Guatemala. Persecution and forest destruction are the cause of the decline of this bird, which is rapidly decreasing.

According to recent information received by the International Council for Bird Preservation, it seems as though the imperial woodpecker (*Campephilus imperialis*) has become extinct or is very near disappearing forever. Its last stronghold was the Sierra Madre forests, but these habitats are no longer spared the ax. Eradication and direct human predation are more than this bird can withstand. Also, the thick-billed parrot (*Rhyncopsitta pachyrhyncha*) of the mountain forests of the Sierra Madre is for the same reason disappearing and endangered. Two subspecies, *R. p. pachyrhyncha* and *R. p. terrisi,* live in the occidental and the oriental parts of the Sierra. The latter race is near extinction.

LAKES, MARSHES, AND RIVERS

Thanks to its geological past and its great glaciers, North America is very rich in lakes and marshes. In their retreat northward the glaciations left thousands of wetlands. But after the arrival of the white man the continent was again reshaped as violently as if by a new geological force. Marshes and sloughs in particular have been changed. Of 127 million acres of wetlands in the United States in colonial times, more than 45 million acres have been drained for dry land use. Enormous areas that once grew cattails, wild rice, and pond weeds now support agricultural crops, factories, villages, towns, and airports. What this drastic transformation means for waterfowl that require wetlands and fields for breeding, for resting along migration routes, and for wintering is obvious. Nevertheless, North America is still surprisingly rich in ducks and geese.

The most productive wildfowl areas of North America are the prairie potholes and marshes, the northern watersheds and deltas, and finally the northern forests and tundras. The prairie pothole region makes up only 10 percent of the total waterfowl breeding area of the continent, but it produces 50 percent of the duck crop in an average year and more than that in bumper years. Unfortunately, the Canadian and Alaskan deltas and wetland flats are being exploited by dam projects and oil-field development. Three-fourths of the Saskatchewan delta were seriously altered in the late Sixties, the Yukon is endangered, and so are the Mackenzie River and Old Crow flats. The Rampart Canyon Dam project of the Yukon River would have been a catastrophe for waterfowl and a disaster for fishing resources. It would have blocked the migration of the salmon into a third or more of the upper Yukon watershed.

Fortunately, the Rampart Dam Project was turned down. But in July, 1968, some oil companies announced the discovery of "one of the largest petroleum accumulations known to the world today" along the arctic slope of the Brooks Range of Alaska. This is one of the most important remaining wilderness areas of North America, harbouring the Arctic Wildlife Range, the largest single federal biological reserve of the U. S. All this may now be endangered by the new oil discoveries. Oil pollution may threaten all waters of the area and their inhabitants. Of course, terrestrial habitats may also be destroyed.

Americans have learned a little from their mistakes. The National Wildlife Federation with an affiliated membership of about three million chose "Save America's Wetlands" as the theme for its National Wildlife Week in 1955. Minnesota and North Dakota, two states where drainage has been most rapid, are now the scene of concerted action for the preservation of marshes. There are other plans to restore destroyed wetlands to their former productivity.

Many birds of forests and bogs make their homes in the coniferous-forest region, to which they have retreated before advancing man. One of those most threatened by man was the trumpeter swan (*Cygnus cygnus buccinator*). At the arrival of the white man it ranged from Alaska and Canada to Missouri and Indiana. But it suffered severely from hunters and by the 1930's all the traditional breeding sites had been abandoned, and sixty-nine birds remained in 1932. This swan was apparently near extinction in the United States when a refuge was established in Montana in 1935. It increased slowly and began to breed in the Yellowstone National Park. Other successful reintroductions followed and today trumpeter swans are breeding in southern Alaska, central British Columbia, western Alberta, southwestern Montana and Wyoming. The population in Alaska was estimated at about thirteen hundred birds in 1961, and in the rest of the United States at more than seven hundred birds in 1963. Since then the trumpeter swan has increased in number. In the fall of 1968 an aerial survey indicated a total population of four to five thousand birds in the U. S. with more in Canada. That year more than 2,848 birds were counted in Alaska. Although still rare, this swan may now be considered saved as a result of protection from hunting and of population management programs.

The Yuma clapper rail (*Rallus longirostris yumanensis*) is one of the rarest birds of North America. It occurs in six localities along the lower Colorado River in Arizona and California. The population is estimated at less than two hundred birds. Flooding and draining of swamps seem to be the main factors behind the decrease of this rail.

A bird at the other extreme in size is Bachman's warbler (*Vermivora bachmanii*), which is localized to some river swamps in Missouri, Kentucky, Arkansas, South Carolina, and Alabama. It frequents wooded thickets in such swamps, and it is therefore difficult to estimate its numbers, but it has been described as perhaps the rarest songbird of North America.

Several aquatic reptiles are threatened by destruction of habitats. To them belongs the bog turtle (*Clemmys muhlenbergii*), which occurs in isolated populations from Connecticut to North Carolina. Its decline is due not only to drainage but also to over-exploitation by collectors furnishing the pet trade.

Many amphibians in North America are restricted to single localities situated in isolated mountains, pools, wells, and cave systems, a fact which makes them vulnerable to extinction. Examples of such species are the Georgia blind salamander (*Haideotriton wallacei*), which is known only from a well two hundred feet deep in Albany, Georgia; the Ocoee salamander (*Desmognathus ocoee*) from Ocoee Gorge in Tennessee; the Valdina Farms salamander (*Eurycea troglodytes*) from a cave in Texas; the San Marcos salamander (*E. nana*) from a spring in Texas; and the Mariposa salamander (*Hydromantis brunus*) from a hillside in California. There are also a toad and a frog in a similarly endangered situation: the black toad (*Bufo exsul*), limited to Deep Springs, California, and the Las Vegas frog (*Rana pipiens fisheri*) from Nevada. The latter may now be extinct owing to drainage of its springs. The Texas blind salamander (*Typhlomolge rathbuni*), living in Ezell's Cave of the underground Purgatory Creek in central Texas, is endemic, extremely rare, and near total extermination. Other American salamanders sharing this fatal position are the Santa Cruz long-toed salamander (*Ambystoma macrodactylum croceum*) and the California tiger salamander (*A. tigrinum californiense*). Both occur in California. The former is on the verge of extinction, the latter is also rapidly declining. The garden slender salamander (*Batrachoseps pacificus major*) from southern

California is menaced to disappear entirely by habitat changes due to the rapid urban growth of Los Angeles.

Also, several other American toads and frogs are endangered because of environmental modifications. Human overexploitation of water resources and the use of pesticides have brought the Amargosa toad (*Bufo boreas nelsoni*) to the verge of extinction within its limited range in California and Nevada.

To the best of my knowledge, on no other continents but Asia and North America have such a great number of fishes been totally exterminated by man. According to Dr. Robert Rush Miller of the American Society of Ichthyologists and Herpetologists, at least seven species of freshwater fishes have become extinct in the United States and Mexico since 1900. About thirty other species are either rare, very restricted in range, or threatened with extinction.

At least three trouts, one grayling, and one killifish are now probably extinct. They are the emerald trout (*Salmo smaragdus*) from Pyramid Lake in Nevada, the regal silver trout (*S. regalis*) from deep waters of Lake Tahoe in Nevada and California, the San Gorgonio trout (*S. evermanni*) from the Santa Ana River in California, the Michigan grayling (*Thymallus signifer tricolor*) from the Great Lakes basin, and the killifish (*Empetrichtys merriami*) from the Death Valley system. The latter has not been taken since 1957. The Gila trout (*Salmo gilae*) from the Gila River system in New Mexico and Arizona is now almost extinct, and its near relative, the Apache trout (*S. sp.*), whose taxonomic status is unclear, is restricted to two small streams on the Fort Apache Indian Reservation in Arizona. Previously this fish was widespread in tributaries of the White and Colorado rivers, but the introduction of competing species and the modification of the habitat by deforestation have wiped out these populations.

Other fishes that are near extinction include the Owens Valley pupfish (*Cyprinodon radiosus*) from California, four races of the pupfish *C. nevadensis* (*mionectes, pectoralis, calidae,* and *shoshone*) from Nevada and California, the killifish *C. salinus* from the Death Valley system, the harelip sucker (*Lagochila lazera*) from the Mississippi Valley, and the thicktail chub (*Gila crassicauda*) from California. The Mohave chub (*G. mohavensis*) is at present surviving only in a pool near Baker, California. The humpback chub (*G. cypha*), a minnow whose former status is little-known, now occurs only in the Green and Colorado rivers of the Grand Canyon. Its upper range along the Utah–Wyoming border has been altered by the Flaming Gorge Dam. Improper utilization of rotenone has placed the Colorado chub (*G. robusta*) among threatened fishes in Colorado and Utah. The Devil's Hole pupfish (*Cyprinodon diabolis*) is a small, specialized fish, probably a relict of the Ice Age, that now exists with only about two hundred individuals in a single spring-fed pool in Death Valley in southern Nevada. It requires warm water and heavy algae growths. These requirements are met only above just one ledge a few feet under water, so habitat changes may well doom this species.

The case of the four species of pupfish (*Cyprinodon*) from the California-Nevada desert valleys mentioned above is interesting from an evolutionary point of view; because, isolated for thousands of years since the Ice Ages, when their habitats were formulated, they have evolved from an ancestral pupfish to four distinct species and several subspecies. This evolution is, of course, still going on. Moreover, these fish show a remarkable physiological ability to survive at temperatures as low as 38° F. and as high as 108° F., hence withstanding temperatures over a range of 70° F.

Other threatened fishes in Nevada are the desert dace (*Eremichtys acros*), the moapa dace (*Moapa coracea*), the woundfin (*Plagopterus argentissimus*), and the pahrump killifish (*Empetrichthys latos*). Two races of the latter species are already extinct. The seriously endangered species include the White River spinedace (*Lepidomeda albivallis*) of Nevada, the Little Colorado spinedace (*L. vittata*) and the Gila topminnow (*Poeciliopsis occidentalis*) of Arizona, the Sacramento perch (*Archoplites interruptus*) of California, the Comanche Springs pupfish (*Cyprinodon elegans*), the Alamito pupfish (*C. exinius*), the Clear Creek gambusia (*Gambusia heterochir*), the Big Bend gambusia (*G. gagei*) and Peros gambusia (*G. nobilis*) of Texas, the Maryland darter (*Etheostoma sellare*) of Maryland, the Niangua darter (*E. niangue*) from Missouri, the fountain darter (*E. fonticola*) from Texas, and the Waccamaw darter (*E. perlongum*) from North Carolina. The flannelmouth sucker (*Catostomus latippinus*) is slowly disappearing from the streams of Arizona and Colorado because of siltation and pollution. The modoc sucker (*C. microps*), once thought to be extinct, still exists in a single creek in California. A squawfish, *Ptychocheilus grandi*, from northern California cannot withstand the impounding of habitat waters and the introduction of exotics. The meda spinedace (*Meda fulgida*) is swiftly disappearing from its last stronghold, the Gila River in New Mexico, from where the loach minnow (*Tiaroga cobitis*) has also nearly vanished.

Other species of fish listed as very rare and endangered in the United States and Mexico, chiefly owing to overfishing, pollution, and habitat destruction, are the following:

Shortnose sturgeon (*Acipenser brevirostrum*). At present restricted to the Hudson River.

Lake sturgeon (*A. fulvescens*). In the Great Lakes the catch for 1885 records 8.5 million pounds, but at present this fish is rare.

Longjaw cisco (*Coregonus alpenae*). Formerly abundant in the Great Lakes, but now rare.

Lahontan cutthroat trout (*Salmo clarki henshawi*). Now very rare in a few creeks and lakes in California and Nevada.

Piute cutthroat trout (*S.c. seleniris*). Existing in two tiny streams in California.

Greenback cutthroat trout (*S.c. stomias*). Only a few pure individuals of this race live in a creek in Colorado.

Mexican golden trout (*S. chrysogaster*). Very rare and vulnerable in streams of northern Mexico.

Olympic mudminnow (*Nuvombra hubbsi*). A rare relict in a few streams of the Puget Sound and on the Olympic peninsula, Washington.

Monterey platyfish (*Xiphophorus couchianus*). Existing in three localities in Mexico.

Cui-ui (*Chasmistes cujus*). Confined to Pyramid Lake, Nevada.

Klamath sucker (*C. brevirostris*). Rapidly disappearing from its range in California and Oregon.

Widemouth blindcat (*Satan eurystomus*). Restricted to artesian wells around San Antonio, Texas.

Toothless blindcat (*Trogloglanis pattersoni*). Restricted to artesian waters near San Antonio, Texas.

Mexican blindcat (*Prietella phreatophila*). Near extinction. Confined to a well in Coahuila, Mexico.

Checkered killifish (*Cualac tesselatus*). Exists only in a spring-fed ditch in San Luis Potosí, Mexico.

Waccamaw killifish (*Fundulus waccamensis*). Restricted to Lake Waccamaw, North Carolina.

Ozark cavefish (*Amblyopsis rosae*). Confined to a few caves in Missouri.

Suwannee bass (*Micropterus notius*). Restricted to some springs in Florida.

Unarmoured threespine stickleback (*Gasterosteus aculeatus williamsoni*). Exists only in a restricted area of California.

Rough sculpin (*Cottus asperrimus*). Confined to Lake Waccamaw in North Carolina.

THE COASTS AND ISLANDS

The coast around North America is marked by a tremendous variety of habitats: arctic tundra islands, foggy and rainy cliffs, estuaries, deltas, tidal marshes, sand beaches, coral reefs, mangrove forests, kelp beds, and so on. Animal life varies in relation to these habitats. In this section we shall move southward along the Pacific and Atlantic coasts.

Three coastal mammals of North America have disappeared forever. Newfoundland once had a carnivore of its own, the Newfoundland wolf (*Canis lupus beothucus*), that had developed differences from the mainland wolf. In 1875 this wolf was common in Newfoundland, where it fed on caribou and rodents. But it also preyed upon young cattle, and therefore a bounty was put on it. By the end of the century it had been decimated and the last specimen was killed about 1911.

Another species or subspecies that has become extinct is the sea mink (*Mustela vison macrodon*), which at the arrival of the Europeans was restricted to the mainland coast and islands of Maine. Because of its large size and valuable fur it was hunted avidly and skins were procured regularly until about 1860. Then the number shrank rapidly and by 1880 the sea mink was gone.

The Gull Island vole (*Microtus nisophilus*) from Long Island Sound became extinct in 1898.

Many other animals with economic value were pursued without any regard for their survival. Some marine mammals along the Pacific coast were slaughtered in such tremendous numbers that it was merely by chance that any survived until people realized the need to protect them. The most dramatic story is that of the sea otter (*Enhydra lutris*). In 1741 Russian sailors were wrecked east of Kamchatka on what today is called Bering Island. There they discovered a sea otter (*E. l. lutris*) living in the seaweed beds offshore. Because the otter ranged along Pacific Alaska as well as the

Old World coast, Russian ships hunting the otters began to sail along these coasts. Thus, it is due to the sea otter and other marine mammals that the Russians opened up these northern lands. Since one ship alone could collect as many as five thousand skins during a season, the numbers of otters killed must have been tremendous, but the animals were so abundant that it was not until the 1860's that the depletion seems to have become noticeable. In 1867 the U. S. bought Alaska and the surrounding islands from Russia. Although the slaughter of otters continued, the number taken dropped every year. The rising price of pelts stimulated continuing persecution, so that the species was near extinction when in 1910 the United States, Great Britain, Russia, and Japan agreed to ban otter hunting. When the years passed and no sea otters were observed, it was thought that the measure had been taken too late. However, a small group was discovered in the Commander Islands and by 1935 this colony had increased to between six and seven hundred animals. In 1936 a colony of sea otters was found in the Aleutian Islands and was immediately made part of a wildlife refuge. The population around Alaska has now increased to about thirty thousand. The entire population of the northern sea otter is about fifty thousand and the species has recolonized almost a third of its former range. In Russian waters there were about 7,500 sea otters in 1969. It can once more be hunted locally within limits and utilized as a valuable natural resource. In 1971 forty-two northern sea otters captured off Alaska were released off the British Columbia coast, which so far has not been recolonized in a natural way. However, the future of the sea otter is not entirely rosy. The species is facing new perils such as marine pollution, limited feeding grounds, and antagonism from abalone fishermen who fear that the sea otters reduce their harvest.

A southern race (*E. l. nereis*) of this otter was formerly distributed along the Pacific coast from Washington to Baja California. It was abundant but was hunted mercilessly, which led to its disappearance off Oregon in 1876, and off California in 1915, when it was considered extinct. There was no further record of this otter until 1938, when single individuals began to appear almost yearly off Monterey in California. In 1938 a resident colony of about ninety-four sea otters was found at Monterey. The otter expanded southward, and in 1957 its range extended from Santa Barbara to Carmel Bay. One can easily see these interesting mammals lying among the kelp off the coast of Monterey. An aerial census in this area in 1966 yielded 312 animals. In the same year the whole population off California was 618 animals, nearly one hundred more than the year before. In 1968 the number was 1,014 animals. Of course, this is a dangerously small population and oil pollution could easily wipe out all these otters in a short time. So the southern sea otter is not yet quite safe.

The northern misty ocean waters are also the home of another animal of great commercial value, the northern fur seal (*Callorhinus ursinus*). Here again we have a useful marine mammal that once existed in incredible numbers, but after about two decades of hunting was near extinction.

The northern fur seal was first observed by Bering's sailors in 1741 off the island that now bears his name, but the seals did not use this area for breeding. Despite an intensive search, it was forty-five years later before man discovered where the fur seals congregated for calving and mating. This is not surprising, because the Bering Sea is one of the most foggy waters in the world. In 1786 the Russian explorer Gerasim Pribilof, sailing among the group of islands that today are called by his name, came upon the greatest concentration of marine mammals ever observed, at least by Europeans. Millions of fur-seal bulls, cows, and pups covered the beaches and rocks of one of the islands, now known as St. George. About a year later another island in the Pribilofs, St. Paul, was discovered to have even more fur seals than St. George.

Immediately the exploitation of the species was begun by the Russians and within twenty years the enormous herds had been so sharply reduced that the species was endangered. In 1834 it was decreed that only mature bulls could be killed, and this measure saved the species. In 1864 the population was estimated at between two and three million, and yielded between eighty and ninety thousand bulls every year, seemingly without any drastic effect on the size of the population.

When in 1867 the United States bought Alaska from Russia, the fur trade was taken over by Americans. In 1870 the United States limited the number shot to a hundred thousand fur seals each year. But Canadian and British sealers continued indiscriminate shooting in the open sea, where it was impossible to determine the sex of the animal. Moreover, the majority of the dead seals sank to the bottom before they could be secured. The annual harvest on the Pribilofs dropped continuously and in 1910 only twelve thousand pelts were taken. Fortunately, the United States arranged an international treaty in 1911 which banned all sealing in open waters. From a low of about 125,000 seals, the population has increased until it now seems to have reached its former abundance. The species can now be used as a renewable natural resource with a harvest based on the reproductive capacity of the seal. By 1943 the annual crop exceeded a hundred thousand animals, although only three-year-old males without harems could be killed. This is a splendid result of wildlife management based on biological facts.

At present the breeding range of the northern fur seal comprises the Pribilof Islands, Alaska, the Bering and Copper islands, Robben Island off Sakhalin, and probably Lovushki Island in the Kuril Islands. Since the U. S., Canada, and the U.S.S.R. share the responsibility of maintaining the northern fur seal and are conservation-minded, the future of the species now appears quite safe. In 1958 the summer populations were estimated at about 1,800,000 on the Pribilof Islands, sixty thousand on the Commander Islands, sixty thousand on Robben Island, and several thousand on Lovushki. In 1968 a colony of up to one hundred northern fur seals was found as far southward as San Miguel Islands off California.

We have elsewhere discussed the slaughter of two other northern seals, the harp seal and the hooded seal, around Newfoundland and elsewhere.

The Aleutian Canada goose (*Branta canadensis leucopareia*) is now very rare and breeds only on the islands of Amchitka and Buldir in the Aleutian Islands. Formerly there was a large population on the Aleutians. Intensive hunting and the introduction of the arctic fox are believed to account for the decline. However, there are no arctic foxes on Buldir Island, the most isolated of the Aleutian archipelago, and the number of geese there increased from sixty-three in 1962 to about three hundred in 1963. It is to be hoped that the breeding area on Buldir will be set aside as a reserve.

The Pribilof wren (*Troglodytes troglodytes alascensis*) is an isolated subspecies with a very small population. So is the Ipswich sparrow (*Passerculus princeps*), which lives only on Sable Island off Nova Scotia and is decreasing in number, possibly owing to the erosion of its small island world.

The beach meadow vole (*Microtus breweri*) is found only on Muskeget Island between Martha's Vineyard and Nantucket. It is adapted to sandy habitats but its burrows, made in loose sand, do not give it much protection from cats, owls, and the elements. It was last observed in 1956. The Block Island meadow vole (*M. pennsylvanicus provectus*) also has a restricted distribution, occurring only on Block Island off Rhode Island, where it is endangered by cultivation.

The brown pelican (*Pelecanus occidentalis*), a coastal bird in the southern U. S., has within ten years decreased to such an extent that it is now on the verge of extinction and has been added to the long list of endangered species by the U. S. Department of the Interior. Pesticides are the reason for this catastrophe.

It is chiefly in California and Mexico that coastal and island animals of North America have been exterminated or seriously reduced in numbers. Some belong to the mainland coast but most of them live on islands. One of the former is the salt-marsh harvest mouse (*Reinthrodontomys raviventris*) from a few localities in the San Francisco Bay area which are constantly being reduced in size by industrialization.

No area in North America has been so badly treated by man as Guadalupe Island, which lies about 135 miles off Baja California, Mexico. An oceanic island of volcanic origin, surrounded by deep waters and reaching an elevation of about 3,400 feet, it is about twenty-two miles long and from four to seven miles wide. Virtually all the native shrubs, many of them endemic, have disappeared and have been replaced by introduced grasses. Sparse groves of native trees, mostly cypresses, pines, oaks, and palms, still exist on the northern ridge and slopes. Tremendous destruction of habitats by domestic goats, predation by feral cats, and plundering by man are the chief causes of the decline of many members of the native fauna.

The most famous animal in the history of Guadalupe Island is the Guadalupe fur seal (*Arctocephalus philippii townsendi*). It was originally found off California and Mexico from the Farallon Islands in the north to the San Benito Islands in the south. Early in the nineteenth century it was avidly hunted for skins and oil. In 1810, for example, a party of only eight men killed 33,740 seals on the Farallon Islands; next year they took 21,153; and in 1812 the catch was 18,509. By 1826 this seal was almost extinct on the Farallons. The most important remaining population was that of Guadalupe Island, where about thirty thousand fur seals still survived. They decreased rapidly: in 1880 there were three to four thousand seals and by 1892 only seven seals were left, the last seen in that century.

For thirty years the Guadalupe fur seal was considered extinct, but in 1928 a fisherman captured two specimens and reported that he had seen a herd of about sixty animals on Guadalupe. But searchers could not locate them. In 1950 Professor George Bartholomew visited San Nicolas Island off southern California and discovered one Guadalupe fur seal. This lone specimen was observed several times between 1949 and 1951. In 1954 a breeding colony of fourteen seals was seen at Guadalupe by Professor Carl L. Hubbs. In 1965 the population was reported to be about two to five hundred and in 1972 at least five hundred. This fur seal is now protected.

There are no terrestrial mammals, reptiles, or amphibians on Guadalupe Island, but there are birds, and these have declined greatly. No less than five birds became extinct between 1897 and 1922, and five are now threatened by the same fate. The first bird to disappear was the Guadalupe rufous-sided towhee (*Pipilo erypthrophthalmus consobrinus*), exterminated in 1897. Then followed the Guadalupe Bewick's wren (*Thryomanes bewickii brevicauda*) also in 1897, and the Guadalupe caracara (*Caracara lutosa*) in 1900, the Guadalupe red-shafted flicker (*Colaptes cafer rufipileus*) between 1906 and 1922, and the Guadalupe storm petrel (*Oceanodroma macrodactyla*) between 1912 and 1919. Seriously threatened by extermination are the Guadalupe kestrel (*Falco sparverius guadalupensis*), the Guadalupe rock wren (*Salpinctes obsoletus guadalupensis*), the Guadalupe house finch (*Carpodacus amplus*), the Guadalupe junco (*Junco insularis*), and the Guadalupe kinglet (*Regulus calendula obscura*). A small population of McGregor's house finch (*Carpodacus mcgregori*) is found on San Benito and Cedros islands, off Baja California.

The birds of the Rivella Gigedo Islands, west of the tip of Baja California, have also been drastically reduced in numbers. One is extinct; others are endangered. One of these four volcanic islands, San Benedicto, was the home of the San Benedicto rock wren (*Salpinctes obsoletus exsul*), which was exterminated by a volcanic eruption in 1952. Another island of the group, Socorro Island, is the home of three endemic and threatened birds: the Socorro Island wren (*Thryomanes sissonii*), the Socorro Island thrasher (*Mimodes graysoni*) and the rufous-sided towhee (*Pipilo erythrophthalmus carmani*). The Cozumel curassow (*Crax rubra griscomi*), an endemic race of one of Mexico's finest game birds, lives on Cozumel Island off Yucatan; it is very rare.

BALANCE FOR NORTH AMERICA

Since the arrival of the Europeans in North America, in fact after 1825, nine mammals, fourteen birds, and at least nine fishes have become extinct. In addition one bird, one amphibian, and five fish are probably extinct. (The twelve "species" and the four "subspecies" of grizzlies, which have been claimed to be extinct [cf. pages 181–183], as well as the various presumed races of the prairie bison, are not included in these figures.) Forty-five mammals, thirty-nine birds, eleven reptiles, thirteen amphibians, and fifty-six fishes are at present in danger of extermination. Five of these threatened mammals are shared with Eurasia. Many more species have in the last hundred years been brought to the verge of extinction by reckless exploitation, but measures taken at often the very last moment arrested the decline of certain species and even permitted them to increase. In some instances this has allowed the use of these animals as a valuable resource.

Compared with the balance sheet of Africa and Europe, more vertebrate species and races have been exterminated by man during the last three hundred years in North America, but today the conservation movement is stronger on this continent than anywhere else in the world. The future for the remaining North American wildlife therefore looks brighter than that of any other continent except for Antarctica.

Species and subspecies of vertebrates extinct during historic time, probably extinct, and at present endangered by extinction. All figures refer to extinctions which have occurred after 1825.

CLASS	EXTINCT	PROBABLY EXTINCT	ENDANGERED
Mammals	9	—	45
Birds	14	1	39
Reptiles	—	—	11
Amphibians	—	1	13
Fish	9	5	56
Total	32	7	164

CHAPTER FIVE

South and Central America

South America is mostly tropical, with the southern part extending into a temperate zone and the Andes showing a wide spectrum of climates. It has more rain forests, mainly in the Amazon Valley, than any other tropical continent. The variety of vegetational zones is very great, ranging from deciduous temperate forests and steppes to arid brushlands, deserts, and subantarctic moors.

Called the "island continent" because it was long isolated (probably during most of the Tertiary), South America once had an astonishingly rich mammalian fauna with an extraordinary number of unique hoofed animal species. All these animals disappeared and were partly replaced by others that entered the continent from the north after the isthmus connecting it with North America was formed in the late Pliocene, presumably one or two million years ago.

According to geological and fossil evidence, man did not invade the South American continent until after the latest glaciation in North America. Radiocarbon datings indicate that man has not been in South America more than six thousand years. If this is correct, he has spread over the entire continent and settled as far south as Tierra del Fuego in an astonishingly short time. Man is, however, an extraordinary species and does accomplish almost unbelievable feats.

But findings in 1968 seem to indicate that man was already in Chile about eleven thousand years ago. Bone and stone tools were associated with extinct fauna (horse and mastodon). Charcoal thought to be contemporary with the fossils and the artifacts could be dated at about eleven thousand years ago.

Despite his long prehistoric occupation of South America, man did not have a harmful influence on the environment, although it

is not known exactly how many of the larger mammals vanished
during the late Pleistocene through human pressure. Prior to the
arrival of the Europeans, the situation in South America was with
few exceptions much like that in early North America: The Indians were a more or less harmonious part of nature. However,
in Central America man's agriculture began far back and developed rapidly. In Tamaulipas in tropical Mexico there are remains
of cultivated plants that date back several millenniums B.C. Apparently agriculture spread southward in Central America at an
early stage and this greatly affected the natural landscape, at least
locally. But it was only after the appearance of the white man that
the destruction of nature began on a tremendous scale, particularly
in the Caribbean, where most of the larger islands have been
almost entirely modified during the last few centuries. There are
still large areas of South America that remain more or less untouched, particularly in the Amazon and some of the forested
parts of the Andes. For example, only 2 percent of the enormous
acreage of Brazil is at present cultivated; but, a larger area than
that has been destroyed. The destruction will accelerate very rapidly in the future because great development projects are in the
planning stage.

   As a result of habitat destruction, a great number of mammals
and birds have been exterminated in South America, particularly
in the Caribbean, where endemic island species are very vulnerable
to abrupt changes in environment. Removal of forests and introduction of exotic species have proved catastrophic for the native
animals. For the same reason an appallingly large number of species are on the verge of vanishing forever.

ANIMAL FAMILIES PECULIAR TO SOUTH AMERICA

   South and Central America as well as the West Indies belong
zoogeographically to the Neotropical region. This region is exceptionally rich in animals. There are more birds breeding or wintering here than in any other faunal region, so that South America
has been called the "bird continent." About half of the avian
species and subspecies of the world belong to the Neotropical
region and there are more endemic families (thirty of sixty-seven)
of land and freshwater birds than we can conveniently list here.
In addition, the Amazon River and its tributaries possess the greatest abundance of freshwater fish in the world.

Among the mammals there are several families which are exclusive to the Neotropical region: opossum rats (*Caenolestidae*), hare-lipped bats (*Noctilionidae*), true vampire bats (*Desmodontidae*), long-legged bats (*Natalidae*), smoky bats (*Furipteridae*), disk-winged bats (*Thryopteridae*), flat-nosed monkeys (*Cebidae*), marmosets (*Callithricidae*), anteaters (*Myrmecophagidae*), tree sloths (*Bradypodidae*), and ten families of hystricomorph rodents (*Hystricomorpha*). There are fewer unique reptiles; only two families, with one species in each, are exclusively South and Central American: a turtle (*Dermatemydidae*) and a lizard (*Anelytropsidae*). Among the amphibians only one family is endemic, the *Rhinophrynidae*. The fish fauna of South America is dominated by characins and catfishes, and certain groups are remarkable for a great number of species that do not occur elsewhere. However, on the family level only gymnotid eels (*Gymnotidae*), flying characins (*Gasteropelecidae*), and twelve families of catfishes are peculiar to this region.

In dealing with the extinct or endangered animals of Latin America, we begin in the north with the Bahamas, the Antilles, and Central America.

THE BAHAMAS

The Bahama Islands, east of Florida, are considered the northern part of the West Indies. Lying in the subtropics and tropics, these islands surrounded by sparkling emerald-green and blue waters have many biological affinities to South America. Geologically, however, they have never been connected with any mainland.

Some of the islands have been exploited intensively; others still possess natural habitats. Compared with the Caribbean islands, animal life on the Bahamas has been less disturbed and reduced by man. However, two rodents have been exterminated and four birds are endangered. Two races of the Bahaman hutia (*Geocapromys ingrahami irrectus* and *G. i. abaconis*) disappeared during the seventeenth century, probably as a result of clearing and burning after the European occupation. The species was long thought to be extinct until 1966, when an abundant population was found on a small unhabited island in the Bahamas. This surviving population seems to belong to the nominate race, *G. i. ingrahami*. The Bahamas parrot (*Amazona leucocephala bahamensis*) vanished from Great Abaco in 1933 and from Acklins Island in 1940. It still survives on Great Inagua Island, but it is rare and decreasing in numbers. We looked for it in vain there in 1965, but it is still well-known to the inhabitants. Three races of the red-bellied woodpecker (*Melanerpes superciliaris*) are confined to coastal forests of Grand Bahama (*M. s. bahamensis*), Great Abaco (*M. s. blakei*), and San Salvador (*M. s. nyeanus*), and seem to be declining in numbers.

THE CARIBBEAN ISLANDS

On a map, the chain of the Antilles looks like a gigantic reef separating the Atlantic Ocean from a vast lagoon—the Caribbean Sea. But the impression one gets from an airplane is that they are far apart—lonely little expanses of land that barely break the oceanic waves rolling into the Caribbean Sea. And the Caribbean is hardly a lagoon—more than 1,500 miles from west to east and from four to seven hundred miles from north to south.

Before the arrival of the Europeans, most of the West Indies were covered by tropical forests and scrubs. Of this luxuriant greenery not much remains; however, for urban man many of the islands still have the reputation of being like paradise. Such names as the Caribbean, the Virgin, and Windward Islands conjure up visions of lush tropical havens. True, these islands are rich in fascinating plants and animals, but it is also true that a shamefully high proportion of the original wildlife is gone forever. Forty percent of the world's vertebrate extinctions in historic time have occurred in the Caribbean. The Caribbean Islands particularly have been victims of man's mania for introducing exotic animals wherever he goes. Tremendous damage to the native animals has been done and is still being done by these aliens. Worst of all has been the introduction of the mongooses (*Herpestes auropunctatus* and *H. griseus*) to many islands of the West Indies. It has led to a complete or nearly complete extirpation of numerous native mammals and birds. Not only do introduced dogs, rats, pigs, monkeys, cats, and opossums prey extensively on the indigenous species, but introduced goats destroy the vegetation, which releases an accelerating erosion of soils. The intruders have displaced many large native rodents that constituted an important food item for the human inhabitants, as shown by rich deposits in the kitchen middens of the aborigines. However, even prior to the presence of

Europeans in the West Indies a great number of mammals had been exterminated after the arrival of Indians two to four thousand years ago.

Since space does not allow for a detailed account of all extinct and vanishing animals after the appearance of Europeans in the West Indies, the information is given in tabular form for each island.

Cuba

Apparently most vertebrates that have difficulty in crossing large expanses of salt water have migrated to the West Indies from the west by way of Cuba and Jamaica. Many of these animals went no farther, and Cuba is therefore relatively rich in relicts and endemic forms. Several of these unique animals are now extinct. Among mammals the following have disappeared:

> Cuban solenodon (*Solenodon cubanus cubanus*), probably extinct by about 1890. Represents the last living form in New World of a very peculiar group of shrews. Fortunately, another race (*S. c. poeyanus*) still survives in the mountains of northeastern Cuba, where Cuban conservation organizations have suggested a reserve for its protection.
>
> Two primitive shrews (*Nesophontes mirus* and *N. longirostris*). Disappeared several centuries ago.
>
> Lesser falcate-winged bat (*Phyllops vetus*). Apparently extinct at an early stage of historic time.
>
> Cuban yellow bat (*Natalus primus*). Probably extinct since the nineteenth century.
>
> Cuban short-tailed hutia (*Geocapromys columbianus*). Became extinct during the eighteenth or nineteenth century.
>
> Larger Cuban spiny rat (*Boromys offella*). Extinct in the nineteenth century.
>
> Lesser Cuban spiny rat (*B. torrei*). Extinct during the nineteenth or twentieth century.
>
> Black-tailed hutia (*Geocapromys melanurus*) of eastern Cuba and the dwarf hutia (*G. nana*), which lives in the Zapata Swamp on Cuba. Very rare and endangered.

Among the birds, the Cuban red macaw (*Ara tricolor*) became extinct about 1885 and the Grand Cayman thrush (*Turdus ravidus*) in 1938 or some time later. Species that are becoming increasingly rare and are already extirpated locally include:

Cuban tree duck (*Dendrocygna arborea*). Also occurs elsewhere is the Greater and Lesser Antilles as well as on the Bahamas.

Cuban hook-billed kite (*Chondrohierax wilsonii*). Restricted to one area in eastern Cuba.

Gundlach's hawk (*Accipiter gundlachi*). Found in the Cuban mountains. Has increased during recent years.

Cuban sharp-shinned hawk (*Accipiter striatus fringilloides*). Decreasing rapidly owing to persecution and habitat destruction.

Cuban sandhill crane (*Grus canadensis nesiotes*). Once widespread on Cuba and on the Isle of Pines, but today extremely rare on both islands and decreasing. In 1950 the population on the Isle of Pines was estimated at about one hundred, but it has since been reduced to about fifty. Total population is about 150 birds.

Zapata rail (*Cyanolimnas cerverai*). Known only from the Zapata Swamp, part of which has been drained.

Jamaica black rail (*Laterallus jamaicensis jamaicensis*). Extinct on Jamaica and Puerto Rico since the 1870's, and very rare if not already extinct in Cuba.

Cuban ivory-billed woodpecker (*Campephilus principalis bairdii*). By 1956 only twelve or thirteen individuals remained in eastern Cuba, but in 1969 there were thirteen pairs. The disappearing forests make survival difficult for this magnificent bird.

Fernandina's flicker (*Nesoceleus fernandinae*). Confined to central Cuba.

Zapata wren (*Ferminia cerverai*). Restricted to the Zapata Swamp.

Zapata sparrow (*Torreornis inexpectata*). One race (*T. i. inexpectata*) is limited to the Zapata Swamp and another (*T. i. segmant*) to a desert area.

On the Isle of Pines, the Isle of Pines solitaire (*Myadestes elisabeth retrusus*) has not been observed since the early 1950's and may be extinct. On Grand Cayman Island, south of Cuba, the Grand Cayman troupial (*Icterus leucopteryx bairdi*) has not been observed since 1938. It may already be extinct.

The famous Zapata Swamp is not only rich in birds but also is the only place in which the Cuban crocodile (*Crocodylus rhombifer*), which is peculiar to the island, can always be found. A reserve has been established for the estimated three hundred crocodiles in the swamp, but there they must compete with the much larger American crocodile (*C. acutus*), which is also endangered by extermination in its wider range.

The Cuban ground iguana (*Cyclura macleayi*), represented by three island races around Cuba (Isle of Pines: *C. m. macleayi;* Little Cayman: *C. m. caymanensis;* and Grand Cayman: *C. m. lewisi*), is estimated to exist in about five thousand lizards but is threatened because of predation by man, mongooses, and cats.

Jamaica and Hispaniola

Like Cuba, Jamaica is a mountainous island with a varied vegetation and a rich fauna. Several mammals and birds have been exterminated there during recent centuries and others are thought to be extinct. They are:

> Jamaica long-tongued bat (*Reithronycteris aphylla*). Extinct since 1898.
> Jamaica rice rat (*Oryzomys antillarum*). Extinct since about the 1880's.
> Jamaica diablotin (*Pterodroma hasitata caribbea*). Extinct since about 1880. There are rumors that this bird is still heard at night in the mountains in the northeast.
> Jamaica wood rail (*Amaurolimnas concolor concolor*). Extinct since about 1890.
> Jamaica red macaw (*Ara gossei*). Extinct since about 1765.
> Jamaica green and yellow macaw (*A. erythrocephala*). Extinct since the early nineteenth century, probably about 1810.
> Jamaica pauraque (*Siphonorhis americanus americanus*). Extinct since about 1859.

The only survivor of Jamaica's original land mammals, with the exception of bats, is the Jamaican hutia (*Geocapromys brownii brownii*). A small population still lives in inaccessible mountainous areas of eastern Jamaica. Even rarer is the Caribbean monk seal (*Monachus tropicalis*), which has its last stronghold in Jamaican waters. Its situation is extremely precarious. Formerly this seal was distributed throughout the Caribbean Sea and the Gulf of Mexico eastward to the Bahamas. In 1707 the latter islands were "filled with seals" and one hundred animals could be caught in a night. The species was rapidly destroyed and has long since been extremely rare. It has no protection whatsoever.

The American crocodile (*Crocodylus acutus*) is endangered throughout its range. Once it had a wide distribution in South and

Central America, the West Indies, and southern Florida. Owing
to unwise exploitation for hides and destruction of habitats, the
species has decreased tremendously and occurs at present only in
a few localities in the Florida Keys, the Caribbean—particularly
Jamaica—Mexico, British Honduras, Venezuela, and perhaps still
Colombia. Jàmaica seems to hold the largest population. Professional hunters estimated in 1971 the remaining number of American crocodiles at about two thousand, but this figure is certainly
too high and biased, because the hunters want to continue the
harvesting of this species. Two areas in Mexico also seem to hold
viable populations.

The following endemic reptiles are all considered to be either
extinct or endangered.

> Jamaican iguana (*Cyclura collei*). Since at least 1910 re-
> stricted to Hellshire Hills and Goat Island. Since 1940 it has
> not been recorded from the latter locality, but in 1969 one
> individual was found in the Hellshire Hills, the first recorded
> there in sixty years. The species is extremely rare and near
> extinction.
>
> Galliwasp (*Diploglossus occiduus*). This skink has not been
> recorded in over a hundred years and is now probably extinct.
>
> Snake-waiting skink (*Mabuya spilonota*). Not observed since
> the end of the 1950's. Near extinction due to predation by
> mongooses, cats, and rats.
>
> Jamaican snake (*Alsophis ater*). Not observed since the
> early 1940's. Probably extinct.
>
> Jamaican boa (*Epicrates subflavus*). Decreasing in number
> owing to predation and persecution.

On Little Swan Island, 110 miles off Honduras and about 330
miles from Jamaica, there lives the Little Swan Island hutia
(*Geocapromys brownii thoracatus*), which is interesting because
it is a near relative to the Jamaican hutia. This hutia is also endangered.

Hispaniola, including Haiti and the Dominican Republic, is the
second largest island in the West Indies. When Columbus discovered it in 1492, he became enthusiastic about its beauty: "Its
lands are high, and there are in it very many sierras. . . . All are
most beautiful . . . and filled with trees of a thousand kinds and
tall, and they seem to touch the sky. And I am told that they never
lose their foliage. . . . And the nightingale was singing, and other
birds of a thousand kinds, in the month of November. . . ." The

nightingale was probably a mockingbird, which is still called a nightingale (ruisenor) in the West Indies. Hispaniola has changed so much that if he returned Columbus would not recognize it.

Habitat destruction in Hispaniola has wiped out the following animals:

Three primitive shrews (*Nesophontes zamicrus, N. parmicrus,* and *N. hypomicrus*). Extinct after the European occupation.

Smaller Hispaniolan ground sloth (*Acratocnus comes*). Probably exterminated by man prior to or just after the arrival of Europeans.

Larger Hispaniolan ground sloth (*Parocnus serus*). Possibly disappeared after the arrival of Europeans.

Haitian long-tongued bat (*Phyllonycteris obtusa*). Probably disappeared during the twentieth century.

Hispaniolan spiny rats (*Brotomys voratus* and *B. contractus*). Extinct after the arrival of the Europeans.

Haitian hexolobodon (*Hexolobodon phenax*). Presumably disappeared soon after the European occupation.

Least Hispaniolan hutia (*Plagiodontia spelaeum*). Extinct in historic time.

Haitian isolobodon (*Isolobodon levir*). Probably disappeared soon after the arrival of Europeans.

Narrow-toothed hutia (*Aphaetreus montanus*). Probably disappeared just before or soon after the arrival of Europeans.

Quemi (*Quemisia gravis*). The largest rodent of Hispaniola, became extinct about the first half of the sixteenth century.

The following are endangered and extremely rare:

Hispaniola solenodon (*Solenodon paradoxus*). Survives only in certain parts of the Dominican Republic.

Hispaniola hutia (*Plagiodontia aedium*). Has long been close to extinction.

Dominican hutia (*P. hylaeum*). Confined to a few localities in Haiti and the Dominican Republic.

Hispaniola least pauraque (*Siphonorhis americanus brewsteri*). Limited to a few localities on the main island and on Gouave Island.

Puerto Rico

Few islands of the West Indies have been so drastically altered since the European occupation as Puerto Rico. During the nineteenth century its rich forests and other habitats were destroyed almost everywhere. This had a disturbing effect on agriculture, the water table, local climate, and so forth. During the 1920's the United States authorities began forest restoration and today there is probably no other Caribbean area where man has worked so hard and effectively to repair the damage done by earlier generations. Forests have regained a considerable acreage and cover about a quarter of Puerto Rico. About 1 percent of the forests are still primeval, rich in species and abounding in tree ferns. In these forests most of the island's threatened animals have found a refuge. However, the following species had already become extinct by the time wildlife restoration was begun:

A large shrew (*Nesophontes edithae*). Presumably extinct since the early sixteenth century.

Puerto Rico long-nosed bat (*Monophyllus frater*). Probably extinct since the eighteenth or nineteenth century.

A fruit bat (*Stenoderma rufum*). Extinct since the eighteenth or nineteenth century.

Puerto Rico long-tongued bat (*Phyllonycteris major*). Probably extinct since the eighteenth century.

Smaller Puerto Rico ground sloth (*Acratocnus odontrigonus*). Disappeared in historic time, probably before the arrival of Europeans.

Larger Puerto Rico ground sloth (*A. major*). Disappeared probably before the arrival of Europeans.

Puerto Rico isolobodon (*Isolobodon portoricensis*). Probably abundant in Puerto Rico, the Virgin Islands, and Hispaniola as late as the European occupation, but then soon became extinct.

Two agoutilike rodents (*Heteropsomys insulans* and *Homopsomys antillensis*). Probably extinct before the arrival of Europeans.

A hystricomorph rodent, *Heptaxodon bidens*. Probably extinct after the arrival of Europeans.

Puerto Rican quemi (*Elasmodontys obliquus*). The largest rodent of Puerto Rico. Probably extinct before the arrival of Europeans.

Puerto Rico conure (*Aratinga chloroptera maugei*). Extinct since about 1892.

The following birds were until recently close to extinction and are still very rare:

Puerto Rico plain pigeon (*Columba inornata wetmorei*). Considered extinct after 1927 but rediscovered in 1961.

Puerto Rico parrot (*Amazona vittata vittata*). The establishment of the Loquillo National Forest saved this species from extinction or at least delayed its disappearance. I visited Loquillo in 1963 and 1965 and observed this parrot in small numbers during both years. In 1966 the population was estimated at about 150 birds. In 1969 a census gave 124 birds, but in 1970 only a little more than twenty of them remained, which indicates a population crash. In 1971 there were probably not more than fifteen to twenty parrots.

Puerto Rico short-eared owl (*Asio flammeus portoricensis*). Extremely rare and last observed in 1942.

Puerto Rico whippoorwill (*Caprimulgus vociferus noctitherus*). Considered extinct after 1911 but rediscovered in 1961.

Elfin Woods warbler (*Dendroica angelae*). Discovered in 1971 in the Loquillo National Forest, where the population probably does not exceed 300 pairs. These birds are restricted to a habitat of high elevation comprising an area of about 450 hectares.

Puerto Rico bullfinch (*Loxigilla portoricensis portoricensis*). Extremely rare, decreasing, and confined to the mountain forest of El Yunque, where I observed it in 1965.

Other Caribbean Islands

Culebra, near the eastern coast of Puerto Rico, was the home of a parrot (*Amazona vittata gracilipes*) that became extinct about 1899.

St. Thomas, in the Virgin Islands, has an endemic screech owl (*Otus nudipes newtoni*) that is very rare and probably vulnerable to habitat destruction.

St. Croix, also in the Virgin Islands, was thought to have lost its endemic ground lizard (*Ameiva polops*) during the early twentieth century. However, in the 1960's a small colony was found in Frederiksted on the west coast, where it still occurred in 1968. This lizard also persists in low numbers on two islets off St. Croix, Protestant Cay, with about two hundred individuals, and Green Cay, with about three hundred. The former islet is undergoing hotel development, while Green Cay is undeveloped. Probably the species once occurred also on nearby Buck Island, which is now a reserve, but became exterminated there by the Indian mongoose, which was introduced in 1884. As a conservation effort sixteen ground lizards were released on Buck Island in 1968. By 1970 they had increased to at least twenty-four individuals.

Anegada of the British Virgin Islands has an endemic species of iguana (*Cyclura pinguis*) that is menaced by tourist development.

St. Christopher Island, in the Lesser Antilles, lost an endemic bullfinch (*Loxigilla portoricensis grandis*) about 1880, probably because of the introduction of African vervet monkeys.

Barbuda Island, in the Leeward Islands, lost the Barbuda muskrat (*Negalomys audeyae*), probably soon after the European occupation.

Antigua lost its burrowing owl (*Speotyto cunicularia amaura*) about 1890.

Guadeloupe, the Lesser Antilles, has lost the following birds:

> Guadeloupe conure (*Aratinga labati*). Extinct since early eighteenth century.
> Guadeloupe parrot (*Amazona violacea*). Extinct since the early eighteenth century.
> Guadeloupe red macaw (*Ara guadeloupensis*). Extinct since the early eighteenth century.
> Guadeloupe violet macaw (*A. purpurascens*). Extinct about 1640.
> Guadeloupe burrowing owl (*Speotyto cunicularia guadeloupensis*). Extinct since about 1890.
> Very rare is the Guadeloupe house wren (*Troglodytes aëdon guadeloupensis*), which was thought to be extinct since about 1914. It was rediscovered in 1969.

The montane forests of the island of *Dominica,* between Guadeloupe and Martinique, have been somewhat less subject to damage than other islands of the Lesser Antilles. Therefore, Dominica harbours the only large extent of tropical rain forest in the Lesser Antilles. Nevertheless the following animal species have been exterminated there or are endangered there:

> Dominica green and yellow macaw (*Ara atwoodi*). Extinct since the early eighteenth century, probably about 1791.
> Imperial parrot (*Amazona imperialis*). Restricted to high mountains, where it is rare and declining in numbers owing to deforestation and hunting.

For *Martinique* the record is as follows:

Martinique muskrat (*Megalomys desmarestii*). Extinct since the end of the nineteenth century.

Martinique parrot (*Amazona martinicana*). Extinct since the early eighteenth century, probably about 1722.

Martinique macaw (*Ara martinica*). Extinct since about 1658. Another macaw, *A. erythrura,* possibly another name for *A. martinica,* is said to have been seen shortly before 1658.

Martinique house wren (*Troglodytes aëdon martinicensis*). Exinct since about 1886.

Martinique brown trembler (*Cinclocerthia ruficauda gutturalis*). Perhaps already extinct. In 1964 a few pair were seen but later in the year they disappeared.

Martinique white-breasted thrasher (*Ramphocinclus brachyurus brachyurus*). Restricted to one locality. Not seen after 1886 until rediscovery in 1950.

The snake *Dromicus cursor* has long been considered extinct but it was found in 1962.

St. Lucia has suffered the following:

St. Lucia muskrat (*Megalomys luciae*). Extinct since the end of the nineteenth century.

St. Lucia parrot (*Amazona versicolor*). The only parrot on the island, it has declined rapidly owing to destruction of forests and killing despite protection by law.

St. Lucia forest thrush (*Cichlherminia l'herminieri sanctae-luciae*). Extremely rare. Not observed since 1968. The decline is caused by predation by introduced mongooses.

St. Lucia wren (*Troglodytes aëdon mesoleucus*). Restricted to one area and near extinction.

St. Lucia white-breasted thrasher (*Ramphocinclus brachyurus sanctae-luciae*). Restricted to one area and near extinction.

Semper's warbler (*Leucopeza semperi*). Extremely rare. Last collected in 1932, last seen in 1947, and last heard in 1962.

On *Barbados* the local yellow warbler (*Dendroica petechia petechia*) has decreased in the last decade to a dangerously low level and is now found only in two or three localities.

The "black list" from *St. Vincent* is as follows:

St. Vincent rice rat (*Oryzomys victus*). Extinct since about 1897.

St. Vincent parrot (*Amazona guildingii*). The only parrot on the island, it has decreased in numbers through forest destruction and intensive hunting.

St. Vincent wren (*Troglodytes aëdon musicus*). Extremely rare and near extinction until recent years, when a sudden increase took place.

St. Vincent thrush (*Myadestes genibarbis sibilans*). Last reported in 1950.

Grenada, the southernmost of the British Windward Islands, is much cultivated in the lowlands, while the hills and the valleys of the interior are covered by rain forests that show the effects of violent hurricanes. Its record follows:

Grenada hook-billed kite (*Chondrohierax uncinatus mirus*). This endemic species is extremely rare and is in danger of extinction. It is specialized in its feeding, preying chiefly on giant land snails, which are decreasing.

Grenada dove (*Leptotila wellsi*). An endemic species that is very near extinction, probably owing to habitat destruction.

Euler's flycatcher (*Empidonax euleri johnstonei*). Also peculiar to Grenada, it has been observed only once in this century.

Trinidad, off Venezuela, is zoogeographically more related to continental South America than to the West Indies. Habitats are diverse, from lowlands to mountains. In the remaining dense forests lives the white-headed curassow (*Pipile pipile pipile*), which is endemic in Trinidad, very rare, and decreasing.

Bonaire in the Netherlands Antilles and the Venezuelan island of *Blanquilla* are homes of the yellow-winged parrot (*Amazona barbadensis rotschildi*), which in Bonaire breeds with only about fifty pairs. They are threatened by persecution.

CENTRAL AMERICA

Central America has probably had its present form for about the last two million years. Whether it was previously a peninsula of North America, an island, or a chain of islands is still open to question. Although parts of Central America are thus young lands, man has misused the land earlier than elsewhere in the Americas. Guatemala saw the pre-Mayan culture rise in the fifth century, prosper for almost six hundred years, then decline and fall. There are many explanations of this, but the ecological factors seem to have predominated. The deforestation and agricultural methods of the Mayas apparently so impoverished the country that it could not support a large human population. Thus a splendid civilization and a mighty kingdom disappeared.

Central America is situated almost entirely within a region that in its natural state is dominated by tropical forests and scrub. Much of this forest is now gone or has been greatly modified. Some of it remains in the lowland, some in mountainous country. Fortunately there are plenty of mountains in Central America, some of them covered by wonderful cloud forests partly protected by steep slopes and rain forests with a rich animal life, but the original habitats diminish steadily, the forests cleared and burned and the marshes drained. Much of this is unavoidable, but much is also the result of carelessness and ignorance of proper land use and wildlife management.

The destruction of habitats in Central America has, as far as we know, not yet led to the total extermination of any animal species, but several are endangered. One of them is Baird's tapir (*Tapirus bairdii*), which is intimately associated with virgin rain forest in the vicinity of rivers, marshes, and lakes. Formerly it occurred from Mexico to Ecuador west of the Andes, but because of habitat destruction and hunting pressure it has been exterminated in much of its original range, so that it is now restricted to some remote, undisturbed forests of southeastern Mexico, Panama, northwestern Colombia, and western Ecuador. Perhaps it also still exists in other Central American countries. Strictly protected rain forest reserves seem to be the only way to preserve a species that is an important food resource.

Certain birds are also menaced in Central America. The population of the Lake Atitlán grebe (*Podilymbus gigas*), consisting of about eighty-five birds in 1965, is restricted to a single lake in Guatemala, where it is threatened by introduced largemouth bass, human predation, and habitat destruction. However, recent efforts of conservation work seemed in 1968 to have turned the decrease of this grebe to a slight increase. In 1969 this trend continued and the number rose to 130 birds. Another marsh bird, the Nicaragua grackle (*Cassidix nicaraguensis*), is very rare and is confined to the shores of lakes Nicaragua and Managua in Nicaragua. The yellow-green sparrow (*Pselliophorus luteoviridis*) from Cheriqué, Panama, is also extremely rare and is, in fact, known from only one specimen. The famous quetzal (*Pharomachurus mocinno*), the sacred bird of the Aztecs and the national bird of Guatemala, is threatened by the rapid destruction of its cloud-forest habitats, which are shared by another endangered bird, the horned guan (mentioned in the section about Mexico, page 201). The Cocos Island finch (*Pinaroloxias inornata*) is confined to the Costa Rican island of Cocos.

The second rarest crocodile in America, Morelet's crocodile (*Crocodylus moreleti*), is confined to Yucatan. Formerly it occurred also in Guatemala and British Honduras. This crocodile was long thought to be extinct but it was rediscovered in the 1920's. It has unfortunately been rapidly exterminated in one locality after the other, the victim of excessive exploitation for hides, and its future looks very dark. Attempts to breed the species in captivity are going on in Mexico, where in 1971 fourteen specimens were kept for this purpose. Obviously it would be much more effective for the species' reproduction to protect it strictly on its natural breeding grounds.

THE TROPICAL SELVAS OF SOUTH AMERICA

The South American rain forest is the largest tropical forest of the world. It covers much of the immense plain of the Amazon basin, but is drained not only by this river but also partly by the Orinoco and La Plata river systems. It extends westward to the slopes of the Andes, where it changes to other types of forest. This rain forest supports thousands of plants and animals, including at least 2,500 species of trees. The equatorial rain forest in South America is very similar in structure to those in Africa and Asia, but very different in species.

The vast tropical selva of the Amazon has so far been relatively little disturbed by man, but anyone who travels along the main watercourses may get a quite different impression. There the forest has been destroyed, and what the river traveller sees of the selva is often only a cleared, seasonally flooded zone of shores where the animal life is poor.

In addition to the river courses, the Amazonian forests of Brazil in particular are increasingly traversed by roads and even a four-thousand-kilometer highway is transecting the Amazonas. These routes open up the forest country to timber and mineral exploiters, hunters and collectors for skins and pets, livestock, farming, and other activities which will destroy vast areas of the Amazonian rain forests. According to investigations, 70 percent of the animal species living in these primary forests will vanish when their habitats are transformed into secondary growths. The destruction also leads to the deterioration of waters and soils from erosion, sedimentation, and laterization. It might also be the end of many tribes of Indians which here, for thousand of years, have utilized the environment without destroying it.

Several arboreal, terrestrial, semiaquatic and aquatic mammal species peculiar to the lowland rain forest of South America are at the moment threatened. All three existing species of uakaris, monkeys living in the treetops of the Amazonian forest and having a restricted range, are very rare and at least locally endangered. The bald uakari (*Cacajao calvus*) inhabits western Brazil, the red uakari (*C. rubicundus*) western Brazil and eastern Peru, and the black-headed uakari (*C. melanocephalus*) a narrow strip along Rio Negro. Other monkeys which show a numerical decline are the white-nosed saki (*Chiropotes albinasus*) in Brazil, and the woolly spider monkey (*Brachyteles arachnoides*) in southeastern Brazil, rarest of South American primates. Goeldi's tamarin (*Callimico goeldii*) in western Brazil and Peru, the golden-headed tamarin (*Leontideus chrysomelas*), the golden lion marmoset (*L. rosalia*), and the golden-rumped tamarin (*L. chrysopygus*) in eastern Brazil are other monkeys with an insecure future. The wild population of the golden lion marmoset now occurs only in a shrinking forest in eastern Brazil. The population is estimated at fewer than one thousand, and the one of the golden-headed tamarin at less than five hundred, while the golden-rumped tamarin exists with about one hundred individuals. Extensive deforestation and collecting for trade are the main reasons for the decrease of these monkeys.

Though the smaller South American forest cats have immense areas in which to roam, some species have become rare and are rapidly decreasing owing to man's reckless hunting. The spotted cats are at least locally in danger because their fur is so attractive and in great demand throughout the world. The ocelot (*Felis pardalis*), the little spotted cat (*F. tigrina*), and the margay (*F. wiedi*) have their main range in the rain forests, but the ocelot and the margay go northward to Mexico and Texas. These three cats are the most threatened of the nine South American species of the genus *Felis*. In many districts the jaguar (*Panthera onca*) has also completely disappeared. The small-eared dog (*Atelocynus microtis*) is a very rare carnivore of the Amazon, where it may be endangered. Rapidly approaching extinction is also the giant anteater (*Myrmecophaga tridactyla*), owing to heavy persecution. Another very rare and endangered species is the Brazilian three-toed sloth (*Bradypus torquatus*) from Brazil.

The semiaquatic and aquatic species of the rain forests will be dealt with in the section on lakes and rivers. Several rain-forest birds are apparently very rare, but in such an immense area the status of these birds is not definitely known. The red-billed curassow (*Crax blumenbachi*) has been seriously depleted owing to forest destruction and predation by hunters. About fifty birds survive in a small, partly artificial reserve in Brazil. It is doubtful whether the species still exists in the wild. Other forest birds on the list of endangered or extremely rare species are: the black-headed tinamou (*Crypturellus atrocapillus*) from Peru; the barred tinamou (*C. casiquiare*) from only one area in Venezuela; the pygmy swift (*Micropanyptila furcata*) from the Lake Maracaibo area in Venezuela; the yellow-throated oriole (*Icterus xantholemus*) from Ecuador; the Honda oriole (*I. hondae*) from the Magdalena valley in Colombia; Simon's atlapetes (*Atlapetes simonsi*) and Celica atlapetes (*A. celicae*) from Ecuador; the buff-throated ground finch (*Embernagra longicauda,* a somewhat doubtful species, known only from one specimen) of unknown distribution. Moreover, there are twenty-one species of hummingbirds representing fourteen genera, of which little is known except that they all seem to have a very restricted distribution.

THE TROPICAL LLANOS AND CAMPOS

The llanos of South America are tropical and subtropical savannas of two types: bunch grass savannas composed chiefly of such grasses as *Hyparrhenia rufa* and *Andropogon condensatus,* with scattered trees or groups of trees; and high grass savannas, dominated by the tall *Paspalum fasciculatum.* The forest bordering the llanos is in the main of a dry deciduous type, generally important for the animals of the area. The largest true savanna areas of South America are the llanos in Venezuela, but Colombia, Bolivia, Brazil, Paraguay, and Argentina also have typical llanos. The vegetation of most llanos seems to be greatly affected by periodic fires, and probably corresponds to a fire-climax habitat, at least on some soils. This presents a parallel to many African savannas, and like them the South American llanos are in some parts heavily overgrazed by cattle.

A large part of the Brazilian planalto, including Paraguay, Uruguay, Argentina, and Bolivia, is occupied by drier savannas or arid brushlands, or sclerophyll woodlands and forests. These habitats, depending on their character are called montes, campos, or caatingas. The campos and montes have a larger distribution in South America than any other tropical grasslands and include a wide range of open habitats, from temporarily flooded grasslands to very dry, steppelike areas. Some campos remain under water during much of the year; others are treeless expanses; and still others are patched with woods and junglelike forests. Many campos penetrate deep into the rain forests, while some are entirely isolated within the selvas. Areas such as the Mato Grosso in Brazil and the Gran Chaco in Argentina and Paraguay are essentially campo savannas (brushlands), but their proximity to the Amazon rain forests and the Andean slopes influences them a great deal. The Gran Chaco, for example, is during much of the year an extremely hot semidesert where the winds whirl up clouds of dust, and only cactus that grows from twenty to thirty feet high and xerophilous trees up to sixty feet high seem to survive. But in the summer the area is transformed into an immense, mosquito-infested swamp, flooded by rains and swollen streams from the melting snows of the Andes and the cloud forests. The Gran Chaco is truly a place of contrasts.

The caatingas occupy areas both in and outside the rain-forest region. There are both evergreen caatingas and deciduous caatingas. The former seem to be determined by soils which are poor in nutrients and deficient in water, while the latter respond to areas having soils characterized by nutritional elements and a climate of severe dry seasons where evapotranspiration exceeds precipitation.

The giant armadillo (*Priodontes giganteus*) is a species that in the past had a vast range, but is now found chiefly on the monte and campo llanos, where it lives at the edge of primeval forests. Formerly distributed over the plains and woods of tropical and subtropical South America, it is today restricted to a few scattered areas from southeastern Venezuela and the Guianas, across Brazil to northern Argentina, Bolivia, and Paraguay. But everywhere the giant armadillo is very rare and declining in numbers. Man does not eat it in some regions, but he does so in others. The main threat to this species comes from deforestation and other habitat changes. Like edentates that have already vanished, the giant armadillo seems to be opposed by natural factors which we do not understand.

Three other armadillos show a pronounced decline, perhaps caused by the gradual cultivation of their habitats as well as hunting pressure. One is the greater pichiciego (*Burmeisteria retusa*) from the Chaco region; a second is the lesser pichiciego (*Chlamyphorus truncatus*) from central Argentina; and a third is the Brazilian three-banded armadillo (*Tolypeutes tricinctus*) from northeastern Brazil.

One of the most characteristic mammals of the campos but now rare in many districts or already gone is the maned wolf (*Chrysocyon brachyurus*), a slender animal with long, almost stiltlike legs. It occurs in parts of Brazil, eastern and northern Bolivia, Paraguay, northern Argentina, but it seems to be diminishing rapidly in numbers. A canine that has very short legs is the bush dog (*Speothos venaticus*), a wild dog with one relative in Asia. It lives in woods and savannas from Panama in the north to Paraguay in the south but is rare everywhere within its wide range. The thin-spined porcupine (*Chaetomys subspinosus*), which only exists in southeastern Bahia, Brazil, is menaced by rapid deforestation.

The Colombian red-eyed cowbird (*Tangavius armenti*) seems to be confined to the llanos of southernmost Colombia. It was thought to be extinct because no specimen had been reported since 1866, but it was rediscovered in 1956. A very rare and perhaps endangered savanna bird is Baer's cardinal (*Paroaria baeri*) from Goiás, Brazil.

THE PAMPAS

The pampas of Argentina are among the most fertile areas of South America from a cultivator's point of view, but the intensive cultivation has caused the retreat of several animals. The pampas are a sea of grass—immense plains without trees or hills. Many kinds of grasses grow there in tussocks, and several of them are green throughout the year, but compared with the overwhelming animal richness of the African grassland, the pampas are poor in wildlife. There are several characteristic species, but few of them live in herds. Peculiar to the pampas are its many species of rather large rodents.

Today much of the tall pampas grass has disappeared and with it the habitats of some wild animals. Several species have been reduced to only a fraction of their former population. Most in danger is the pampas deer (*Ozotoceros bezoarticus*). It was once common not only on the Argentine pampas (including the steppes of Patagonia) but also on the campos of Uruguay, Paraguay, Bolivia, and Brazil. It still occurs in this area, and is even common in certain districts, but in general it is very rare and decreasing in numbers as a result of habitat destruction, overhunting, and diseases transmitted by cattle. Moreover, this little deer does not seem to tolerate human disturbances. Once the tall grass of the pampas is gone, it has no shelter and is forced to live in the open, which has caused it to develop an extraordinary shyness. The pampas deer is protected in Argentina but since there is no control, this measure does not seem to have had any effect. There are three races and all are threatened.

The pampas deer often used to graze or browse in association with the common rhea (*Rhea americana*), an American ostrich that has decreased considerably because of the same factors affecting its mammalian associate on the pampas. The pampas gerbil (*Reinthrodon physodes*), a small rodent of the open plains, has also declined greatly and is on the verge of vanishing completely.

THE SIERRAS OF THE ANDES

The Andes form a western border for the whole of South America and are a formidable barrier separating the Pacific Ocean and its shores from the interior of the continent. Among the mountain chains of the world the Andes are second only to the Himalayas in height.

The Andean highlands are almost a world unto themselves. Great valleys, plains, slopes, and cordilleras divide this enormous chain, with its tremendously high peaks, transversely as well as from north to south. The range of climate as well as of vegetation is very wide not only because of the extreme variations in altitude from the ocean shore to Aconcagua's 22,867-foot peak but also because of the range in latitudes from the Caribbean in the north to Tierra del Fuego in the south. Moreover, the forest formations and plant communities on the western and eastern sides of the Andes are different because of differences in the climate. Roughly, the climatic belts of the Andes can be distinguished as tropical up to 4,500 feet, subtropical to 10,500 feet, and temperate up to twelve thousand feet.

Many areas of the Andes were colonized by man at an early period. In the vicinity of Peru the Incas developed a system of irrigation agriculture; thus valleys, plains, slopes, and wildlife were already being modified by man in pre-Columbian days. When the Spaniards reached South America the llama (*Lama peruana*) and the alpaca (*L. pacos*) were already domesticated. Whether they are true species or domesticated forms deriving from the guanaco (*L. guanacoe*) is difficult to say, since the llama and the alpaca apparently have lived in domestication so long that they have lost certain characteristics. However, the wild herds of the vicuña (*Vicugna vicugna*) and the guanaco, which were abundant in the Andes, had enough grazing land despite cultivation and grazing by domestic relatives, but when European man arrived with his firearms the herds were considerably reduced. Conservation measures have, however, changed the rate of decline, but the guanaco is still in imminent danger of extinction due to hunting. The total Peruvian population still hardly exceeds five thousand animals.

The vicuña is also threatened despite the Peruvian government's having taken up measures to conserve it. Hunting vicuña and trading or exporting vicuña have been strictly prohibited in Peru since 1920, and in Bolivia the killing of vicuña and wool trading are also forbidden. In 1969 Peru issued one of the toughest conservation laws ever proclaimed: three years in jail—no bail—for trading vicuña wool. Nevertheless, there is a big illegal trade going on. Unfortunately, there are no restrictions except in the U. S. and Great Britain on the import of vicuña wool although governments and importers know that it is obtained illegally from poached animals. In Peru an 125,000-acre reserve twelve thousand feet up in the mountains was set aside in 1966. Two years earlier a herd of some one thousand vicuña was discovered there, the largest concentration of this species in South America.

Between 1950 and 1970, about 400,000 vicuñas were killed. In 1957 the whole vicuña population was estimated at about 400,000, with about 250,000 in Peru. In 1966 these figures had dropped to about eight thousand vicuñas in Peru and 1,500 in Bolivia. Two years later there were five to ten thousand in Peru and one thousand to 1,500 in Bolivia, and a few herds in Chile and Argentina. The total in these last two countries was in 1971 about one hundred individuals. In Ecuador the vicuña is almost exterminated. In 1970 the total population was estimated at less than ten thousand animals. The largest single concentration of vicuñas is in Reserva Nacional de Pampa Galeras in Peru, which held 1,079 animals in 1970. With the vicuñas living in surrounding areas of the reserve the total is over 4,500.

Another Andean animal of great economic importance is the chinchilla (*Chinchilla laniger*), a rodent that is famous for its valuable fur. It is a highland species, formerly widely distributed in the Andes from Peru and Bolivia to Chile and Argentina. It occurred in three races, of which one, *C. l. brevicauda,* from Peru, is probably already extinct; while another, *C. l. boliviana,* from the eastern Andes of southern Bolivia and northern Argentina, is on the verge of extinction if not already extinct; and the third, *C. l. laniger,* from the western Andes in northern Chile, is also declining in number.

Once chinchillas were extremely abundant and could be seen in the thousands during a single day. The Incas used chinchilla as furs, but it was not until these pelts were introduced into Europe that the demand increased tremendously. In 1905 alone, 217,836 pelts were checked by the customs office of one city alone, Coquimbo in Chile; a year later the number dropped to about half that, and by 1909 the figure was 27,936 and the price was five hundred dollars for a dozen pelts. Since then it has been increasingly difficult to catch chinchillas, but the trappers continue to do their work without regard for the breeding periods of the species and laws protecting the animal.

If no effective measures are taken immediately, the wild chinchilla will disappear. However, chinchilla farms have been established, chiefly in Chile and the United States but also in Europe. Fortunately the species breeds very well in captivity and there are probably more than ten thousand animals in the United States alone. Most of the captive stock belongs to the Chilean race (*C. l. laniger*), but the Bolivian chinchilla (*C. l. boliviana*) was imported in the 1930's, so the races may have become mixed. If not exterminated, wild chinchillas would doubtless in the long run produce more valuable pelts than do the captive animals. It would therefore be economically wise to preserve the species in the wild state.

The spectacled bear (*Tremarctos ornatus*), the only represent-

ative of the bear family in South America, is distributed in the
Andes from Venezuela and Colombia to southern Peru and southwestern Bolivia. It inhabits cloud and rain forests in the subtropical
and temperate zones of the Andes, but also visits habitats above
and below the forest-covered slopes of the mountains. It seems to
be disappearing from Venezuela and Colombia, and almost all
recent reports of it have come from Ecuador and northern Peru.
The total Peruvian population is less than two thousand animals.
Despite its great ecological adaptability this bear is now very rare
all over its range and seems to be facing extermination, chiefly due
to persecution by man.

The mountain tapir (*Tapirus pinchaque*) is another of South
America's larger mammals threatened by extinction. At present it
occurs in the Andean forests and the adjacent grasslands of Colombia and Ecuador, and a very few turn up in a restricted part
of northern Peru, where the population cannot number more than
one to two hundred individuals. It is perhaps also in Venezuela.
Its decline has been very rapid as a result of deforestation, cultivation, and hunting. No measures whatsoever have been taken to
protect it although it could easily be utilized as a food resource.

The pudu (*Pudu pudu*) is a little deer that occurs in the Andes,
found in the temperate zone of southern Chile and Argentina
southward to the Straits of Magellan. It is also found on the island
of Chiloé. Despite the pudu's wide range its status has been critical since the 1940's because it is intensively hunted. It is now
protected within the Nahuel National Park in Argentina. The Ecuadorian pudu (*P. mephistophiles*), even rarer than its relative,
seems to be limited to the Papallacta area of the Ecuadorian
Andes, and in Peru, where it will not survive for much longer
unless the hunting is restricted. Two other species of deer that
occur in the Andean forests and grassy hills are very rare and endangered. The huemul (*Hippocamelus antisensis*) ranges in the
Andes of Ecuador, Peru, Bolivia, and northern Chile, while the
southern species (*H. bisulcus*) is restricted to the Andes of southern Chile and Patagonia. The latter is locally not uncommon in
Argentina.

Five birds of the Andes or nearby sierras are also extremely
rare. Sclater's spinetail (*Asthenes sclateri*) is known only from the
Sierra de Córdoba, an Argentinian offshot of the Andes, where it
is near extinction or may already be extinct. Garlepp's mountain
finch (*Compsospiza garleppi*) from Vacas in Bolivia, and Baer's

mountain finch (*C. baeri*) from the sierra of Tucumán in Argentina have very restricted ranges.

PATAGONIA AND TIERRA DEL FUEGO

Temperate forests, steppes, deserts, and subantarctic moors are the major vegetation types of Patagonia and Tierra del Fuego, the southernmost regions of South America. But the biotic zones are even more various, owing to differences in altitude and climate south of 40° S. latitude. As one moves south from Chile to the region south of the Strait of Magellan, the vegetation changes from forests consisting of many trees covered with epiphytes and lianas to areas where the tree species are few, about 50 percent of the forests being composed of southern beeches (*Nothofagus*). Some epiphytes still appear in the latter area but the lianas have given up. The fauna diminishes in the same way. Large areas of Patagonia consist of temperate pampas which formerly were rich grasslands, but where ignorance or carelessness by the cultivators has led to a serious degradation of the soil. It is chiefly as pastures for cattle that the pampas are valuable to man, but this resource has declined because of overgrazing. The vegetation has disappeared over large areas, erosion has set in, and dust fills the air. The herds of guanacos which once roamed the Patagonian pampas have been greatly reduced.

Southern South America lies nearer to Antarctica than does any other continent, and Tierra del Fuego is thus bitterly cold, with glaciers covering the mountains of the archipelago, and mists and clouds often sweeping around them.

It was in Patagonia that a remarkable mammal was exterminated, the Patagonian giant ground sloth (*Glypotherium listai*). This species still existed in Patagonia after the coming of man. No white man has ever seen this sloth alive, but large pieces of rather fresh skin and broken bones were found in a large cavern in southern Patagonia in 1898 and subsequently. It is believed that this cavern had served as a corral where the sloth had been kept and fed by man.

Kleinschmidt's falcon (*Falco kreyenborgi*) is the rarest bird breeding in the southwesternmost part of the Strait of Magellan. It appears in Tierra del Fuego and Patagonia during the winter. It is known only from four specimens from two localities there and from one in the Rio Negro province in Argentina.

LAKES, MARSHES, AND RIVERS

There are many marshlands and swamps and thousands of rivers
in South and Central America, but the number of lakes is not as
great as in North America. Drainage and reclamation of lakes as
well as marsh and slough areas have eliminated many of the wetlands of South America. This has, of course, affected not only
migratory waterfowl, which had their winter quarters in Central
or South America, but also sedentary species among mammals,
passerine birds, and reptiles.

Several aquatic and semiaquatic mammals of South America
have been greatly reduced by reckless hunting. The largest of the
South American deer, the swamp deer (*Blastocerus dichotomus*),
belongs in this category. It lives in swamps, wet grasslands, and
temporarily inundated forests in British Guiana, Brazil, Paraguay,
Bolivia, Uruguay, and Argentina. It is much persecuted by the natives because they esteem it highly as food and because medicines
and aphrodisiacs are prepared from the antlers. Another vanishing
species is the giant otter (*Pteronura brasiliensis*), a commercially
valuable animal that occurs in rivers of Venezuela, British Guiana,
and Brazil as well as in the Peruvian Amazon southward to Paraguay, Bolivia, northeastern Argentina, and Uruguay. Except in
Bolivia and Venezuela this species has become so rare that it is
now difficult to obtain any pelts of it. In Peru the giant otter is
gone from most areas, a fact which is reflected by the decline in
export figures of skins from this country: in 1947 the export was
2,248 pelts, in 1957 1,006, and in 1966 210. It is not protected
even though its great commercial value would seem to make its
preservation worth a considerable effort. Also, the La Plata otter
(*Lutra platensis*) is rapidly decreasing owing to persecution. It
still occurs in southern Brazil, Paraguay, northern Argentina, and
Uruguay. The southern river otter (*L. provocax*) from Chile and
Argentina is endangered in Argentina owing to overexploitation,
while its situation in Chile seems to be a bit better.

The Amazonian manatee (*Trichechus inunguis*) has also been
severely persecuted, resulting in its drastic decline. It is confined
to the Amazon basin, where it was formerly found far up the
rivers of this immense system. The westernmost occurrence was at
Iquitos on the Ucayali in Peru, and in the south it went down to
19° S. latitude. It has now vanished from many rivers it formerly
occupied in the lower Amazon but it still survives in small numbers
in their upper reaches. It is protected by law, but since there is no

enforcement the manatee is constantly being speared, harpooned, and shot. Its meat is considered a delicacy and its hide is useful. Up until recently the meat was canned commercially near Manaus on the Amazon River, but this industry has now died out. Thus, the Amazon manatee is another example of the ruin of a valuable food resource. Effective protection combined with management measures could certainly restore the population to a level that would yield a considerable annual harvest.

Also, the Amazon River porpoise (*Inia geoffroyensis*) has practically disappeared from the river systems where its ubiquitous presence is a thing of the past. This decline is due to the industrial use of the skin, which has resulted in a tremendous overexploitation by fishermen. In Peru catching of this river porpoise was prohibited in 1969. Locally in Peru this dolphin is remarkably plentiful.

Commercially, the most important food resource of the Amazon and Orinoco river systems was probably the South American river turtle (*Podocnemis expansa*). During the 1650's it was said that people living in the regions where this turtle occurred "never knew what hunger was." The turtle was so numerous that in certain seasons it impeded the passage of canoes and smaller boats. This tremendous primary food resource has been utilized for more than three hundred years and was the basis of the economy along the river. The exploitation concentrated chiefly on the eggs, though the turtles themselves were hunted for meat and oil. The oil was used for lighting and as an edible fat. Without any consideration for the future of the animal, eggs were collected in heaps twenty feet high. The reckless exploitation, combined with destruction of the shores where this turtle nested, caused such a decline in its numbers that by the middle of the nineteenth century it had become rare all over its original range. Since then the river turtle has continued to decrease in numbers and distribution. Nesting is at present restricted to an area in the Trombetas River near Oriximiná (Brazil), where the species is still rather common; to remote headwaters of the Amazon and the Orinoco; and Bolivia's rivers Beni, Madre de Dios, and several others, but even in these the species is threatened.

Although the river turtle is protected in Venezuela and Brazil, the Venezuelan government only recently began to enforce the legislation. The government has also successfully introduced the species into Lake Valencia in the Andes, and artificial nesting beaches have been constructed. However, attempts to build up the

242 *Let Them Live*

populations in the Amazon and Orinoco river basins should be more systematic; they would then yield a much greater harvest without considerable investment.

Another river turtle, the Terecay turtle (*P. unifilis*), which at present occurs in Colombia but formerly also in Venezuela, the Guianas, and northern Brazil, has been the victim of the trade in hatchlings and the collecting of eggs, which yield an oil for cooking.

The spectacled caiman (*Caiman crocodilus crocodilus*) and the Magdalena spectacled caiman (*C. c. fuscus*) are both threatened by extinction and have locally already become extinct in large areas. The species is distributed in Colombia, Venezuela, the Guianas, and in parts of the lower Amazon River. The black caiman (*Melanosuchus niger*) also is in great danger of vanishing completely from its remaining range in Colombia, Ecuador, Peru, and Brazil. All over it is near extinction. Formerly it had a much wider distribution in the rivers of the Amazonian system. Excessive exploitation for hides and human consumption are the prime reasons for the decrease of these three caimans.

The Orinoco crocodile (*Crocodylus intermedius*) is almost gone in Venezuela and Colombia, its last area, after having become eliminated in the Amazon river system and in most of the Orinoco basin through excessive hunting for hides.

Several South American birds are restricted, each to a single lake, resulting in small populations very vulnerable to disturbance. We have already mentioned the Lake Atitlán grebe of Guatemala. Similarly, the Lake Junín grebe (*Podiceps taczanowskii*) is confined to one lake in Peru, and the flightless Titicaca grebe (*Rollandia microptera*) to Lake Titicaca in the high Andes of Bolivia and Peru. Lake Junín is increasingly polluted which kills many fish in the lake and therefore also threatens the Lake Junín grebe. The Andes are also the home of two species of flamingoes, James's flamingo (*Phoenicoparrus jamesi*) and the Andean flamingo (*P. andinus*). Both are limited to a few lakes high in the mountains. Their local distribution makes them vulnerable, but fortunately they breed in remote areas. However, Indians are hunting both species, which is a danger particularly to James's flamingo, which breeds only in Laguna Colorada at 14,000 feet in Bolivia. The Andes eared grebe (*Podiceps andinus*) is known from a few lakes in the Colombian Andes, where it is near extinction, apparently as a result of persistent hunting. The great horned coot (*Fulica cornuta*) is limited to small lakes above twelve thousand feet in the Andes of southern Bolivia, northern Chile, and northwestern Argentina.

Finally, Forbes' marsh bird (*Agelaius forbesi*), known only from one specimen from Pernambuco in Brazil, and perhaps a doubtful species, must be very rare if not already extinct.

Threatened fishes of South America are the following:

> *Cynolebias constanciae.* Exists in a single pond in eastern Brazil.
> *C. marmoratus.* Lives in ditches below the Organ Mountains, Brazil.
> *C. minimus.* Occurs in a few ditches near Rio de Janeiro.
> *C. opalescens.* Lives in ditches below the Organ Mountains, Brazil.
> *C. splendens.* Restricted to the same localities as *opalescens* and *marmoratus.*
> *Orestias cuvieri.* Only known from Lake Titicaca, where it is perhaps extinct and was not taken during the 1960's.

THE COASTS AND ISLANDS

There are thousands of islands along the coasts of South America. The Caribbean islands and Tierra del Fuego have already been dealt with, and such major groups of islands as the Galápagos, the Juan Fernández, and the Falklands will be treated in the chapter on the Oceanian islands. Of the other islands off South America, a few contain animals that have their last strongholds there.

The West Indian manatee (*Trichechus manatus manatus*) was formerly very abundant along the coasts and in the coastal rivers of the West Indies as well as of Central and South America eastward to the Guianas. In the seventeenth century manatees were so common in the Guianas that ships were specially chartered in Holland to hunt the animals and transport the meat to the West Indies. The species was also intensively hunted for skins and oil. Populations are still to be found along the coasts of Venezuela, Surinam, and British Guiana and locally in the West Indies and Central America, particularly British Honduras. Manatees are not only a food resource but they also clear canals and waterways of seeds and other aquatic vegetation whose growth is a menace to boat traffic.

The South American fur seal (*Arctocephalus australis gracilis*) has decreased sharply in numbers during recent decades and few people seem to be concerned with its preservation. Formerly it occurred along both the Pacific and the Atlantic coasts from the Strait of Magellan to Peru and Brazil. At present it is gone from

most coasts, particularly the Pacific, while the situation along the
eastern coast is somewhat better. The last refuges of this race are
in Uruguay. Various races of the colpeo fox (*Dusicyon culpaeus
culpaeus*), and particularly the Magellanic fox (*D. c. magellani-
cus*), inhabiting Patagonia, southern Chile, and Tierra del Fuego,
are extremely rare. This is also true of the Magellanic otter
(*Lutra felina*), which has disappeared from many coastal areas
from Peru to Tierra del Fuego. This marine and littoral otter is
in Peru estimated at two to three hundred animals, but seems to
be commoner in Chile.

The Tumaco seedeater (*Sporophila insulata*) is restricted to
Tumaco Island off southwestern Colombia, where the population
is probably very small. This also applies to the slender-billed vireo
(*Vireo gracilirostris*) from Fernando de Noronha off Brazil, to the
red-rumped ant-thrush (*Myrmotherula erythronotos*) from Nova
Friburgo, a province of Rio de Janeiro, and to the Masafuera
creeper (*Aphrastura masafuerae*) from small Masafuera Island
off Chile.

The story of the guanay cormorant (*Phalacrocorax bougain-
villii*) on islands in the Humboldt Current of the Pacific south of
the equator is well known. The populations of this cormorant, the
Peruvian booby (*Sula variegata*), and the brown pelican (*Pelecanus occidentalis*) breeding on the Chincha Islands are estimated
at four to five million birds. They base their existence on a super-
abundance of food provided by the sea. As far back as the Incas
the guano produced by these birds was used as fertilizer in agriculture, but it was not until the nineteenth century that the enormous accumulations of guano were industrially exploited. Between
1851 and 1871 about ten million tons of guano are estimated to
have been shipped from the Chincha Islands alone. By the end of
the nineteenth century there was hardly any guano left, and the
populations of cormorants, pelicans, and boobies had been so
depleted that the industry was ruined. Tens of thousands of
nestlings and even more eggs and nests had been destroyed by
workers on the islands. By 1909 the Peruvian government had
taken strong measures to protect not only the islands but also the
birds and their nests. Then guano export increased from year to
year. Between 1946 and 1950 the guano production was at the
highest level in fifty years and the bird population was estimated
to be about thirty-five million birds. The economic yield was
enormous.

Latterly a new menace to the guano birds has developed. Their staple food, the Peruvian anchovy (*Engraulis ringens*), has decreased considerably owing to overfishing. This fish normally lives in the waters of the Peruvian coastal current. It is one of the greatest fishing resources in the world, representing almost 18 percent of the total world production of fish.

Since 1955 the fishing industry off Peru has been operated by boats owned by multimillion-dollar companies as well as single owners. The sea birds indicate better than modern devices where shoals of fishes are to be found, causing a race of the fast boats to the fishing grounds and disturbing the birds' feeding. In addition, many birds are certainly drowned in the nets. However, it is the human overfishing of anchovies which has created a threat to the existence of the Peruvian sea birds and consequently to the guano industry.

In less than ten years the fisheries of the Peruvian anchovy increased from an annual catch of about two million tons to nine-and-a-half million tons. The fishing fleet utilizing this resource has increased to such an extent that the anchovy is overexploited, resulting in a reduction of the guano-producing fishing birds off Peru to about one-fifth of their former numbers. Guano production has gone down so far that Peru itself will be forced to import fertilizer. Moreover, the birds did not nest in the sanctuaries in 1966 and many of them, weakened by hunger, died from disease and starvation. However, this loss was partly due to another dramatic change.

In addition to the heavy fishing pressure on the anchovy, another factor from time to time drives away the fish from the coastal waters where the guano birds can catch them. A warm current mixes every few years with the cold Humboldt Current, killing the plankton en masse and driving the anchovies to greater depths. This is a catastrophe for the guano birds, especially since it takes about two years for the plankton populations to recover and the anchovy to return in previous numbers. In one such disaster for the guano birds, in 1957–58, over thirteen million birds died, that is, 64 percent of the total population. It took the bird populations eight years to grow from the low of five-and-a-half million after the plankton crash in 1957–58 to seventeen million in 1965. The same year saw a new crisis, and the guano birds decreased in one year from seventeen million to four million. Since then the birds have not increased, so the cycle regulating the food chain—plankton-anchovies-guano birds—has apparently been upset by a new, unknown factor. This is a dramatic situation and may not only threaten the birds but also jeopardize Peru's economy.

Normally the guano birds catch two to three million tons of anchovies every year. Hence the decrease in number of anchovies reduces the production of guano. This is an outstanding example of the relationship within a marine ecosystem in which man is in two ways a consumer of animal productivity. Conservation organizations have urged the Peruvian government to restrict any further increase in the fishing fleet. It would also be wise to introduce closed seasons, net limits, and catch quotas as well as other ecological management of the anchovy population.

BALANCE FOR SOUTH AMERICA

The record of exterminated or endangered vertebrates in South and Central America would not be so deplorable if the Caribbean area were excluded. We could then say that only the Patagonian giant ground sloth had been wiped out and that that had occurred shortly before the arrival of the Europeans. In addition, one mammal is by now probably extinct. The endangered animals would then include "only" forty-seven mammals, thirty-two birds, seven reptiles, and six fish. These figures are nothing to be proud of, but if the number of species exterminated and threatened in the Caribbean (in which we have included the Bahamas) is added, the statistics become frightful. In the Caribbean alone forty-two mammals and eighteen birds have become extinct in historical time. Three more birds and two reptiles are probably extinct. In addition, ten mammals, forty birds, and eleven reptiles—not counting the marine turtles—are seriously threatened. Among the continents not even Australia can rival this record of destruction.

With very few exceptions these extinctions have occurred after the arrival of Europeans in the Caribbean. It is a record that emphasizes how islands and their species of plants and animals are vulnerable to environmental disturbances such as habitat alterations by man and through introduced exotic animals, particularly mammals.

Not only from a scientific but also from an economic point of view, it is important to save the South American mammals and reptiles from becoming extinct. They are in general useful as a primary food resource, one that can convert terrestrial and aquatic vegetation into excellent meat, hides, and pelts. Scientifically, they as well as the birds are still little-known and represent many species that do not occur anywhere else.

Species and subspecies of vertebrates extinct during historic time, probably extinct, or at present endangered by extinction. (Figures within parentheses show extinctions after 1700.) In the table, the Bahamas are included in "Caribbean," and Central America in "South America."

Class	Extinct			Probably Extinct			Endangered		
	Caribbean	South America	Total	Caribbean	South America	Total	Caribbean	South America	Total
Mammals	42 (16)	1 (1)	43 (17)	–	1	1	10	47	57
Birds	18 (18)	–	18 (18)	3	–	3	40	32	72
Reptiles	–	–	–	2	–	2	11	7	18
Amphibians	–	–	–	–	–	–	–	–	–
Fish	–	–	–	–	–	–	–	6	6
Total	60 (34)	1 (1)	61 (35)	5	1	6	61	92	153

CHAPTER SIX

New Guinea, Australia, and New Zealand

Australasia, comprising New Guinea, Australia, and New Zealand, extends from the equator to 50° S. latitude. It ranges from tropical to temperate regions and covers a wide spectrum of habitats from rain forest to deserts and high mountains.

Australasia seems to have been isolated by water barriers longer and more effectively than any other continent, except perhaps for Antarctica. This explains why it is so rich in unique animals of great scientific interest. However, the three island blocks have quite different geological histories. New Guinea functioned as a bridge for animal migration between Asia and Australia. Geologically, it is less stable than Australia and its mountains seem to be rather young. Except for several marine invasions, Australia seems to have been geologically stable at least since the late Paleozoic, that is, for about 300 million years—long before the appearance of mammals. New Zealand is the most isolated of all the three areas, and there is no evidence that it has been connected with Australia or Antarctica. If it was ever connected with another landmass, it was probably Antarctica, but before recent vertebrates could make use of the connection.

Compared with prehistoric man in Africa and Asia, man entered New Guinea and Australia relatively late, arriving on the Australian scene about eleven thousand years ago. (Recently it has been suggested that man may have penetrated Australia more than thirty-one thousand years ago.) The Maoris reached New Zealand only about one thousand years ago. But the tremendous destruction of habitats and animal life did not begin until the arrival of the Europeans in Australia and New Zealand nearly two hundred years ago. Paradoxically, of the three areas discussed here, it is on New Guinea, where man has been present longest, that nature has been least affected by human influence. In fact, in its interior, New Guinea is to a great extent a virgin island, one of the last large natural areas of the world that is still untouched.

ANIMAL FAMILIES PECULIAR TO AUSTRALASIA

In terms of animal distribution, New Guinea and Australia belong to the Australian region. Although New Zealand lies about one thousand miles from Australia, we include it as part of the Australasian region. The vertebrate fauna of this region represents several ancient elements that do not exist elsewhere. They came from Asia a long time ago, were geographically isolated, and survived after their Asian ancestors died out. They then evolved and radiated into many different species which adapted to local habitats. The great specialization and differentiation of the marsupials is an outstanding example among mammals of such evolution and adaptation. They have filled habitats that on other continents are occupied by a large number of placental mammals of various other classes: primates, rodents, carnivores, and ungulates.

There are eight families of mammals peculiar to Australasia: echidnas (*Tachyglossidae*), the platypus (*Ornithorhynchidae*), marsupial mice, cats, and others (*Dasyuridae*), marsupial moles (*Notoryctidae*), bandicoots (*Peramelidae*), wombats (*Phascolomidae*), kangaroos, wallabies, rat kangaroos and others (*Macropodidae*), and finally a family of insectivorous bats (*Mystacinidae*) with one species from New Zealand.

Of the birds, several endemic families have evolved: cassowaries (*Casuariidae*), emus (*Dromaiidae*), New Zealand wrens (*Xenicidae*), lyrebirds (*Menuridae*), scrubbirds (*Atrichornithidae*), Australian tree creepers (*Climacteridae*), Australian magpies (*Cracticidae*), magpie larks (*Grallinidae*), wattlebirds (*Callaeidae*), bowerbirds (*Ptilorhynchidae*), and birds of paradise (*Paradisaeidae*).

Of reptiles there are only three families peculiar to Australasia: *Carettochelyidae*, a turtle (one species) confined to New Guinea; the famous tuatara from New Zealand, belonging to the family *Sphenodontidae;* and pygopodid lizards (*Pygopodidae*).

There are no amphibians of endemic families, but of fishes there is one very old relict in Australia, a lungfish belonging to the family *Ceratodontidae*.

New Guinea

New Guinea has been geographically isolated from Asia by
water at least since the Tertiary, that is, about sixty million years.
This is still one of the very few places in the world where one may
find oneself literally in the Stone Age and wander through regions
where hardly anyone has been before. It takes almost a whole day
to fly over New Guinea, a distance from east to west of about
1,500 miles. The flight passes over snow-covered summits rising
to a height of 16,500 feet. Below the snow limit are alpine heaths,
and below these are forests. Dense rain forests cover the lower
slopes up to about ten thousand feet. The bottoms of valleys are
frequently covered by an unbroken canopy of forest, through which
a river has cut a winding corridor. Here and there the rivers swell
out into marshes, which the forest has not been able to colonize.
In both the south and north the highlands sink to lower plateaus,
mostly covered with lowland rain forest but otherwise consisting of
savannas and wet, sometimes flooded grassland. The coastal plains
of north and south New Guinea are dominated by the Sepik River
in the north and the Fly River in the south. Both rivers seem magnificent from the air, meandering through mighty basins, crossed
and recrossed by many tributaries. Typical, too, are the vast wetlands just inside the Casuarina coast in the southwestern part of
the island.

The plane takes hours to pass over the rain forests. Here and
there are little clearings with a few grass huts in them. These
dwellings seem to be scattered haphazardly in the virgin forest,
but generally they are on slopes above a river valley. Looking
down on this landscape, where precipitous ravines and deep valleys are hidden by the forest canopy, it is easy to understand why
the Papuans remained isolated for such a long time, not only from
the world outside New Guinea but also from each other. A few
miles between villages often mean that their respective inhabitants
speak different languages, making communication difficult if not
impossible.

Two visits to eastern New Guinea, in 1964 and 1966, gave me
opportunities to get to know two diametrically different worlds on
the island. New Guinea is just below the equator, and nine-tenths
of the island is in the tropical rain-forest belt, with high humidity
and luxuriant vegetation. The remaining one-tenth has a dry cli-

mate with little precipitation. Thus, some areas are reminiscent of the jungles of India, while others recall the wooded savannas of Australia. The dry regions are in the south, north of Torres Strait and in the area around Port Moresby. The vegetation, dominated by *Eucalyptus,* is strikingly similar to that on the Cape York peninsula, the most northerly part of Australia. This is probably not a coincidence: The distance between New Guinea and Australia is only about seventy-five miles here, and it was probably Cape York that once or perhaps several times formed a land connection with New Guinea.

The vegetation and wildlife of the dry regions of eastern New Guinea are relatively poor in species compared with those of the mighty rain forests of the interior. Nevertheless, there is much of interest also in the dry regions in spite of the effect of forest clearance, cultivation, and the introduction of Australian eucalypts. A few miles from the centers of population, forests free of exotic species flourish. Native eucalypts dominate in light open woods, which here and there turn into savannas, covered mostly with *Themeda australis* or a similar grass. The most interesting plant is a primitive cycad, *Cycas,* that does not grow more than five feet high. This genus, of which there are about ninety species in the tropical parts of the Old World, is the oldest flowering plant in existence and had its great period 140–180 million years ago. In the neighbourhood of Port Moresby in particular, these ancient palmlike trees are common in the eucalyptus woods. Many birds, among them numerous parrots, frequent these open woods.

But it is mainly the mountain rain forests of the interior that contain the remarkable forms of plants and animals usually associated with this gigantic, sparsely populated (only about 2,300,000 people) island. Many species of New Guinea's mammals, birds, and reptiles are endemic.

On eastern New Guinea the luxuriant montane, closed-canopy rain forests, rich in plant and animal species, climb about 7,500 feet. Above this, southern beeches (*Nothofagus*) form a belt of extensive stands up to about 9,300 to 10,300 feet. The next higher vegetation zone, only about three hundred feet, is a cloud forest characterized chiefly by hardwood trees like *Decaspermum* and *Xanthomyrtus,* a conifer (*Phyllocladus*), and an abundance of mosses. This belt, going up to more than 13,000 feet, is succeeded by a subalpine vegetation of tall plants, among which rhododendrons are an important element. The highest zone is composed of tussock grasslands. Animals occur in all these zones, but the majority live in the lowland and montane rain forests.

Thus, New Guinea is a vast wilderness full of seething life. The tree vegetation with all its tropical attendants—aerial roots, lianas, epiphytes, giant ferns, and screens of bamboo—is an orgy in green, with flowers, especially orchids and fungi, introducing sharply contrasting colours. Enchanting effects are created by butterflies and other insects and by brilliantly coloured birds flashing among the branches and leaves. Among the most beautiful of the latter are the famous birds of paradise, a group unknown elsewhere except for a few relatives on the Molucca Islands and in northern Australia. There are about forty species of birds of paradise. They are related to crows, as their cries reveal, but in beauty of plumage and in the colour and shape of their ornamental feathers they differ not only from these humble relatives but from all other birds in the world.

The glorious colouration of the birds of paradise seems to have influenced their human neighbours, the Papuans. I know of no other people who decorate themselves with such bright colours as the tribes living around Mount Hagen in eastern New Guinea. On festive occasions, the so-called sing-sings, the Papuans use not only birds of paradise but emerald-green beetles, shells, parrot feathers, the hairlike quills of the cassowary, the tail feathers of honey buzzards, the striped pinions of eagles, and the skins of snakes and lizards—not to mention gaudily painted robes and bizarre masks. The effect of a hundred or more natives dancing in these costumes, with plumes a yard high, is a fascinating sight, but it is difficult to suppress indignation at the number of creatures that have been sacrificed to provide all these ornaments. Many of the animals and birds may have been eaten, and this is of some use, but the main reason for their slaughter is human vanity. This would not be a problem if it were not that many species of birds of paradise have long been threatened. Even before New Guinea had been discovered by white men, skins of birds of paradise were being exported to Asia and even Europe. These birds have always been coveted for their beauty.

The Papuans kill birds of paradise not only for ceremonial plumes but also for the skins, which young men use in payment for a bride. Thus birds of paradise have the same monetary function as, for example, cows in Africa. Despite the fact that this situation has prevailed for a thousand years, the birds of paradise still survive. However, in the last thirty years, since civilization has brought peace to the Papuan tribes, they have increased their hunting of birds of paradise considerably. Formerly, they were constantly at war with neighbouring tribes and did not penetrate forests far from their villages. Tribal wars having been ended and tribal boundaries abolished, the Papuans can kill birds of paradise almost everywhere. And they do.

Moreover, formerly, that is, before civilization came to New Guinea, the Papuans were not equipped with shotguns. At present rifles are freely used. This fact together with the demand on skins of birds of paradise has made the trade in these birds a way of earning money. One skin is today worth about ten dollars.

In the territories of New Guinea administered by Australia there are no restrictions on the traditional hunting rights of natives. This is in the long run a threat to the birds of paradise. The situation in the Indonesian part of the island is at the moment unclear; there is very little control of how the natural resources there are used. In the Australian part an ordinance now being drafted will prohibit natives from trading in bird-of-paradise plumes, and this may in some measure reduce the destruction of these birds.

On the other hand, the administration of Papua encourages the Papuans to perform their sing-sings as a tourist attraction, particularly in connection with the annual agricultural shows. These gatherings bring together about twenty thousand Papuans, who try to outdo one other in decoration and adornment. A single man may have twenty bird-of-paradise skins on his headdress. It has been calculated by Roy D. Mackay of the newly formed New Guinean Bird Society that on the average there are five skins per dancer, making an annual slaughter of a hundred thousand birds of paradise. This number is rising each year.

One way to overcome this problem seems to be to create possibilities to store the headdresses so they can be used many times and to try to eliminate the competition of decoration among the dancers.

No species of bird or other vertebrate on New Guinea seems to be in immediate danger of extinction, a unique situation for such a large landmass so rich in endemic animals. The survival of much of the wildlife of New Guinea is largely attributable to the fact that it has been exploited by modern man only in very recent times. However, there is still insufficient knowledge about the status of many birds on New Guinea. It has been claimed that the safe survival of certain birds of paradise is in question owing to the increasing numbers of shotguns available. Concern has also been expressed about the Watut leaf warbler (*Sericornis nigro-viridis,*) which is known only in one single specimen (found in 1964) from the Watut River area in the district of Morobe, eastern New Guinea. Also, the parrot (*Psittrichas fulgidus*) from Papuan New Guinea is limited in distribution and is said to be endangered by a greatly increased local demand, because it forms a part of Papuan bride-price payments.

The golden-fronted bowerbird (*Amblyornis flavifrons*) is known only from three or four skins purchased on the European millinery market in the nineteenth century. During the 1960's several expeditions have searched for it in vain. In the same way the yellow-breasted bowerbird (*Chlamydera lauterbachi*), known only from the type specimen of 1896, remained long unobserved until it was rediscovered in 1964.

Unfortunately, exotic species have been introduced to New Guinea and have already had adverse effects on native species. The marine toad (*Bufo marinus*) from America has been intro-duced and has spread rapidly over wide areas, eradicating lizards such as geckos and skinks wherever it goes. Similarly, introduced carp and trout in New Guinea have led to local exterminations of indigenous fish.

AUSTRALIA

In terms of its animal life, Australia is unique. Its small size as a continent, its isolated location, and the length of time it has been separated from other continents have led its flora and fauna to follow other lines of evolution than those that can be traced elsewhere. Only during the past two hundred years, moreover, has man had any important effect on nature in Australia. But during this brief period, he has caused violent changes, mostly for the worse.

Human exploitation of Australia contains many dramatic phases and instructive mistakes. It is enough to consider the introduction of the rabbit to realize what enormous biological and economic risks are taken when foreign animals are introduced into a coun-try. The rabbit was introduced in 1859; three years later the animal was regarded as a national catastrophe. For a hundred years countermeasures were tried, such as the introduction of other animals to kill off the rabbits, but in vain. Instead they exterminated valuable native species. The staggering increase in the number of rabbits in Australia is reflected in the statistics on the export of skins: thirty-three thousand in 1873, about nine million in 1882, about 17,600,000 in 1945. In 1950 an imported viral disease, myxomatosis, proved at first to be an effective destroyer of rabbits, but after six or seven years the rabbits became partly immune, and now the number of survivors is greater after each outbreak of the disease.

Australia is mainly lowland with a few large rivers, and has therefore no true geographical barriers to the spread of animals and plants. But there are climatic boundaries. Thus, low precipitation has had a tremendous influence. Practically the whole continent is arid, one-third of it having an annual rainfall not exceeding ten inches. The average precipitation throughout Australia is fifteen inches (380 millimeters), and the evaporation is high. From the aspect of land exploitation, this is a very great problem. In Europe, by comparison, practically the whole of a journey from The Hague to Volgograd is through agricultural and forest regions. Over the same distance through Australia, from coast to coast, 76 percent of the journey is through desertlike country with only a little steppe vegetation. At present only one-third of the continent can be cultivated. It is chiefly the coastal fringe that receives sufficient rainfall to grow crops or artificial pastures. Twenty-five percent of Australia is desert and 47 percent arid or semiarid grassland. Despite the dry climate, the vegetation varies greatly, ranging from tropical in the north to temperate in the south.

For more than 50 million years, Australia has been separated from Asia. The islands of Indonesia and New Guinea are the remnants of former land connections between the two continents. It was in the Malay archipelago, where the fauna is so unlike that of Australia in spite of the short distance between them, that Darwin's contemporary, Alfred Russel Wallace, independent of his compatriot and isolated in the wilderness, worked out his thesis on evolution. The fauna of Indonesia and Australia was for Wallace what the fauna of Galápagos was for Darwin: one of the foundations of the hypothesis of natural selection. A hundred years ago, Wallace wrote that South America and Africa, although separated by the Atlantic, do not differ so much by far as do Asia and Australia.

All the vertebrate fauna of Australia (229 mammals, 531 birds,

380 reptiles, 112 amphibians, and 180 species of freshwater fishes) provides important evidence on the history of Australia and the evolution of the animal kingdom. The remarkable mammalian fauna of Australia is of most interest. Of the 229 species, no fewer than 119 are marsupials (pouched animals) and two are *Monotremata* (cloacal animals). Both groups are primitive mammals which have followed, in the main, a line of evolution different from that of animals in other parts of the world.

The predominance of pouched animals among the mammals of Australia will be realized when it is noted that before the colonization of the continent by Europeans there were only two other orders of mammals, rodents and bats, if man and the dingo he introduced about twelve thousand years ago are excepted. The success of pouched animals in Australia must be seen in the light of the fact that they had no competition from other orders of mammals, and that they were peculiarly able to adjust themselves to the rather difficult conditions of life in Australia. It is wrong, therefore, to regard—as is often done—pouched animals as failures because they have not evolved into the higher forms found on other continents. On the contrary, marsupials have shown a degree of adaptability that not even the most specialized mammals on other continents can equal.

It cannot be easy for a fish to thrive in such a dry country, and many species are therefore specialized. Not infrequently they have overcome problems of climate more successfully than their relatives elsewhere, for some Australian fishes have existed for millions of years, long after their relatives in other parts of the world became extinct. One such "living fossil" is the lungfish (*Neoceratodus forsteri*). In terms of distribution and evolution, the fishes of Australia are very remarkable, and it is a pity that the introduction of fishes from other continents has driven out native species before they could be studied.

The present dry climate of Australia has been characterized by fluctuations approximately every hundred years. European colonization was begun when precipitation was rather favourable. In blissful ignorance of the climatic cycle, it was assumed that rainfall would remain constant, and the stock of sheep was increased enormously. By 1890, there were no fewer than a hundred million sheep in New South Wales alone. Then came a dry period, which culminated around the turn of the century. The pasture was insufficient, and the overexploitation of the land brought on an economic crisis. The number of sheep and the arable land were both reduced drastically, for the natural grass that had supported the sheep had been destroyed by grazing and trampling. The grass gave way to other plants that adapted to the ravaged earth but were of no use as pasture. This situation persisted for a long time, even after the climate had taken a turn for the better. In some areas, for example in Western Australia, much of the land became worthless after only fifty years of occupation by livestock. (Under natural conditions erosion during drought periods would have been slow or negligible, because there would in general always have been a grass cover protecting the soil despite grazing by wild herbivores and occasional fires by the Aboriginals. And where local damage occurred, rapid recovery followed immediately during lush years. Therefore no unnatural changes of vegetation took place.)

One of the striking features of present Australia is the extent to which the indigenous vegetation has been invaded by exotic plants which gradually replace the native ones and completely change the landscape. This ecological transformation has taken place after the European settlement. It has had profound effects on Australian animals.

Other changes in the vegetation have also occurred in recent times. Large areas have been deforested completely, altering the landscape from forests and woodlands to treeless fields. Drainage, damming, and other effects of so-called development are still today changing the Australian environment at a faster rate than ever.

The present Australian grasslands are extremely vulnerable when exposed to grazing by sheep and cattle. Much damage is already irreparable. These fragile rangelands amount to nearly three-quarters of the continent. Ecologists predict that these areas will degenerate into unproductive wastelands if destructive livestock grazing is permitted much longer. In addition to the over-sized livestock population, introduced banteng cattle (*Bos banteng*), water buffaloes, Arabian camels, goats, and donkeys have gone wild and degrade habitats considerably.

Kangaroos, produced by Australia's arid grasslands, are much more efficient than sheep and cattle at converting vegetation to animal protein, and they do it without destroying the environment. But this well-adapted and productive natural resource is unwisely depleted, eradicated, or wiped out by habitat alterations.

Forest destruction is also pronounced. More than half of Western Australia's state forests are under mining tenements. Clearing of tropical rain forest in Queensland has taken place to such an extent that very little now remains of the distinctive lowland rain forests of Australia. The chemical and general ecological values of most tree species and other plants of these disappearing forests have not even been investigated.

The decline of grasslands and forests leads to serious soil erosion. The New South Wales Soil Conservation Service claims that not less than forty-eight million acres in the eastern and central parts of this state alone are affected by gully, sheet, and wind erosion. As a result of the adverse land use in Australia, the traditional rural exports have decreased sharply. The mining industry has saved Australia financially in recent years but inflicts terrible environmental wounds.

In such a dry continent as Australia, water is a precious and invaluable resource for environmental quality and health. Yet, all over Australia the water resources are being devastated by pollution and wasteful use affecting the underwater table, lakes, swamps, and rivers to such a degree that human society is now threatened. Control of streams and rivers for flood mitigation, irrigation, and dams as well as drainage of lakes, marshes, and billabongs for agriculture have had far-reaching, adverse effects on ecosystems, habitats, and species, particularly aquatic animals such as birds and fish. In several lakes and rivers introduced carps are destroying the environment for important native fish, especially the Murray cod (*Maccullochella macquariensis*).

Marine life along and off the Australian coasts is rapidly deteriorating owing to industrial pollution and oil spillage. No fewer than 305 spills in bays, ports, and harbours were found on the Australian coast in twelve months between April, 1970, and March, 1971. In Victoria and New South Wales alone there were 245 spills within the same period. One of the world's marvels, the Great Barrier Reef, is also endangered because of industrial pressure for development such as mining for lime and drilling for oil.

Most of what we have said about human activity in Australia has referred to Europeans. Human beings first appeared on the continent rather late, long after Australia had become isolated. Discoveries dated by the carbon-14 method show that in Australia people were using stone implements about eleven thousand years ago. Many hold the view that, in spite of more than ten thousand years of occupation, the Aborigines with their stone tools had little effect on the living nature around them, while others believe that grass fires periodically lit to catch lizards—a practice that still continues—contributed greatly to changes in environment. Regardless of which view is correct, it was the arrival of Europeans, with sheep, cattle, and rabbits in their wake, that led to the collapse of the ancient balance of nature.

The dingo, the wild Australian dog, has often been a subject of zoogeographical controversy. There is no longer any doubt that it came to Australia from Asia, but it is not known whether it arrived with the first human beings or was introduced later. There is evidence that it was there about eleven thousand years ago, after which it disappeared, to return again five thousand years later. Whether or not it was introduced once or several times, it probably had a devastating effect on many native elements of the fauna, in the long run doubtless much more serious than the grass fires mentioned above.

There are few regions of the world more suitable for the study of man's relation to his environment than Australia, for there it is possible to follow almost in detail what has happened since the first European colonists arrived in 1788. At present the population of Australia is only about twelve million, but already all the most suitable regions are being exploited. Nevertheless, it is calculated that Australia could support between thirty and forty million people at the current standard of living if all utilization of pasture for domestic animals were based on the productivity of the land. In view of the enormous destruction of the land by the hitherto small population, these figures seem fearfully high. The native population, now about forty thousand, probably never exceeded three hundred thousand. If the natural law of the carrying capacity of the land is ignored, the results will sooner or later be catastrophic. The deterioration of Australia's dry lands due to overuse by the sheep industry has now become so serious that it is imperative to stop the opening up of more land for sheep grazing and to initiate restoration of lands devastated by sheep.

Although most Australian mammals have suffered from the man-made and sheep-made damages to the environment, a few species have locally benefited. For example, an increase in num-

bers of red kangaroos or marloos (*Macropus rufus*) occurred in
the lower-rainfall areas used for pastoral settlement. In western
New South Wales this species was rare in 1844–46 but is nowadays numerous there. Sheep grazing in this area has converted a
shrubby saltbush vegetation with myall and other lower trees to a
short grass association with less tree cover. This seems to have
favored the red kangaroo. Changes induced by cattle in central
Australia have also led to an increase of the red kangaroo. Similarly, overgrazing by sheep in northwestern Australia has been
an advantage to the euro (*M. robustus*) but resulted in a decline
of the red kangaroo, because its food was suppressed by the sheep.
However, these examples of livestock grazing are just exceptions
to the generally adverse effects on wildlife.

In order to avoid confusion when discussing kangaroos, walla-
roos, euros, and wallabies, an explanation must be given about
these names, which are used in various parts of Australia and in
the literature. Kangaroos are the largest members of the family
Macropodidae, which comprises kangaroos, wallabies, and rat
kangaroos. "Wallaroo" and "euro" are names for the same species,
Macropus robustus, which is divided into four subspecies. In various parts of Australia these four races are called by the one or
the other vernacular name. Hence, when using the name euro in
this book we refer to the species and not to a particular subspecies.
The red kangaroo (*M. rufus*) is often placed in a separate genus,
Megaleia. The grey kangaroo, often called *Macropus canguru,*
does in fact exist in two species, the eastern grey kangaroo (*M.
giganteus*) and the western grey kangaroo (*M. fuliginosus*), which
has been recently demonstrated on the basis of serological characters, coat colour, gestation periods, and other criteria. Therefore,
when in the following we refer to the grey kangaroo in the old
sense, it means one or the other of the two species.

Australia was the worst possible continent for the introduction
of exotic plants and animals because of the vulnerability of its
unique, highly specialized flora and fauna. No less than seventeen
wild mammals have been brought into Australia since 1788, the
fatal year of the introduction of the rabbit. The destructive effect
of these exotics combined with overgrazing by enormous numbers
of livestock and predation by domestic cats and dogs has been
monumental. Sheep together with rabbits certainly have done more
to change Australian natural habitats and damage wildlife than
any other introduced species. Man's clearing of scrub, deforesta-

tion, and bush fires have also affected the fauna, as has ruthless hunting for sport and for pelts with dogs and modern firearms.

Eighteen mammals and thirteen birds have been exterminated in Australia during the last two hundred years and many more are approaching extinction entirely because of the activities of civilized man. However, it is also clear that some mammals had declined considerably before the arrival of the Europeans, according to evidence in Aboriginal middens and caves.

Deserts

A large part of Australia is desert. Vast plains of gravel and stone with a minimum of vegetation as well as semiarid deserts with sparse tussocks of sclerophyllous grass, chiefly spinifex (*Triodia*), occupy the lowlands of the interior. After the sporadic rains, some areas explode into verdure but it is, in general, of short duration. Of all Australian habitats it is the deserts that have been the least modified by man, but this does not mean that desert animals are not endangered. Several desert mammals and birds have become extremely rare. One of them is the long-tailed sminthopsis (*Sminthopsis longicaudata*), a mouselike creature that may still survive in Western Australia although it has not been observed since the 1930's. Formerly it had a wider range. The same is true of the crescent nail-tail wallaby (*Onychogalea lunata*), which is now on the verge of extinction. Its former distribution included the deserts of Western and South Australia. The last known of this species was of one killed in 1956, but reports indicate that it still occurs in a restricted desert area. The desert bandicoot (*Perameles eremiana*) is extinct in most of its former range but still known to the Aborigines to occur rarely in the desert. The spectacled hare-wallaby (*Lagorchestes conspicillatus*) is probably exterminated in livestock country but still exists in unstocked desert areas. A fifth endangered and perhaps already vanished species is the desert rat kangaroo (*Aloprymnus campestris*) from the Lake Eyre basin in South Australia and Queensland; it has not been seen since 1935. The Alice Springs pseudorat (*Pseudomys fieldi*) is known only from a single specimen and is probably extinct or extremely rare. Finally, the Australian night parrot (*Geopsittacus occidentalis*) of the deserts of Western and South Australia has not been observed for many years and only one specimen has been collected this century.

Scrub and Grassland

With deserts and subdeserts, the scrub and grasslands, ranging from steppelike plains to true savannas, occupy the largest part of Australia. In a belt of varying width the scrub and grasslands almost entirely surround the deserts of the interior, but they are also found along some of the coasts, particularly in the northern parts of the continent. The broadest expanses of grassland are in eastern Australia west of the Great Dividing Range and east of the desert. There are two main types of scrub: the mulga scrub and the mallee scrub, the former dominated by mulga (*Acacia aneura*), while the latter is formed mostly of dwarf eucalypts, some shrubs, and sclerophyllous grass.

Many former savannas have been converted into cultivated fields and grazing areas for livestock. Some grasslands still show their original vegetation, dominated by feather grass (*Stipa*), wallaby grass (*Danthonia*), and kangaroo grass (*Themeda australis*). The latter, a very nutritious grass, was once of great importance to Australia's rich animal world, apparently playing the same role as its relative *T. triandra* does for many species of antelopes on the savannas of Africa.

It was to such rich grassland that a multitude of grazing marsupials as well as many birds had adapted. The product of millions of years of natural selection, they roamed the plains freely and in harmony with the vegetation. Suddenly, with the arrival of the Europeans, the whole system was altered and disaster followed for many living things. Numerous smaller marsupials disappeared forever, destroyed not only by the competition of sheep but also directly by human hunters. In many areas nutritious plants disappeared and were replaced by less palatable species like spinifex. However, some wild animal species such as the euro were probably favoured by this change. As mentioned above, the red kangaroo was also benefited by the changes of grassland brought about by livestock. It has been claimed that the present vegetation of Australia's inland plains is probably supporting a higher biomass of livestock and red kangaroos than it could of either alone (Newsome in 1971). Therefore, both kangaroos and domestic animals should be harvested instead of treating the wild animals as pests. This unwise policy has led to a number of marsupial extinctions and has brought many species to the category of rarities.

The eastern barred bandicoot (*Perameles fasciata*) of New South Wales has not been recorded since 1867; the western barred bandicoot (*P. myosura myosura*) of Western Australia has not been seen since 1900; the Nalpa bilby (*Macrotis lagotis grandis*) from South Australia was probably exterminated during the 1930's; the brown hare-wallaby (*Lagorchestes leporoides*) from New South Wales and South Australia became extinct in the latter state during the 1930's and in 1966 was listed by A. J. Marshall as "almost certainly lost forever"; and the toolach (*Wallabia greyi*) from South Australia and Victoria disappeared in the same decade.

The history of extermination of the toolach, a very handsome species, is indicative. It had a restricted range, but locally (for instance, near Kingston) it was so numerous that it "swarmed," to quote Professor F. W. Jones. The toolach's extraordinary speed (in 1863 John Gould said, "I never saw anything so swift . . . leaving the dogs far behind it") made it great sport to hunt. Its beautiful pelt became popular, and great numbers were marketed in Melbourne. Human persecution reduced the larger colonies and dispersed them, and by 1870 the species had become so rare that extinction could be foreseen. Hunters became eager to kill the last survivors for their pelts or as trophies. Finally, in the 1930's, a doe, rescued from dogs, was all that survived of Australia's most beautiful kangaroo. With her, the species disappeared forever.

At present, a number of other marsupials of scrub and grasslands (some of them are also living in deserts), are threatened by the same fate: the dibbler or the freckled marsupial mouse (*Antechinus acipalis*) of Western Australia was thought to have become extinct in the 1930's but was rediscovered at one locality in southern Western Australia in 1967; the dusky planigale (*Planigale rufus*) in Western and South Australia; the rabbit bandicoot (*Macrotis lagotis lagotis*) in Western Australia, Northern Territory, and Queensland; the lesser rabbit bandicoot (*M. leucura*) in Western and South Australia; the pig-footed bandicoot (*Chaeropus ecaudatus*) in central Australia that has not been seen for perhaps fifty years and is now probably extinct; and the hairy-nosed wombat (*Lasiorhinus latifrons latifrons*) in southern Western and South Australia. All of these were formerly widely distributed. The last mentioned species is less threatened than the others.

In recent years vast numbers of kangaroos have been killed for use as pet food. Some kangaroo meat is also used for human consumption. This slaughter began in the 1950's and has increased abnormally. Since 1964 about two million kangaroos are being slaughtered each year. The killing is particularly encouraged in areas where the red kangaroo (*Macropus rufus*) and the euro (*M. robustus*) are considered pests that compete with the sheep. In Western Australia poisoning campaigns were conducted in 1959–60 against the euro, because it was said to hinder pasture-regeneration programs. This was a completely erroneous charge: Scientists found that the primary cause of the deterioration of the pastures was not the marsupials, but overgrazing by sheep! One of the scientists, Dr. E. H. M. Ealey, working for the Commonwealth Scientific and Industrial Research Organization (CSIRO), tried to find out why the vegetation on lands where sheep once grazed in huge herds had deteriorated and why kangaroos in great numbers had replaced the sheep. He found that kangaroos grow fat on the apparently poor food. Given shade, moreover, they can do without water (the annual rainfall averages nine to twelve inches, while temperatures soar to 120° F. in the shade); they reproduce quickly; and because of occasional heavy mortality their numbers fluctuate considerably, giving the pasture an opportunity to recover. In other words, he found that the kangaroos were in balance with the habitat; the sheep were not. The main cause of the deficiency of nutritious plants was the injurious practices of the farmers themselves, especially the habit of burning the grass during sheep mustering when nutritious plants carried seed. The farmers were also guilty of overstocking and of concentrating sheep in the same paddocks year after year. The campaign against the euro was vigorous. In one farm alone, running 2,300 sheep over seven square miles, over 12,800 euros were killed, mostly by poisoning waters, in two months.

Kangaroos are a useful and highly productive natural resource. The meat is excellent and has little fat and much myoglobin. It is not wrong to crop, that is, thin out in order to utilize, these animals, but the harvest must be in proportion to the populations. It is said that in New South Wales red kangaroos have been slaughtered at the rate of two hundred thousand a week and that the hunters are taking smaller animals than in previous years. A study between 1960 and 1963 by Dr. H. J. Frith, director of the Wildlife Research Division of the CSIRO, shows that the population fell sharply during that period. "There is little doubt that a drastic decline occurred," says his report, and it was not due to heavy natural mortality; there was no mass exodus of kangaroos, and no "crash." But there was an enormous increase of shooting for skins and for the new meat trade. In 1959 in Queensland alone, 584,000 red kangaroo skins were marketed, compared with ninety thousand the previous year, and this figure included only a part of those killed for meat and none of those killed in pest-control operations. In 1970 the high levels of shot kangaroos in New South Wales and Queensland continued. Conservationists there fear that this unlimited shooting will destroy the stocks of both the red and grey kangaroos (*M. giganteus*). So far, the Australian government has failed to put even a temporary embargo on the export of kangaroo meat and thus give zoologists time to find out how much damage is being done to the species. In his report to the Eleventh Pacific Science Congress in Tokyo in 1966, Dr. D. L. Serventy of the CSIRO declared:

> The wholesale killing of the larger Macropods in pastoral and farming areas in recent years transcends in public opinion most other conservation issues in Australia at the present time. The three species involved, the Red or Plains Kangaroo or Marloo (*Macropus rufus*), the Grey Kangaroo (*M. giganteus*) and the Euro, Wallaroo or Biggada (*M. robustus*), have been harried by the pastoralists for years. However, because of the recent trade in kangaroo meat for pet food and in some cases for human consumption in overseas countries (mainly Japan, United Kingdom, and Hong Kong, Malaysia and the Federal Republic of Germany), the slaughter has now reached wholesale proportions. It is estimated that one million kangaroos are killed in Eastern Australia every year. The Red Kangaroo is the main species involved and it had had no legal protection under the fauna laws and virtually no control as to hunting.

However, the findings of the CSIRO Division of Wildlife Research, the Northern Territory Administration biologists, and other institutions have completed official cognizance of the seriousness of the situation.

All evidence indicates that kangaroos and wallabies are a valuable natural resource that has already developed to a growing industry. The meat has been exported to forty-eight countries. Therefore this resource should be managed properly. Generally, four species of kangaroos and wallabies are killed regularly in

266

Australia for export. In 1965–66, 5,242 tons of meat were exported, worth in Australian dollars $1,435,508. The weight of exported skins has fluctuated from 718,540 to 1,212,695 pounds between 1950 and 1964. It is interesting to note that during the drought in 1967–68, the value of a sheep was only A$.50, while a kangaroo returned A$4.50. Yet kangaroos are shot as pests!

At the Australian Fauna Authorities Conference in 1965, there was alarm at the way the situation had deteriorated in New South Wales and the Northern Territory. The conference resolved that if the kangaroo population was to be maintained, urgent attention must be given to controlling the age, sex, and number of animals harvested. Severe drought conditions have further jeopardized the survival of the red kangaroo stocks. Research indicated that over 90 percent of the young near Wilcannia were not surviving the drought conditions. The state most concerned, New South Wales, has at last taken remedial action. Professional kangaroo hunters must now be licensed and these licenses are issued with restrictions. No action has been taken yet in other states, but it appears that the situation, outside of New South Wales, is serious only in the Northern Territory.

The public concern about the cropping of kangaroos caused the Australian Parliament to set up a Select Committee on Wildlife Conservation to make a report on kangaroos based on public hearings and field inspections. In November, 1971, this committee stated that none of the four large species of kangaroo is under present threat of extinction whether from destruction of habitat, drought, or commercial harvesting, or from any combination of those factors, except for the Tasmanian eastern grey kangaroo (*M. giganteus tasmaniensis*), which is endangered owing to habitat loss. However, this conclusion does not seem to correspond entirely to the views expressed by many Australian scientists, who fear that several of these kangaroos cannot withstand the present persecution.

Not only the larger kangaroos and wallabies have been victims of adverse land-use practices and direct persecution. A number of other marsupials apparently disappeared or became extremely rare before they were scientifically described and are thus in general very little known. All of them may be considered in danger or even extinct. Since the majority are found in the grasslands, we list all of them here:

Fawn marsupial mouse (*Antechinus bellus*) from the Northern Territory, described in 1904.

Harney's marsupial mouse (*A. bilarni*) from the Northern Territory, known from a single specimen.

Northern fat-tailed marsupial mouse (*A. mimulus*) from the Northern Territory, known from a single specimen described in 1906.

Frogatt's sminthopsis (*Sminthopsis frogatti*) from Western Australia, known from a single specimen described in 1887.

Daly River sminthopsis (*S. nitela*) from the Northern Territory, known from four specimens described in 1897.

Large desert sminthopsis (*S. psammophila*) from central Australia, known from a single specimen described in 1895.

Hairy-footed sminthopsis (*S. hirtipes*) from central and Western Australia.

Stripe-faced sminthopsis (*S. lumholzi*) from Queensland.

Northwestern marsupial mole (*Natoryctes caurinus*) from Western Australia, known from a single specimen described in 1920.

The invasion of the Europeans and their retinue of domestic and exotic animals has also wiped out a number of endemic rodents of scrub and grasslands, including the following:

Eastern pseudo-rat (*Pseudomys australis*) from New South Wales and Queensland. Probably became extinct between 1910 and 1920.

Stick-nest rat (*Leporillus conditor*) from South Australia and New South Wales. A. J. Marshall (in 1966) listed this species as probably extinct.

White-tailed stick-nest rat (*L. apicalis*) from South Australia and the Northern Territory.

Marshall's hopping-mouse (*Notomys mitchelli*) from Australia, Victoria, and New South Wales.

Big-eared western hopping-mouse (*N. megalotis*) from Western Australia. Known only from a single specimen collected about 1840.

The New Holland mouse (*Pseudomys novaehollandiae*) from New South Wales was long known from only four specimens, of which the last was taken prior to 1887. Hence, the species was considered extinct, but in 1967 a fifth individual was collected in the Ku-ring-gai Chase National Park, near Sydney. In 1968 this mouse was found in abundance in a limited area near Port

Stephens, New South Wales. However, its future in the area is insecure because its habitat is threatened by industrial and urban development.

Before the European invasion the scrub, grassland, and light wooded savannas of Australia were inhabited by a wide variety of birds. The number of these has much decreased, several species have become very rare, and some are near extinction.

The paradise parrot (*Psephotus pulcherrimus*) was formerly widespread in Queensland and New South Wales, but excessive hunting for commercial purposes, perhaps combined with such other factors as introduced rats (this parrot nests in termite mounds) has led almost to its extinction. The population is estimated at about 150 birds confined to light woods in Queensland and perhaps still northern New South Wales. The scarlet-chested parrot (*Neophema splendida*) has also been persecuted by aviculturists because it is very attractive and of high commercial value. It is found in Western Australia, South Australia, Victoria, and New South Wales but is everywhere very rare and endangered. The western and southern whipbirds (*Psophodea nigrogularis nigrogularis* and *P. n. leucogaster*) have declined sharply owing to loss of habitats. The former race was thought to be extinct but in 1939 was rediscovered in southwestern Australia. The southern race is confined to Victoria, where it has not been seen since 1932 and may be extinct. The Eyrean grass-wren (*Amytornis goyderi*) from South Australia had not been observed since 1875 when one pair was found in 1931 in the Lake Eyre region. It was considered extinct during the 1950's but was again seen in 1962. Since then there are no records.

The Australian bustard (*Eupodotis australis*), one of the largest birds on the continent, was once a common species on the plains and wooded savannas. There it became an easy prey for foxes and hunters. Sportsmen recklessly shot this bird to such an extent that it was exterminated except in remote areas not visited by Europeans. It is now protected, but illegal shooting continues. Probably man and the fox are also responsible for the disappearance and rarity of the plains wanderer (*Pedionomys torquatus*), a quail from South Australia, western Victoria, and western New South Wales.

The history of the flock pigeon (*Histriophaps histrionica*) resembles that of the North American passenger pigeon. These pigeons are nomadic and millions of them used to congregate on the grassy plains of northern Australia, New South Wales, and northern South Australia. Immense flocks visited drinking pools and there became easy prey for hunters. Since the flesh of this pigeon is excellent it was shot without any regard for its survival as a species. It soon dwindled almost to extinction. But recently the population has in some places shown an astonishing recovery, which has given rise to hope that the species may yet be saved.

Surprisingly enough, the wedge-tailed eagle (*Aquila audax*), largest of Australia's birds of prey, seems to have withstood the intense persecution to which it is constantly subjected by man. Large numbers are killed annually all over Australia under the pretext that it is harmful to lambs. Although the statistics are fragmentary, available data seem to indicate that the total kill of eagles in Australia exceeds thirty thousand birds a year. Bounties on the wedge-tailed eagle were paid in Western Australia and Queensland until 1968, when the former abolished the bounty system. In these two states payments were made for an average of 13,056 scalps a year for the period 1958–1967. The species is nowhere protected except in Tasmania and the Australian Capital Territory. This lack of protection affects many other birds of prey in Australia. In this respect the Australian authorities are far behind more conservation-minded countries.

The justification for such a drastic control does not exist. An investigation of the food habits of wedge-tailed eagles in southeastern Australia carried out during eight months showed that rabbits constitute the primary prey of the eagles. Rabbits have long been controlled by man in attempts to get rid of what is regarded as a national pest. So it seems illogical to control eagles, which are most efficient controllers of rabbits. In fact, in the Canberra area the prey of thirty-one pairs of wedge-tailed eagles consisted of 65.4 percent rabbits and hares and only 12.2 percent sheep. In another area in New South Wales and Queensland the percentages were 46.6 rabbits, 19.5 kangaroos, 11.7 magpies, 9.7 reptiles, and 4.8 sheep. However, these figures do not give the whole story, because an unknown percentage of the sheep is presumed already to be carrion. There are good reasons to believe so, because other surveys in Australia of lamb mortality show that the predation is not responsible for most of the losses. In fact, nearly half the lambs starve to death after the suckling relationship between mother and offspring has been broken or when the suckling has failed to establish. There are ten million or so deaths of newborn lambs that occur in Australia each year! Obviously this abundance of carrion is utilized by the wedge-tailed eagles, which are then blamed by the sheep owners for having killed the lambs and, therefore, the eagles have to be killed, too.

Eucalyptus Forests and Other Woodlands

Australian vegetation and animal life are unusual in that a few groups of plants and animals show a very broad ecological range, occupying almost every terrestrial habitat. Chief among these groups are various eucalypts (more than five hundred species), acacias (more than six hundred species), and marsupials (119 species), which have representatives on all levels from the seashore up to the timber line.

The woods and forests of Australia are dominated by eucalypts. They grow in open or closed communities with thin or dense undergrowth of shrubs and herbs in wet or dry habitats.

Australia's relatively few forests, covering only about 4 percent of the continent, are unfortunately concentrated along the eastern coast, the most populated and exploited area. The resulting destruction of forests has had serious repercussions on the fauna, because many species were restricted to this habitat and other species took refuge in the woodlands when they were persecuted in the plains. But also in parts of central Australia mulga woodlands have disappeared in areas covering hundreds of miles owing to erosion through bad land use.

Among the animal victims of man's rape of the forest is the broad-faced rat kangaroo (*Potorous platyops*) of Western Australia, which disappeared between the 1840's and the 1880's, probably owing to the introduced cats and the bush fires of Europeans. A century ago, the white-footed rabbit rat (*Conilurus albipes*) had a wide range from South Australia and Victoria to New South Wales and Queensland. Settlement, domestic cats, and introduced foxes apparently exterminated this species soon after 1910.

Many woodland species are now endangered, for example, the eastern jerboa marsupial (*Antechinus laniger*) from Western Australia, Victoria, New South Wales, and Queensland. Leadbeater's possum (*Gymnobelideus leadbeateri*) was restricted to Victoria, where it was discovered in 1867. A disastrous fire burned out a large part of this possum's range and no signs of it could be found, but in 1961 it was rediscovered in a dense forest area only seventy miles from Melbourne, where it is now protected. The brush-tailed rock-wallaby (*Petrogale penicillata penicillata*) had formerly a wide range in eastern Australia, but habitat destructions, hunting, and predation by foxes and dogs pressed down its number, and today it occurs only in scattered populations in Victoria, New South Wales, and Queensland. The bridled nail-tail wallaby (*Onychogalea fraenata*), common about a hundred years ago from New South Wales to central Queensland, is at present probably extinct, again as a result of forest destruction. The white-throated wallaby (*Protemnodon parma*) was long believed to have been extinct, but in 1968 some individuals were found in one locality in New South Wales, where the species once existed before it was assumed to have been exterminated before the end of the nineteenth century! In 1966 it was discovered that the white-throated wallaby exists on Kawau Island, New Zealand! The animals were imported and released there about 1870 together with three other species of Australian wallabies, but until 1966 it was unknown that the rare Australian white-throated wallaby had a refuge in New Zealand, where it is rather common and became officially protected in 1968. Between 1966 and 1970, 384 individuals were exported alive from Kawau to zoological gardens all over the world for establishing breeding nuclei.

Perhaps the most famous of Australian animals of eucalypt forests is the koala (*Phascolarctus cinereus*). The koala is entirely dependent for food on a few species of *Eucalyptus*. Before the arrival of Europeans it was plentiful throughout eastern Australia. It was some time before the Europeans discovered that the fur of the koala was valuable; then a reckless persecution was initiated. The koala was a peculiarly helpless prey: sitting or climbing slowly among the light foliage of the crowns of the eucalypt trees, myriads were shot or trapped. The koala was also vulnerable in the sense that it was too attached to the eucalypts and could not move to safer habitats. Moreover, it is a slow-breeding animal and the young were killed or captured with their mothers. The slaughter brought the koala near extinction. In 1920 only five hundred koalas remained in Victoria. In 1920 the Australian export was two million skins. Three years later, ten thousand licensed trappers in Queensland took half a million koalas, only half the number taken in 1921. By 1930 the koala had become extremely rare in New South Wales as a result of exploitation and disease. This extermination of a valuable and unique animal is one of the more shameful episodes in the destruction of nature in Australia during the past two hundred years. Fortunately public opinion finally reacted strongly to the slaughter, so the authorities proclaimed complete protection of the koala and prohibited the export of skins. The koala was saved at the very last moment, but it is still very rare.

Barnard's hairy-nosed wombat (*Lasiorhinus barnardi*) is restricted to one area in Queensland and therefore vulnerable to habitat changes.

Among birds, many species have suffered seriously from changes in forest habitats. The capture and sale of living and stuffed birds has also contributed to the decline of many species, particularly the colourful parrots. One of these, now almost gone, is a race of the orange-bellied parrot (*Neophema chrysogaster mab*) that was formerly found over a wide area of southern Australia and New South Wales but today is restricted to a small range in southeastern South Australia and Victoria. It is occasionally observed during the winter in coastal northwestern Tasmania also and on King Island in the Bass Strait. It is possible that the entire population does not exceed fifty to seventy birds. Habitat destruction and commercial trapping are presumably the main factors for the decline of this bird. The Tasmanian race of the same species has also become very rare. The turquoise parrot (*N. pulchella*), common a hundred years ago, has also undergone an extremely rapid decline. In 1931 it still occurred from Queensland to South Australia and Victoria, but today it seems to be limited to one or two areas in New South Wales. Both Bourke's parrot (*N. bourki*), normally found over a vast range—from Western Australia to Queensland, New South Wales, and Victoria—and the glossy black cockatoo (*Calyptorhynchus lathami*) from Queensland, New South Wales, Victoria, and South Australia have become very rare in recent times.

Among the passerines the helmeted honey eater (*Meliphaga cassidix*) has suffered greatly from habitat destruction. It is now confined to a small area near Melbourne.

The mallee fowl (*Leipoa ocellata*) has its home in open woods of low-growing eucalypts and acacias. It is one of Australia's most interesting birds as a food resource, but unfortunately it is in grave danger of extermination due to environmental changes, grazing by sheep, and bush fires. The mallee fowl is dependent for food and reproduction on more or less untouched forests. The male builds large pyramidal nesting mounds of decomposing leaves and grass which he covers with sand, gravel, and debris. The eggs are deposited in these mounds, but foxes and dogs dig them out, destroying many clutches.

Rain Forests

The northern part of Queensland is covered with rain forest, but patches of similar forests are still found elsewhere in the same state as well as in a few areas of New South Wales and Victoria, all of them situated between the Great Dividing Range and the sea. Many rare mammals and birds have their last strongholds in these pockets.

The grey cuscus (*Phalanger orientalis peninsulae*) is known only from some parts of the Cape York peninsula in northernmost Queensland, and is very rare. There are only two Australian species of cuscuses. Both live on the Cape York peninsula, but several other forms exist in New Guinea and adjacent islands north of Australia; apparently only a few cuscuses arrived in Australia before the land bridge to New Guinea was broken. Another rain-forest species is the musky rat kangaroo (*Hypsiprymnodon moschatus*) of Queensland. Though fully protected, it is threatened by forest destruction.

Among the rain-forest birds only one species seems to be in danger for the moment, the blue-browed lorilet (*Opopsitta coxeni*) from Queensland and northeastern New South Wales. This parrot is very rare and will be doomed if the forests of its habitats are destroyed.

The Mountains

Australia consists mainly of lowland deserts and savannas. But to the east the country rises, culminating along the east coast in true highlands, the Great Dividing Range, running in an arc from Queensland in the north to Victoria in the south. For long stretches these mountains plunge straight into the Pacific Ocean, but here and there they slope gently down, leaving room for a lowland coastal strip sometimes almost one hundred miles wide. This lowland belt in Queensland, New South Wales, and Victoria contains more than one-third of the whole population of Australia, and is often the only part of the continent a casual visitor sees.

Often Australia is identified with this well-known narrow strip of land and the extensive grasslands and deserts, while the mountains are forgotten.

And yet the alpine regions of Australia are quite close to the largest towns and are among the continent's most characteristic and splendid natural features. From tropical Queensland to the subtropical belts of New South Wales and Victoria, the mountains form a barrier of granite, sandstone, and basalt nearly 1,900 miles long between the Pacific in the east and the vast plains in the west. It is also a boundary between climates and vegetation. From the east humid winds blow and from the west desert winds, while in the southern part, the Australian Alps, hurricanes often in conjunction with cyclones from Antarctica storm over the range. These climatic factors have given the Australian mountains a rich variety of natural environments, many of them not found elsewhere on the continent.

From the Blue Mountains the view is breath-taking in its grandeur and recalls the Grand Canyon's fantastic system of eroded cliffs and ravines; its proportions are not so gigantic as those in Arizona, but they are still overwhelming. In addition, the Blue Mountains are mostly wooded. Eucalypts cover the bottoms of the valleys and climb high up the mountain slopes. Unlike any other subtropical mountain woods I have seen, the eucalyptus woods are open and light and have rather dense undergrowth. In some valleys and gorges the vegetation is luxurious, with a tendency to rain-forest character. The cry of the lyrebird (*Menura novaehollandiae*) is among the most common sounds. Here the enormous leaves of the trees and shrubs form a dense canopy, shutting out the light. Rotting vegetation covers the soft damp earth, and from it grow small ferns which under their long fronds hide a miniature world of strange tiny creatures. On the plateaus above the eucalyptus woods are extensive heaths covered with a multitude of flowers in spring. They attract various species of honey birds that hover about like huge butterflies. There are sixty-seven species of honey eaters (*Meliphagidae*). As the main pollinators of several species of *Eucalyptus* and other trees and herbs they are of great importance.

The platypus (*Ornitorhynchus anatinus*), one of Australia's unique animals, is common in the Blue Mountains along virgin parts of the Grose River and its tributaries. This egg-laying mammal lives in long burrows in the banks and finds food at the bottom of the river with its sensitive bill. Platypuses were once hunted, and their skins were used in rug making. In time the animal was endangered, but now the species is strictly protected by law.

Even more interesting as mountains are the Australian Alps farther south in the same range. They form the highest land in Australia, with Mount Kosciusko (7,328 feet) the highest peak on the continent. The central parts of the Australian Alps are the Snowy Mountains, which may be said to be a key area for understanding the phytogeography of Australia.

Within this limited area are floral elements of the most diverse origins. Among the more than seven hundred vascular plants in the Snowy Mountains are many species whose forerunners must have grown in New Zealand, Antarctica, South America, South Africa, the tropics, and even the Northern Hemisphere. It is interesting to observe how plants originating in the colder parts of New Zealand, Antarctica, and South America become more common as one gets higher up the Snowy Mountains. In the lowlands, such plants comprise only about 3 percent of all species, but above six thousand feet the proportion increases to 20 percent.

I visited the Snowy Mountains in the beginning of November— early summer. There were large patches of snow both above and below the tree limit. Farthest up the slopes, to a level of about 6,500 feet, were woods of snow gums (*Eucalyptus niphophila*) with white trunks. Many were standing in three feet of snow. These low, wind-cut trees present a pattern very much like those in subarctic areas of Alaska, Canada, and Eurasia. Significantly, Mount Kosciusko is the only part of Australia that underwent glaciation at the same time as did the Northern Hemisphere. Although the plant communities and frost phenomena are also similar, in detail almost everything is different.

It is a fascinating experience in November, the month of flowers and singing birds in Australia, to wander from luxuriant valleys in the Snowy Mountains up to the alpine heaths and fields of snow on Mount Kosciusko. The emu (*Dromaius novaehollandiae*) is still quite common on the savannas in the valleys. Sometimes it visits the mountain meadows just below the tree limit. Although eucalyptus trees dominate the forests, there are also many acacias, whose yellow mimosa blossoms fill the woods with scent. Here the koala finds sanctuary.

Parrots are a striking feature of the woods on the Snowy

Mountains, even when the snow is deep. The magnificent gang-gang (*Callocephalon fimbriatum*) in red and greyish-black, the white cockatoo (*Kakatoë galerita*), the yellow-tailed black cockatoo (*Calyptorhynchus funereus*), and the elegant eastern rosella (*Platycercus eximinius*) with blue wings and tail are especially noticeable.

Though the Great Dividing Range is the largest montane region of Australia, other highlands are scattered all over the continent, from the Hamersley Range and the King Leopold Range in Western Australia, the MacDonnell Range in the deserts of the Northern Territory, to the Musgrave and Flinders ranges in South Australia.

In Australia, as in other parts of the world, mountains are often the last refuge of rare animals. The rare scaly-tailed possum (*Wyulda squamicaudata*) has its only known range in the Kimberleys of Western Australia. It is known only from four specimens, of which two were collected in 1954. Since then no trace of it has been found. The ring-tailed rock-wallaby (*Petrogale xanthopus xanthopus*) was common in parts of South Australia, New South Wales, and Queensland in the 1920's, but it has declined markedly as a result of hunting for its very attractive and valuable pelt. At present this wallaby has its stronghold in the Flinders Range in South Australia, where it is totally protected, but a diversity of control measures in different states makes it rather easy for hunters to kill this extremely rare wallaby in South Australia and market the pelts in the bordering states where the species is not protected. This seriously endangers the survival of this rock-wallaby. The long-nosed rat kangaroo (*Potorous tridactylus*) was formerly distributed across eastern Australia from Queensland to Victoria and South Australia. It is found now only in a few isolated areas in the eastern states, while in South Australia and Western Australia it has been exterminated, chiefly as a result of the deforestation of the mountain slopes.

In August, 1966, a living specimen of a marsupial previously known only from fossil material was discovered on Mount Hotham in the Victorian Alps. This animal is a very small phalangerid, the mountain pygmy possum (*Burramys parvus*), which was thought to have become extinct in historical time. In 1969 a well-established colony was found near the treeline at over 6,000 feet in the Kosciusko National Park in New South Wales. The broad-toothed rat (*Mastacomys fuscus*) occurs at present only in small relict colonies in the Kosciusko National Park in New South Wales and parts of southern Victoria and Tasmania.

Finally, a mountain bird, the black grass-wren (*Amytornis housei*), is very rare, and has been seen only a few times in the Kimberleys in Western Australia.

Marshes, Lakes, and Rivers

As a consequence of its very dry climate, Australia has a poorly developed system of rivers. Relatively few of its watercourses are permanent. The lakes and marshes vary in size in relation to the periods of rain and drought. Occasionally mighty rivers may dry up entirely and their beds remain waterless for several years. A large proportion of rivers fade out before they reach the sea. Erosion has led to silting-up of water holes and billabongs along inland rivers. Such conditions make it difficult for aquatic animals to survive. However, many species, particularly fishes, have solved the problem by developing an ability to aestivate for prolonged periods. These special conditions combined with the long isolation of Australia make the Australian freshwater fishes unique in the same evolutionary sense as the eucalypts and marsupials. Many of these fishes are now endangered, not only by man-made changes in their water habitats but also by the introduction of numerous exotic fishes, which prey on or compete with the Australian species. What has happened so tragically in the land habitats of Australia is also going on in the waters.

The vegetation bordering rivers, marshes, and swamps is also important for many animals. One species that seemed to be confined to riverine and marshy thickets, Gilbert's rat kangaroo (*Potorous gilberti*), was found in 1840 in Western Australia but has never been seen again. At that time the Aborigines frequently captured or speared it, and a tribe could kill a great number in a few hours. So Europeans are not guilty of the extermination of this marsupial. Among other species of swamps and rivers threatened by extinction is the western ringtail (*Pseudocheirus occidentalis*) from Western Australia, which already had a limited distribution when it first became known. Although now protected by law, it was in 1962 considered to be near extinction.

The Australian freshwater crocodile (*Crocodylus johnstoni*) is in danger of extinction due to overhunting. Like its saltwater relative, *C. porosus,* it plays an important and useful role in fish

ecology. Their local extermination in some waters has coincided
with the depletion of the barramundi, a valuable commercial fish.
The same phenomenon in fish is known from Asian and African
waters where crocodiles have been locally exterminated. The freshwater crocodile is protected only in Western Australia and the
Northern Territory, but it is heavily poached in these areas, from
where skins are taken to Queensland and exported from that state.

The Australian tiger snake (*Notechis scutatus*) is chiefly found
in and near freshwater swamps in southern Australia (mainly
Western Australia, Victoria, and New South Wales) and some
off-shore islands, where it has been severely reduced owing to
habitat alterations, diminishing food supply (frogs are the main
diet), and direct persecution. It seems that the tiger snake is not
adaptable to a changing environment and has difficulty in building
up its numbers in localities where they have been depleted. In
1970–72 the situation has become so bad that the species is facing
extinction. The Australian tiger snake is of great value to medicine.
Its venom is frequently used for laboratory research in biochem-
istry.

Coasts and Islands

When Captain James Cook's *Endeavour* anchored on April 29,
1770, in a wide bay in what is now New South Wales about ten
miles south of Sydney, there were two naturalists on board, an
Englishman, Joseph Banks, and a Swede, Daniel Solander, a dis-
ciple of Linnaeus. They made so many discoveries during the
week they stayed there, and became so enthusiastic over all the
new herbs and trees they found, that the water was given the name
Botany Bay. Not much of the wildlife, either plants or animals,
that Banks and Solander found there less than two hundred years
ago remains today. Cook and his men made several remarkable
zoological discoveries around Botany Bay, Cook himself describing
what was clearly a small kangaroo species. Cook is therefore often
credited with "discovering" the kangaroo. Dutch sailors had, however, found and described kangaroos in western Australia as long
before as 1629.

The coming of Europeans began a fateful phase in the natural
history of Australia. Previously the flora and fauna, including man
and in spite of the dingo, had fused into a well-balanced ecosystem.
The arrival of Europeans, with sheep, cattle, rabbits, and many

other foreign animals and plants in their wake, upset an equilibrium that had lasted millions of years. The process of change is now going on at a furious pace, and all the highly specialized native species are in danger. In the coastal area of New South Wales, where the European colonization is most advanced, native animals and plants without too great an admixture of foreign species can be found only in some nature reserves such as the Royal National Park on the coast around the Hacking Inlet.

This reserve is representative of the various natural environments of this high-rainfall coastal area, ranging from seashore and sparsely wooded heath to luxuriant subtropical forests. Near the shore the dunes have been tamed by grass; somewhat higher on the dunes is a dense carpet of various plants. On the dune marsh, wind-cut shrubs, especially *Banksia,* crowd together, making a natural hedge beyond which are vast heaths with dense maquis vegetation. In spring (September–October) the herbs, shrubs, and small trees on this heath bloom in cascades of colour. Many birds live there, too, some of them, such as the parrots, with striking plumage. Lories in blood-red, blue, green, and gold search in pairs for food in the bushes. Never before had I seen such an intense red as on the breasts of these birds. Rosellas, cockatoos, parakeets, and other parrots, large and small, added other splashes of brilliant colour. But even more dazzling sensations awaited me. The bush heaths are the haunt of fairy wrens (*Malurus*), a group of birds found mainly in Australia, where there are thirteen species. These small balls of down with their sweet voices are reminiscent of the European long-tailed tit, both of them with long tails which they hold upright as the American and European wrens do. Fairy wrens can be seen everywhere in the bush, and in all shades from sky-blue to violet.

It is tragic that the habitats of the eastern coast, the richest in plants and animals, have been more devastated than any other area of Australia. But other coasts have also suffered because all denser settlements are situated along the coasts. The animal life not only of coastal areas but of islands is particularly vulnerable to human occupation. Off Australia Kangaroo, Lord Howe, and Norfolk islands have been affected most.

Two coastal mammals from the mainland seem to have disappeared forever: the western chestnut mouse (*Thetomys nanus*) of Western Australia has not been observed since the 1850's; and the long-eared pseudo-rat (*Pseudomys auritus*), which lived along

the edges of dry salt-water lagoons in South Australia, seems to
have been exterminated more than a hundred years ago. Eleven
mammals of the coasts are endangered. The rufous rat kangaroo
(*Aepyprymnus rufescens*), once abundant and dispersed all over
the coast of New South Wales from the seashore to the mountain
slopes, is very rare and its range is reduced to scattered colonies
in northeastern New South Wales and Queensland. The brush-
tailed rat kangaroo (*Bettongia penicillata penicillata*) was once a
common animal in eastern Australia, where it still exists locally in
New South Wales and Victoria. Also, the southwestern race, *B. p.
ogilbyi,* survives only in a small population in southwestern Western Australia. Lesueur's rat kangaroo (*B. lesueuri*), the only burrowing species of the kangaroo family and once distributed almost
throughout Australia, is today restricted to the Bernier, Dorre,
and Barrow islands off Western Australia. This tremendous decrease was caused by the spread of pasture lands, disturbance by
man and cattle, competition for water, hunting, predation by dogs
and foxes, and so on. The species is now protected. Two of the
islands where it occurs have been established as reserves, but
unfortunately there are goats on Bernier Island, so the vegetation
there will certainly be destroyed, thus endangering the rat kangaroo
as well as other rare marsupials.

The barred bandicoot (*Perameles bougainvillei*), formerly occurring over vast areas of Australia, is found only on Bernier and
Dorre islands in Shark Bay in Western Australia. The western
hare-wallaby (*Lagorchestes hirsutus*) is today also confined to
these islands. Perhaps some small populations are left in Western
and South Australia. Habitat changes during the last thirty years
due to the introduction of livestock and cultivation are probably
the main reason for the decline. Bernier and Dorre islands have
become a refuge for endangered marsupials. The banded hare-
wallaby (*Lagostrophus fasciatus*) occurs there after having been
exterminated on the mainland as early as the beginning of the
1910's, perhaps already in 1906. Two other rare species, the
ashy-grey mouse (*Gyomys albocinereus*) and the Shark Bay
mouse (*Thetomys praecornis*), are at present probably occurring
only on these islands. The false water rat (*Xeromys myoides*)
is known only from two coastal locations in Queensland and is
apparently very rare. The New Holland mouse (*Pseudomys
novaehollandiae*) was known only from four specimens collected
in New South Wales between 1840 and the 1880's, and thought

to be extinct until it was found in 1967 and 1968 in two localities at the coast of New South Wales and one in Victoria.

Typical of the many birds of the coasts and islands that are seriously menaced and have become rare is the southwestern Australian ground parrot (*Pezoporus wallicus flaviventris*). Formerly widespread on coastal heaths and offshore islands, this bird is today found only in some swampy areas of the southern coastlands of Western Australia. Here again altered habitat, brush fires, intensive hunting (because its flesh was much esteemed), predation from foxes and domestic cats were more than the bird could withstand. It is now protected. The same reasons caused the decline of the southeastern Australian ground parrot (*P. w. wallicus*), now limited to a few coastal heaths of South Australia, Victoria, and New South Wales. The decline of the golden-shouldered paradise parakeet (*Psephotus chrysopterygius chrysopterygius*) of the Cape York peninsula in Queensland (now estimated to number less than 250 birds) is thought to be its desirability as a cage bird and predation by introduced mammals. According to D. L. Serventy, illegal trapping for trade purposes in the past few years has had adverse effects on this parrot. Another rare race of the same bird, the hooded paradise parrot (*P. c. dissimilis*), is restricted to Arnhem Land in the Northern Territory.

The noisy scrubbird (*Atrichornis clamosus*) is a small passerine that was recently given wide publicity by heartening efforts to save its only remaining habitat from being converted into a town. In the past this bird was confined to dense scrub along the coast of southern Western Australia. Destruction of its habitat led to such a decline in its numbers that it was considered extinct as early as 1889. A population of about fifty birds was discovered in 1961 on the coastal slopes of Mount Gardner. A small reserve of about one thousand acres was established for the bird and 13,600 acres will soon be added to this. Unfortunately, a town site was planned for about one thousand acres of the proposed reserve, including the territories of a few breeding pairs. The IUCN and the World Wildlife Fund joined Australian conservation and scientific organizations in strong protests. Broadcasts and articles in Britain as well as Australia were for months focussed on the noisy scrubbird. It was a major conflict but the efforts of the conservation press were crowned with success. The town site was cancelled and the land was declared a faunal reserve. The whole population of the scrubbird, estimated at forty pairs, will be protected. "May it never be extinct again!" concluded a speaker at the ceremony inaugurating the reserve.

A near relative to the former is the rufous scrubbird (*A. rufescens*) that occurs in a small coastal area on the border of New South Wales and Queensland. Fortunately its habitat is preserved within forest reserves. Environmental changes have reduced its range.

The black-and-white wren (*Malurus leucopterus*), one of the charming little fairy wrens mentioned earlier, is restricted to the Dirk Hartog and Barrow islands off Western Australia. The bird is particularly endangered on Barrow Island, which is heavily exploited. The bristle-bird (*Dasyornis brachypterus*) is also in danger. The western form (*D. b. longirostris*), once found in a coastal swamp between Perth and Albany in Western Australia, was considered extinct, until one bird was collected in 1945. Since then this race has been found in small numbers within the reserve set aside for the noisy scrubbird mentioned above. The eastern race (*D. b. brachypterus*) is also threatened in its last dwelling places in eastern New South Wales and eastern Victoria. A near relative, the western rufous bristle-bird (*D. broadbenti littoralis*) occurs only in a narrow coastal belt in Western Australia. It was last seen in 1940 and may be still found in the coastal thickets which are rarely visited by human beings. However, development threatens the restricted habitat.

The western whipbird (*Psophodes nigrogularis*) is a vanishing species divided in three races, which seem to be all endangered owing to habitat destruction. It is now restricted to some small coastal areas of scrubland in southwestern Australia (*P. n. nigrogularis*), South Australia (*P. n. pondalowiensis*), and Victoria (*P. n. leucogaster*).

Australia's rarest reptile is the short-necked tortoise (*Pseudemydura umbrina*), believed to occur in coastal swamps north and south of Perth in Western Australia. Intensive exploitation of this area reduced the habitats of this tortoise, and it had long been considered extinct when a specimen was recorded in 1953 north of Perth and the species was found to occur on privately owned land that was being subjected to clearing and drainage for agriculture and industrial activities. Here was another emergency for the Department of Fisheries and Fauna of Western Australia. Fortunately the department was again successful, reserving 533 acres containing the only swamps where the tortoise was known to survive. In 1967 more than two hundred tortoises were found in one of the two reserves, and there were about a hundred in the other one.

The Australian saltwater crocodile (*Crocodylus porosus*) has become endangered because of heavy persecution for its highly valuable skin. It is protected only in Western Australia but needs protection throughout.

The dugong found on the East African coast also occurs on the coasts of the northern half of Australia. Because of the scarcity of human beings in this part of Australia, it seems to be better off here than in Africa and Asia. But even here the number is dwindling. It is worth recalling that in 1893 a herd of dugongs over three miles long and three hundred yards wide was reported in Moreton Bay near Brisbane. This is an indication of the capacity of submarine seaweed beds to support a minimum population of a large marine mammal, which in turn could be harvested as a meat source for man. Today the sea-grass areas of the Gulf of Carpentaria support the largest numbers in Australia. At times herds of up to a hundred dugongs can still be seen.

Kangaroo Island, near Adelaide in South Australia, was the home of the Kangaroo Island emu (*Dromaius diamenianus*). Early settlers exterminated this bird in 1803. King Island also had an endemic ostrich, the King Island emu (*D. ater*), which became extinct the same year because of hunting. The mainland emu (*D. novae-hollandiae*) is nowadays also rare in most parts of its reduced range but is still locally common in Western Australia and northwestern Queensland.

Between three hundred and four hundred miles east of Australia is volcanic Lord Howe Island. This island has undergone a tremendous depletion of life forms since Europeans came there. In addition to those birds wiped out by man and his domestic animals, many others were killed between 1918 and 1928 by rats that came ashore from a wrecked ship. The list of extinct or endangered birds is as follows:

Lord Howe purple gallinule (*Porphyrio porphyrio albus*). Extinct before 1834.

Lord Howe Island metallic wood pigeon (*Columba vitiensis godmanae*). Extinct in 1790.

Lord Howe Island green parakeet (*Cyanoramphus novae-zelandiae subflavescens*). Extinct in 1869.

Lord Howe grey-headed blackbird (*Turdus poliocephalus vinitinctus*). Extinct in 1918.

Lord Howe Island grey warbler (*Gerygone igata insularis*). Extinct in 1919.

Lord Howe Island grey fantail (*Rhipidura fuliginosa cervina*). Extinct in 1928.

Lord Howe Island white-eye (*Zosterops strenua*). Exterminated between 1918 and 1928.

Lord Howe Island starling (*Aplonis fuscus hullianus*). Extinct in 1918.

Lord Howe wood rail (*Tricholimnas sylvestris*). Endemic and rare. Endangered by human persecution and predation by pigs and rats.

Norfolk Island, the remotest Australian island included in this chapter, is a volcanic island about eight hundred miles east of Australia and midway between New Zealand and New Caledonia. This island has been greatly affected by man, though not so many birds have become extinct here as on Lord Howe Island. Gone forever are the Norfolk Island kereu (*Hemiphaga novaeseelandiae spadicea*), which became extinct in 1801, and the Norfolk Island kaka (*Nestor meridionalis productus*) which vanished in 1851. The following endemic birds are endangered: the grey-headed blackbird (*Turdus poliocephalus poliocephalus*), the Norfolk Island starling (*Aplonis fuscus fuscus*), and the Norfolk Island parakeet (*Cyanoramphus novaezelandiae cookii*).

Tasmania

Tasmania, south of southeastern Australia, is about 26,000 square miles in size. It is ecologically diverse, sections of the western part being covered with wet, closed, temperate rain forests, including southern beeches (*Nothofagus*), and open forests dominated by eucalypts. Tasmania is chiefly mountainous and moors occur above the timber line. Connected with the continent in geologically recent time (probably about ten thousand years ago during the last world-wide lowering of sea level), Tasmania has harboured some animals after their disappearance from continental Australia, and vice versa. The Anglo-Tasmanians have not been merciful to animal life. They exterminated the Tasmanian emu (*Dromaius novae-hollandiae diemenensis*) in 1838 and repeated the process when the mainland emu was introduced. As late as 1965 the Tasmanian authorities authorized the hunting of Cape

Barren geese (*Cereopsis novae-hollandiae*), a species on the official list of the most endangered species. The shooting took place on the breeding islands and 140 birds were killed, not counting those that may have died at sea.

However, Tasmanians can be credited with having protected certain animals that faced extinction on the Australian mainland. One of them is the eastern native cat (*Dasyurus viverrinus*). This species formerly occurred widely in eastern Australia, but trapping, poisoning, and other sorts of persecution almost completely wiped it out. It is now confined to a few isolated areas, but in Tasmania it is still rather common and completely protected.

One of the most regrettable instances of the disappearances of an animal on the Australian mainland was that of the Tasmanian wolf or thylacine (*Thylacinus cynocephalus*), the largest of the marsupial carnivores. Europeans did not have a hand in the retreat of this predator from continental Australia but they nearly succeeded in exterminating it in Tasmania. In fact, it is very likely that they did. It is thought that the mainland Tasmanian wolf succumbed during the Pleistocene as a result of competion from the dingo. This seems unlikely since there was sufficient prey for both species, and the dingo does not seem to have been numerous. In Tasmania, however, man alone was responsible for the tremendous decrease of the Tasmanian wolf. When the thylacine was still fairly common in many areas of Tasmania it was accused of damaging livestock, and the authorities declared war against it. Bounties were paid beginning in 1888, and up to 1914 at least 2,268 of the wolves were reported killed, but this official figure is much below the true total. About 1910 a sharp decline of the species, thought to have been caused by disease, set in. Of course, destruction of habitats also played its part and the result was the almost complete extinction of the wolf. No specimens have come to scientific attention since the early 1930's, but it is claimed that an animal was killed in 1961. During the past ten years a number of sightings, tracks, and droppings have been reported. An expedition searched for the wolf for six months in 1963–64 without finding any trace of it, but in 1966 footprints and even fresh hair from a lair were reported to have been found in northwestern Tasmania. The Tasmanian wolf is now protected by law and in 1966 a reserve of 1,600,000 acres was set aside for it in southwestern Tasmania, but there is no news about its existence.

The Tasmanian devil (*Sarcophilus harrisii*) is another marsupial carnivore restricted to the island, and like the Tasmanian wolf, it also inhabited the mainland in earlier times. It has been heavily hunted but seems to hold on. The Tasmanian rat kangaroo (*Bettongia cuniculus*), also endemic in Tasmania, is protected against hunting but it is rare and declining owing to invasion of its habitat by farms. However, it also occurs in areas which will probably be less affected by man. As mentioned above, the Tasmanian eastern grey kangaroo (*Macropus giganteus tasmaniensis*) is endangered owing to reduction of habitats.

Flinders Island is located in Bass Strait and is nearer to Tasmania than to continental Australia. It is inhabited by a wombat (*Vombatus ursinus ursinus*) that has disappeared from all other islands in Bass Strait as a result of being hunted for food as well as changes of habitat. It was very common on Flinders Island in the early nineteenth century, but today it is rare and in danger.

Among the birds we must mention the Cape Barren goose again. The bulk of the small population breeds on islands in Bass Strait close to Tasmania and also occurs on islands off the south coast of Australia. Its rarity is due to persecution by man and perhaps the loss of suitable grazing habitats. The Furneaux Islands are by far the most important breeding area of the Cape Barren goose. By 1960 the population was down to 943 birds, but after 1960, when hunting was prohibited, it had increased to over 2,600 in 1964. This level has since been maintained. In 1964 a small breeding population of less than one hundred pairs was discovered on eleven islands lying off Wilson's Promontory, the southeastern tip of mainland Australia and not far from the Furneaux group. Islands in Spencer Gulf, South Australia, are another Cape Barren goose area with about five hundred breeding pairs. Finally, a small population (in 1952 eighty-one birds) exists on islands in the Archipelago of the Recherche, Western Australia. This means that there are all together not more than four thousand Cape Barren geese in the wild.

The Tasmania ground parrot (*Pezoporus wallicus leachi*) is, like the mainland races, very rare; and it is decreasing owing to habitat destruction.

NEW ZEALAND

Because New Zealand is the most isolated large landmass in the world, many of its plants and animals followed lines of evolution that made them unique. In its virgin state New Zealand was a gigantic museum, an experimental garden in a region which, although neighbouring on Antarctica, is within both subtropical and temperate zones. But this treasure trove has by now been largely destroyed.

During the fourteenth century, at the time of the second wave of immigration of Maoris into New Zealand, the country consisted mainly of forests and savannas. Most of these forests, covering perhaps sixty million acres, were intact as recently as a century ago, when European colonization began. Now forests cover only about fourteen million acres, and they are mainly planted forests, with only remnants of the natural forests here and there. Elsewhere there are pastures and arable land. It is no exaggeration to call the consequences for plant and animal life a cataclysm. The remaining natural regions have, moreover, been greatly injured by the many exotic as well as domestic animals introduced during the nineteenth century by the English.

Cultivation in New Zealand has succeeded in supplying great herds of livestock with food, and the vegetation seems able to tolerate the grazing pressure. But it is regrettable that the Europeans did not realize the value of the native timber and the importance of forests in storing and distributing water as well as in preventing erosion. There are, luckily, remnants of the natural forests, particularly in the mountain regions, which can be seen in all their former glory. Outstanding among the trees are the enormous kauri pines (*Agathis australis*), resembling the giant redwoods of California. Such other conifers as cedars (*Libocedrus*), cypresses (*Dacrydium*), and several species of *Podocarpus* occur in both lowland and highland forests. The small-leaved southern beeches (*Nothofagus*) climb the mountains, particularly on the South Island. Most of the forests I have seen on the subtropical North Island are, even more than in southern Australia, typical rain forests with most of the attributes of climax vegetation. Lianas trail, mosses and lichens cover the trunks of trees that often have a girth of fifteen or twenty feet, and epiphytes grow from the branches; the leaves of the understory vegetation are moist and wet; tree ferns (*Dicksonia* and *Cyathea*) in the valleys throw up immense fronds like green fountains. The woods on some of these mountains leave hardly anything to be desired by a lover of tropical forests, but there is still a most striking difference compared with continental tropical rain forests. There are no frog concerts and hardly any reptiles, and the only mammals are those introduced by man. Birds sing beautifully, but it is disappointing to discover that the singers are mostly thrushes and blackbirds brought from Europe. Many European birds—yellowhammers, starlings, dunnocks, skylarks, etc.—meet in New Zealand other birds introduced from Australia, Asia, Africa, and America. Game birds in particular were brought to New Zealand in very great numbers.

The only vertebrate in New Zealand (apart from some birds and introduced species) whose origin and date of arrival are known is man. Men were living in New Zealand when Abel Tasman in 1642 "discovered" the country, but they had not been there very long, the first Polynesians probably arriving about one thousand years ago. But it would seem that it was not until about four hundred years later that a large wave of Maoris reached the islands. Although man has been active in New Zealand for about six hundred years, it is only in the last one hundred years that his influence has made itself felt. The terrible destruction by the white man in 150 years in New Zealand is comparable to what he did in Australia and North America. The Maoris, on the other hand, in over five hundred years in New Zealand, have helped to wipe out birds, including the huge wingless moas.

Zoologically, New Zealand is strikingly different from all other major areas, because it comprises no native mammals except bats. However, there are several birds and a few reptiles and amphibians. The birds are unique. In addition there is the tuatara (*Sphenodon punctatus*), a survivor of the ancient order *Rhyncocephalia* that disappeared 100 million years ago. Among other reptiles there are only two endemic genera of geckos and one of skinks. There is also an amphibian genus, *Leiopelma,* with two very primitive species, the only native frogs of New Zealand.

Birds replaced terrestrial mammals on New Zealand and filled a wide range of habitats. The giant flightless moas, which were represented by twenty-seven species, sometimes reached a height of twelve feet and were thus among the largest birds ever known. They were grazing birds utilizing the grasslands as kangaroos do in Australia and antelopes in Africa. They are all now extinct. Twenty-two species were contemporary with the Maoris, who hunted them for food, as is shown clearly by many finds from the last one thousand years made on both the North and South Islands. Before man arrived, the moas and other birds had few or no enemies, a fact which no doubt made them unwary and easy to catch. Their huge eggs must also have been coveted by the Maoris as food and for domestic utensils.

Maoris brought dogs and rats (*Rattus exulans*) to New Zealand and these helped to wipe out many birds. The last moa (*Megalapteryx didinus*) is thought to have been killed on the South Island as late as 1773. At least forty-three species of birds have been exterminated on New Zealand since the arrival of the Polynesians, who appear to have exterminated in addition to the moas two flightless geese, a large swan, two ducks, an eagle, several flightless rails, and many passerines. The record of Europeans is not much worse: During the last two centuries nine species have become extinct on the islands. However, the introduction of exotic animals combined with the destruction of forests, the burning of scrub, and the drainage of swamps to make way for livestock and agriculture has driven numerous native species to the verge of extinction. Some will surely be wiped out in the near future.

It is highly regrettable that the unique nature of New Zealand was spoiled by Europeans with the introduction of all kinds of exotic mammals and birds. Not only were pigs, goats and other domestic animals brought in to provide meat but also wild mammals, such as deer and rabbits, for hunting and sport. One mistake led to another. Several species soon began destroying grain, forest, and native animals. Not less than fifty-three exotic mammals have been introduced, of which thirty-four are still here. When the rabbits, introduced before 1838, became too abundant, predators such as ermines, polecats, and weasels were brought in; they quickly established themselves, and like rats and dogs, turned on the native birds. The few reptiles and amphibians were also affected. Herds of sheep have changed the islands beyond recognition.

The red deer, introduced in 1851, soon made itself at home and is now found almost everywhere. It multiplied so rapidly and did so much damage that drastic steps had to be taken; in 1931 the protection of deer was ended and bounties were paid for their destruction. From 1932 to 1954, professional hunters engaged by the government killed 512,384 red deer. The total number shot during the same period is said to have been more than two million. Finally, in 1958 a poison campaign was undertaken but the deer are still there.

Another serious mistake was the introduction of the brush-tail opossum (*Trichosurus vulpecula*) into New Zealand in 1858 as a valuable fur-bearing animal. In New Zealand unlike Australia, this opossum, which is herbivorous, caused tremendous destruction in forests and orchards. It increased rapidly and soon the New Zealanders declared a war of extermination against it, and in 1945 alone they killed 922,088 of these animals. To these wild animals must be added domestic animals such as cattle, goats, and sheep. About six million head of cattle and forty million sheep are now grazing in New Zealand. Practically all strata of vegetation from the grasses to the crowns of trees have been seriously damaged, a fact which has led to a further reduction of the area of forest land; the ground layer has been grazed off, preparing the way in many places for serious erosion.

The original nature of New Zealand has been destroyed forever and has been replaced by a composite nature from all continents. It is now too late to change this and to save the native vegetation. One may question if it is now really worthwhile to wipe out deer but keep millions of sheep. Ecologists, for example, Raymond Dasmann (in 1963), now question whether about two million deer as a source of meat, hides, and human recreation are not more valuable than domestic animals grazing in the same area. So it may be decided that the utilization of some lands by deer is more efficient as well as economically profitable than the use of the same areas by domestic herds.

The North Island

The North Island (44,131 square miles) was once covered by a mantle of forests like most of the rest of New Zealand. Magnificent semitropical rain forests had evolved in the absence of browsing animals. These forests were rich in birds, of which two species, now gone, were unique and extremely interesting. The North Island laughing owl (*Sceloglaux albifacies rufifacies*) was exterminated in 1889, probably by rats and cats. The largest of the New Zealand owls, it fed on lizards and insects and had also turned to rats and mice. Another New Zealand bird, the huia (*Heteralocha acutirostris*), was remarkable because the bills of the male and the female looked as if they belonged to two totally different species. The male had a short, arched, thick starling-like bill, while the female's bill was slender, long, and curved like that of a nectar-feeding bird. These differences suggest different feeding techniques: Both sexes fed on insects, but apparently the male chopped rotten bark from trees while the female probed crevices. When the forests were destroyed, the huia disappeared about 1907. There are at least four birds that are perilously rare on the North Island itself. Some of these, such as the New Zealand brown teal (*Anas aucklandica chlorotis*), occur on the South Island as well, formerly distributed all over New Zealand. This teal is now restricted to a few areas on the North Island and to Fiordland on the South Island. In 1957 its population was estimated at one thousand to fifteen hundred birds. It is now protected but most of the swamps, forests, and ponds in which it lived have been destroyed.

The North Island bush wren (*Xenicus longipes stokesi*) occurs only in forests of the Rimutaka range, but it may already be extinct. The North Island kokako (*Callaeas cinerea wilsoni*) still survives in patches of relict forests in the northern part of the North Island. Formerly it occurred throughout the island, but the clearing of forests and predation by opossums, ermines, and rats have led to its decline. The North Island piopio (*Turnagra capensis tanagra*) is another of New Zealand's many peculiar birds. This thrushlike bird was common in southern North Island when the Europeans arrived, but by the 1880's it had become uncommon and is now extremely rare if not extinct.

The South Island

Prior to the coming of the Europeans, the South Island (58,120 square miles) was largely forested with temperate forests of which remnants still exist. There are also rain forests, as, for instance, in Westland. The South Island is more mountainous and alpine than the North Island, a great chain of mountains more than ten thousand feet high dominating the western and central areas. Originally grasslands probably covered a larger area than on the North Island and hence provided somewhat different habitats.

Extinct species on the South Island since about 1600 include a lesser moa, *Megalapteryx didinus,* the last species of two families of the giant birds. The remains of some specimens still have skin and flesh attached to the head; one even had an eye in its socket when it was found. Apparently *M. didinus* survived until the 1770's, probably as late as 1785, while the brawny great moa (*Dinornis torosus*) is estimated to have become extinct about 1670 and the burly lesser moa (*Eurapteryx gravis*) about 1640.

The New Zealand quail (*Coturnix novae-zelandiae*) was reported to be very common on the North Island in the 1770's. On the South Island it was abundant until 1865, when it declined rapidly; by 1880 the species was gone throughout New Zealand. Reports from the period 1865–80 agree that extinction resulted from fires that destroyed food, cover, and the birds themselves, combined with predation by dogs, cats, and rats. Later analyses suggest that diseases imported with pheasants and other game birds may also help to explain the extraordinary rapid disappearance of the New Zealand quail.

Many birds that have been exterminated on the North Island still hold out on the South Island. One of them is the rare southern crested grebe (*Podiceps cristatus australis*). One of the most notable rediscoveries of a bird occurred in 1948 when an expedition in the Murchison Mountains of the South Island found a small colony of the takahe (*Notornis mantelli*), a big flightless rail thought to be extinct since 1898. Subfossil remains in Polynesian kitchen middens on the North Island indicated that the takahe also occurred on that island. With the fate of the moas and other flightless birds in mind, the scientific world was greatly surprised. The government immediately set aside a reserve of 400,000 acres, in which the takahe occupies about five hundred acres close to a lake. The cause of the decline of this species is thought to be changing climate perhaps combined with hunting by the Polynesians. Red deer and wapiti also are a threat to the takahe, because these browsers destroy the vegetation in the bird's habitat. It is also true that the reproduction rate of this rail is very low and severe winters seem to take a heavy toll of the young birds. Twenty years of protection has paid off in results, however, so that the population of the takahe was in 1969 estimated at nearly two hundred pairs.

One of New Zealand's rarest birds at present is the kakapo or owl parrot (*Strigops habroptilus*), a flightless nocturnal bird that lives on the ground and climbs trees, from which it glides to the ground. Formerly the kakapo was widely distributed in both the North and South Islands as well as on Chatham and Stewart islands. It seems to have been exterminated on the North Island by 1906; and it now occurs only in a few isolated areas on the South Island. In 1961 its population was one hundred, with thirty in one area. The kakapo suffered severely from the destruction of forests and the introduction of pigs, cats, dogs, ermines, polecats, and rats. The bird is, of course, protected by law, but this is of little help against habitat deterioration and exotic predators. The situation of the orange-fronted parakeet (*Cyanoramphus malherbi*) seems to be even more precarious. It once occurred on Little Barrier and Hen islands off the North Island, but it is now gone from there. On the South Island it was found in forests and subalpine scrub; today it is apparently limited to a small wood in the higher southern alps of the South Island. It has been reported only five times since 1890 and may be extinct.

The South Island laughing owl (*Sceloglaux albifacies albifacies*) is another race of a species that already has lost a subspecies. It was plentiful in many areas during the nineteenth century, started to disappear about 1900, and is now almost extinct. During the 1930's it was reported from the regions of Canterbury and of lakes Wanaka and Te Anau, but its numbers have continued to dwindle and it may already be extinct. The cause of the decline was habitat changes and predators; for the latter this ground-nesting owl was an easy prey.

The South Island bush wren (*Xenicus longipes longipes*), once common in forests almost throughout the mountain regions, now consists of a small population restricted to Fiordland. The South Island kokako (*Callaeas cinerea cinerea*) is also confined to the Fiordland area. As late as 1888 it was abundant on the South Island and on Stewart Island. From the latter area it has not been observed since the 1940's and the last known record from the South Island is in Otago in 1958. The South Island piopio (*Turnagra capensis capensis*) once fairly common, seems to be on the verge of disappearing forever. Now it is rarely observed only on the southweastern coast of Otago. The last sight record was made in 1963.

Satellite Islands off New Zealand

The islands off New Zealand have lost more birds than the two main islands. There is also a large number of endangered species, many of them endemic, on these islands. Surveying these islands from north to south, we note that the Kermadec Islands, about 550 miles northeast of New Zealand, still have all their known native birds in fair numbers, probably because there has been little disturbance by Europeans.

The tuatara, New Zealand's celebrated "living fossil," once occurred from the northern tip of the North Island to near the southernmost part of the South Island. It apparently disappeared from the two main islands before the arrival of the Europeans. It is possible that the Maoris contributed to the extermination of this lizard, because subfossil remains from their kitchen middens show that they ate it. Maori dogs may also have been involved in the tuatara's decline. Fortunately, it managed to survive on about twenty small islands, most of them off the eastern coast of the North Island. The total population, according to W. H. Dawbin, probably exceeds ten thousand individuals, with most of the populations apparently maintaining themselves satisfactorily.

The fact that the tuatara survives on islands near the New Zealand coast indicates that it can hardly be climate that—as has been thought—wiped it out on the New Zealand main islands. The hatching of eggs takes more than fifteen months, making them very vulnerable to the predators man has brought to the main islands. Of course, the animals themselves are also an easy prey.

The small Taranga, or Hen, Island, off northern North Island, is presumably the last refuge of the North Island saddleback (*Creadion carunculatus rufusater*). Formerly this bird was abundant in the North Island and also occurred on smaller islands. In 1932 it was reported from the Raukumara Range in eastern North Island, where it may still survive. The population on Taranga Island was in 1964 estimated at about five hundred pairs. In the same year twenty-three birds were trapped and then released on Middle Chicken Island and in 1966 twenty-nine birds were reintroduced to Cuvier Island. Since these attempts saddlebacks have been successfully established also on Red Mercury and Fanal islands. In 1969 there were eight populations on the islands.

Little Barrier Island, north of the Hauraki Gulf, was the home of the Little Barrier Island snipe (*Coenocorypha aucklandica barrierensis*), found and captured in 1870, apparently just before it disappeared. It has not been seen since then. This race was one of five on islands around New Zealand. They are all very rare and may be extinct. Subspeciation in a wading bird is unusual. The explanation may be that it rarely flies; this sedentary habit seems to have prevented populations on neighbouring islands from joining one another.

When the Europeans arrived the stitchbird (*Notiomystis cincta*), a honey eater, was distributed almost all over the North Island, but by 1890 it was gone from this island. Today it is still found on Little Barrier Island, which is a sanctuary, but introduced feral cats are a threat to the remaining population.

The Stephen Island wren (*Xenicus lyalli*) is a remarkable example of how delicate the balance of nature can be. Apparently a single domestic cat was responsible for the extermination of this bird in 1894. The wren lived on rocks where it ran about but was never known to fly. The cat, which had come to the island with a lighthouse keeper, brought in a few specimens of the wren, which was then new to science, and continued to do so until there were no more birds left.

The king shag (*Phalacrocorax carunculatus carunculatus*) is confined to five islets lying across the outer reaches of the Marlborough Sound, northwestern South Island. The population is fewer than five hundred birds. Formerly it was more abundant. The reason for the decrease seems to be shooting by fishermen. Now this shag is completely protected by law, protection to which it responds with a slow increase.

The Chatham Islands, 370 miles east of New Zealand, are the largest of the island group belonging to the continental shelf of New Zealand. Several birds have already vanished from these islands and quite an assemblage of species is obviously going the same way. All the factors that have contributed to the extermination of birds on New Zealand have also operated on the Chatham Islands; in addition, commercial collectors of rare birds have been at work on the islands. As a result, the following birds are extinct:

Chatham Island swan (*Cygnus sumnerensis*). Occurred on New Zealand and Chatham Island. Extinct between 1590 and 1690.

Chatham Island banded rail (*Rallus dieffenbachii*). Occurred on the main island only. Exterminated between 1840 and 1845, probably by rats and cats.

Chatham Island rail (*R. modestus*). Occurred on Chatham and Mangare islands. Extinct between 1895 and 1900. Europeans introduced rabbits, goats, and cats, and destroyed the native vegetation.

Chatham Island fern bird (*Bowdleria punctata rufescens*). Occurred on Pitt and Mangare islands. Exterminated by rats between 1890 and 1900.

Chatham Island bellbird (*Anthornis melanura melanocephala*). Occurred on all islands. Last seen on Little Mangare Island in 1906.

A bird with a somewhat tricky subspecific identity on the
Chatham Islands is a rail, the eastern weka (*Gallirallus australis
hectori*). The Maoris used to kill large numbers for food, sometimes bagging as many as two thousand in a single hunt. The
weka was common in the Chatham Islands, but it became extinct
there before 1868. In 1905 specimens were reintroduced from
the South Island; they increased rapidly and are now common
on Chatham Island. But on the South Island they probably became extinct about 1925. In 1961 birds from Chatham Island
were reintroduced in the South Island, but it is doubtful if the
introduction was successful.

Many birds confined to the Chatham Islands are now in danger
of extermination:

> New Zealand shore plover (*Thinornis novae-seelandiae*).
> Formerly occurred on all main islands off New Zealand but now
> breeds only in South East Island of the Chatham group. About
> 140 birds were counted there in 1937–38 and in 1961.
> Chatham Island snipe (*Coenocorypha aucklandica pusilla*).
> Confined to South East Island, where it is threatened by man-
> made fires.
> Chatham Island pigeon (*Hemiphaga novaeseelandiae cha-
> thamensis*). Confined to Pitt Island and Chatham Island. Near
> extinction on the latter island.
> Forbes' parakeet (*Cyanoramphus auriceps forbesi*). Confined
> to Little Mangare Island, where only about one hundred birds
> existed in 1938.
> Chatham Island robin (*Petroica traversi*). Confined to Little
> Mangare Island, where in 1937–38 the population was estimated
> at from forty to seventy birds.
> Chatham Island tui (*Prosthemadera novaeseelandiae chat-
> hamensis*). Found only on this island.

South of the South Island across Foveaux Strait is Stewart
Island, with forests that reach from the hills down to the sandy
beaches. The birds of the Stewart group—which includes some
offshore islets—comprise several interesting species that have their
last stronghold there. Thus, Big South Cape Island, off southern
Stewart Island, is the only place where the Stewart Island snipe
(*Coenocorypha aucklandica iredalei*) was found. Unfortunately
this island is infested with rats, which are a serious threat to the
survival of the snipe. Therefore, in August, 1964, two of the

birds were moved to an island free of predators, but both died. In December of the same year searchers failed to find any snipe left on Big South Cape Island. Perhaps the Stewart Island snipe is already extinct. It should be noted that another endemic race of the same species, the Snares Island snipe (*C. a. huegeli*), occurs in small numbers on Snares Island far to the south of Stewart Island.

Stead's bush wren (*Xenicus longipes variabilis*) seems to exist only on Big South Cape Island off Stewart Island. Rats are a great threat to this bird, and in 1964 some bush wrens were moved to a ratfree islet nearby. This translocation was fortunate, because in 1965 the bush wrens could no longer be found on the Big South Cape Island.

The South Island saddleback (*Creadion carunculatus carunculatus*) once ranged throughout the South Island and nearby islands. It has decreased greatly as a result of rat depredations and is at present found only on a few islands off Stewart Island. During the 1960's this saddleback occurred on Big South Cape Island and the nearby Solomon. The rat depredation on the former island has had disastrous results on the saddleback population—that in 1964 had largely disappeared from the northern Big South Cape Island, while in the southern half only one immature bird was found. By 1969 the saddleback was exterminated on these islands. Fortunately, thirty-six saddlebacks were captured in 1964 and released on the ratfree islands of Stage and Kaimohu; in March, 1965, it was found that these birds had settled and bred successfully on both islands. In 1969 some birds were also introduced to the nearly Bettsy Island in the same group.

The Codfish Island fernbird (*Bowdleria punctata wilsoni*) is endemic to the small island adjacent to Stewart Island whose name it bears. Because of its restrictive habitat it is sensitive to disturbances.

The Antipodes Island snipe (*Coenocorypha aucklandica meinertzhagenae*) is found only on the Antipodes Islands, about four hundred miles southeast of New Zealand, and is rare there. Here also lives the Antipodes Island parakeet (*Cyanoramphus unicolor*) with a small population, extremely vulnerable if rats should come ashore.

Two hundred miles south of Stewart Island lie the Auckland Islands. Situated in the "roaring forties," the Aucklands are much exposed to gales, so that the trees have a creeping, almost horizontal habit. Tussock grasses dominate the vegetation, but there are also thick forests of mountain rata (*Metrosideros*). Despite the strong, almost constant west winds, domestic animals were introduced. In 1807 pigs were released, and in 1850 cattle and goats, and in 1900 sheep. Rabbits were also introduced. The goats were particularly destructive to the vegetation, and the pigs, cats, and dogs have had a disastrous effect on ground-nesting birds, which were generally trusting and unafraid since they had never before met mammalian predators. One bird became extinct.

The Auckland Island merganser (*Mergus australis*), the only merganser of the Australasian region, occurred on the east coast of the South Island, but was already extinct there when the Europeans arrived. It disappeared from the Auckland Islands after man and his domestic mammals invaded the group. Perhaps the ultimate cause of its disappearance in 1905 was hunting pressure.

The last Auckland Island rail (*Rallus pectoralis muelleri*), peculiar to the islands, was thought to be exterminated in 1865 by introduced domestic animals. However, in February, 1966, it was rediscovered on Adams Island in the same group of islands. The Auckland Island flightless teal (*Anas aucklandica aucklandica*), also peculiar to these islands, is rare on Auckland Island proper, where cats and pigs threaten it, but it is commoner on the other islands.

Also, the Auckland Islands have one endemic and menaced race of the New Zealand snipe (*Coenocorypha aucklandica aucklandica*).

About 145 miles southeast of the Auckland Islands lies Campbell Island, surrounded by nine small rocky islands and thirty-nine stacks and rocks. Swamps and dense scrubs cover the lowlands, while tussock vegetation takes over at an altitude above about 450 feet. The island with its rugged cliffs is inhospitable and the climate is harsh, but this has not prevented man from introducing sheep, which have greatly modified the vegetation. The island has a flightless duck that is related to the species on the Auckland Islands. This duck, the Campbell Island flightless teal (*Anas aucklandica nesiotis*), has been collected only three times between 1866 and 1944. Its breeding grounds are unknown and it may already be extinct.

The Macquarie Islands, almost halfway between New Zealand

and Antarctica, although belonging to Australia, are treeless, with tussock grasses and mosses forming vegetation. On these islands, two species of birds have become extinct owing to the introduction of cats, dogs, and rats by sealers: the Macquarie Island banded rail (*Rallus philippensis macquariensis*), common until 1880 but extinct by 1894, and the Macquarie Island kakariki (*Cyanoramphus novaezelandiae erythrotis*), a parakeet, exterminated by 1913.

BALANCE FOR AUSTRALASIA

New Guinea is in the unique position of not having exterminated or seriously endangered any vertebrate species or subspecies during historic time, although four species of birds may be critical. Unfortunately one cannot say the same for Australia and New Zealand; since the arrival of Europeans these areas have lost at least forty-five and probably fifty-seven vertebrate species or subspecies, while 115 are now threatened by extinction. Among extinct and probably extinct vertebrates twenty-six are mammals and thirty-one are birds. Of these, twenty-six mammals and thirteen birds have been exterminated or are probably extinct in Australia, while twenty-one birds have met the same fate in New Zealand.

Of the animals on the verge of extinction there are altogether 120 species or subspecies. Of these, forty-three are mammals, seventy are birds, and seven are reptiles. All the endangered mammals are Australian, while the threatened birds and reptiles are divided almost equally between Australia and New Zealand. To the fourteen birds lost in New Zealand during the European period may be added at least thirty-five species wiped out by the Polynesians prior to the arrival of Europeans.

The conservation situation of fish in Australia is not well known. There may be several species declining from habitat alterations.

All the extinctions of vertebrates in Australia and New Zealand after the arrival of the Europeans have occurred since 1790 in Australia and 1770 in New Zealand.

Species and subspecies of vertebrates extinct during historic time (that is, in this region since 1600), probably extinct, and at present endangered by extinction. (Figures within parentheses show extinctions after 1800 or, to be exact, after 1790 in Australia and 1770 in New Zealand.) There are no extinct or probably extinct vertebrates in New Guinea.

CLASS	EXTINCT			PROBABLY EXTINCT			ENDANGERED			
	AUSTRALIA	NEW ZEALAND	TOTAL	AUSTRALIA	NEW ZEALAND	TOTAL	NEW GUINEA	AUSTRALIA	NEW ZEALAND	TOTAL
Mammals	18 (18)	–	18 (18)	8	–	8	–	43	–	43
Birds	13 (13)	17 (14)	30 (27)	–	4	4	4	37	28	69
Reptiles	–	–	–	–	–	–	–	4	3	7
Amphibians	–	–	–	–	–	–	–	–	–	–
Fish	–	–	–	–	–	–	–	–	–	–
Total	31 (31)	17 (14)	48 (45)	8	4	12	4	84	31	119

CHAPTER SEVEN

Oceania

Mention of the South Sea Islands conjures up visions of paradise. It is only natural that these islands with their palm-fringed beaches, tropical vegetation, dazzling lagoons, coral reefs, and the seemingly carefree life of the inhabitants should appear to many Europeans as a kind of Eden.

It is not surprising that sailors from disease-ridden, poverty-stricken, eighteenth-century Europe should have sung the praises of this world of idyllic islands. How much remains of this enchanting world now that white civilization with its diseases and commercialization has swept over Micronesia, Melanesia, and Polynesia? Since there are thousands of islands in the South Seas, it is difficult to give a simple answer to this question. I have visited all the main groups, from the Marianas in the west, Wake Island and Hawaii in the north, to the Society Islands in the east. My impressions were mixed, for on isolated islands or in remote mountain regions of even the principal islands, one may still find the original flora and fauna. Almost every island I have visited in the South Seas has its special character, or at least certain features, even when only a narrow sound separates two neighbouring islands. Of course, many characteristic features are found on nearly all islands, for example, the borders of coconut palms along the beaches, or the graceful reef herons (*Demigretta sacra*) in the shallow water.

The genesis and evolution of this remarkable world of islands can be better understood when the islands are seen from the air. Hundreds of millions of years ago volcanic eruptions at the bottom of the sea thrust many of the volcanoes high above the sea. The differences in submarine depths in the South Seas are enormous; close to the Tonga Islands, for example, is the Aldrich Deep, more than five thousand fathoms (30,930 feet) deep. Thus the islands are really tall pillars rising from the depths, constantly exposed to the destructive action of rain, sun, and sea. During countless ages, moreover, myriads of small corals have built up strong walls around almost every island. And sometimes the land has disappeared from inside an encircling atoll, leaving only a lagoon in the center. Some low islands consist entirely of coral. Plants and animals have colonized and are still colonizing both volcanic and coral islands, mainly from the west.

Viti Levu in the Fiji archipelago is one of the largest islands in Melanesia and Polynesia. When I visited it I expected to find only strange animals and plants on it; but much of its flora and fauna seemed familiar and related to those I had seen in southeastern Asia, whence many floral elements have spread via New Guinea. The six hundred or so islands of the Fiji group are especially interesting in this respect, for some species from the west have not advanced beyond this area. Among these are several lizards and one snake, and the Fiji Islands are the uttermost outpost of frogs in the eastern Pacific, if introductions by man are ignored. Of course, we cannot be sure that the frogs were not brought in by prehistoric man.

A garden type of agriculture, which has been remarkably stable on the fertile soils of tropical eastern Asia, spread to the Pacific islands, where it was modified by the conditions on the islands. Groves of breadfruit, coconuts, and bananas were easily produced, often without any effect on the soil. The interior of the islands was often left untouched by the settlers, who were also dependent on the sea for food. This form of agriculture combined with fishing was the basis for an idyllic way of human life but did not allow a strong population growth all over the Pacific islands. Tribal wars, cannibalism, and voluntary limitation of excess children kept the human population in balance with the carrying capacity of the soil. The immigrants brought domestic animals such as chickens, dogs, cats, and pigs, which certainly played a role in changing the biocommunity of colonized areas, but as a whole the incursions were not destructive.

When the Europeans reached the islands about two hundred years ago, the biological harmony was destroyed. They brought in exotic plants and animals in large numbers and introduced sheep, goats, and pigs almost everywhere. Rats and mice came ashore. Insects and seeds were carried in with exotic plants. Diseases from Europe spread among the human population. New methods of farming, unsuitable to the islands, caused increasing erosion. The destruction of natural vegetation and animal life upset the ecological equilibrium in many places, making it more and more difficult for human beings to survive.

Along with other parts of the world, the Pacific islands have undergone a population explosion; the number of islanders has doubled in the last fifty years and is increasing at a tremendous rate, making the future of man on these islands quite uncertain. This, of course, affects many animals. A large number of species have disappeared, exterminated by man and his retinue of goats, pigs, and rats, and others are declining rapidly.

ANIMAL FAMILIES PECULIAR TO OCEANIA

Because the islands of the western tropical Pacific have apparently been colonized rather recently by vertebrates, only Hawaii has an endemic family, the *Drepaniidae,* the birds known as honey creepers. It also has six other endemic genera of birds. In Melanesia there are three endemic genera of amphibians and two of reptiles. On the species level the peculiarity of Oceanian terrestrial vertebrates is more pronounced. Most of the vanished species are land birds, which could not survive on volcanic islands once the forest cover was destroyed. Sea birds generally survived on the coral limestone atolls.

MICRONESIA

Among the major groups of islands scattered over the Pacific south of Japan and east of the Philippines are the Bonin Islands, the Marianas, and the Carolines.

The *Bonin Islands* are twenty-seven islands of volcanic origin about eight hundred miles southeast of Japan. Five birds have been exterminated there. The first to be wiped out was Kittlitz' thrush (*Zoothera terrestris*), which was probably endemic on Peel Island, where it was last observed in 1828. Pigs and perhaps rats, escaped from a wreck, were apparently the cause of the extermination of this species. In 1830 the first permanent settlement was established on Peel Island and was followed by a great number of goats, sheep, pigs, dogs, cats, rats, and deer. By 1930 about half of the original forests had been destroyed and four other birds, the Bonin Islands grosbeak (*Chaunoproctus ferreorostris*), not seen since 1828, the Bonin night heron (*Nycticorax caledonicus crassirostris*), the Bonin wood pigeon (*Columba versicolor*), both last observed in 1889, and the Iwo Jima rail (*Poliolimnas cinereus brevipes*), which was hunted by cats and rats and last seen about 1925, had vanished. The status of the short-tailed albatross (*Diomedea albatrus*) is a worrying matter. It is restricted to Torishima Island of the Bonin Islands. By human predation and perhaps other factors it has decreased from over a million birds in the 1800's to only about two thousand in 1940 and twenty-three in 1953. Torishima became a reserve in 1957 and a census made in 1962 showed forty-seven birds.

The *Mariana Islands* are an arc of volcanic peaks once covered by dense forests but today intensively cultivated. Located about thirteen hundred miles east of the Philippines, these islands have been inhabited by Europeans for three hundred years. Cattle and pigs were introduced early. Probably several species of birds were extirpated before zoological exploration began in 1822. As J. C. Greenway recently pointed out this may explain why there are only twenty distinct land and freshwater birds on the large Marianas, but thirty-two on Palau and eighteen on Ponape, both small islands close to and in the Carolines. Moreover, several birds in the Marianas are threatened. Owing to habitat destruction and predation by rats, cats, and dogs, the Marianas megapode (*Megapodius lapérouse lapérouse*) has been exterminated on four of the Mariana Islands, including Guam, and barely survives on only five islands. The Tinian monarch (*Monarcha takafsukasae*) has been reduced to about forty individuals on Tinian Island.

The *Palau Islands* comprise twenty-six coral-reef islands about 570 miles east of Mindanao. Despite the dense jungle on some islands several birds have declined to a dangerously low level. The Palau megapode (*Megapodius lapérouse senex*) has been exterminated on two islands and barely survives on four islands. By 1945 the Palau ground dove (*Gallicolumba canifrons*) was reduced to about thirty or forty birds on four islands and may also occur on two other islands. The Palau owl (*Otus podargina*) has been forced by habitat changes to leave several islands of the Palaus. In 1930 it was still fairly common on Koror but by 1951 it had become very rare there and had disappeared from Peleliu. The Palau fantail (*Rhipidura lepida*), found on only five islands, is also very rare.

The *Caroline Islands* number about five hundred islands extending sixteen hundred miles across the Pacific Ocean between the Palau and Marshall islands. Most of them have emerged from coral reefs but a few are mountainous and of volcanic origin. Several of the islands have become infested by rats brought by whalers, and this probably explains why the Kusaie Island crake (*Aphanolimnas monasa*) and the Kusaie Island starling (*Aplonis corvina*) became extinct by 1828. Among the extremely rare birds of the Carolines occurring only on Truk Island are the Truk Monarch (*Metabolus rugensis*) and the Truk great white-eye (*Rukia ruki*). The latter may well have vanished. On Ponape the Ponape great white-eye (*R. sanfordi*) is very rare and declining; the Ponape mountain starling (*Aplonis pelzelni*) is also endangered.

Wake Island, an isolated low atoll between the Marianas and Hawaii, has lost one species, the Wake Island rail (*Rallus wakensis*). This nearly flightless rail, the only native land bird of Wake Island, was exterminated during its occupation by Japanese troops in World War II, probably in 1945.

MELANESIA

The Melanesian Islands include vast archipelagoes such as the Bismarcks and the Solomons lying between New Guinea in the west and Samoa in the east. In the north they are a continuation of Micronesia and their southern limit is formed by New Caledonia and the Tonga Islands.

The *Solomon Islands* have distinct affinities with nearby New Guinea in their fauna and in the dense tropical vegetation covering their mountain slopes. Several of the islands have been affected by man and his domestic animals. Cats probably caused the extermination of the Choiseul crested pigeon (*Microgoura meeki*), an endemic species and unique representative of its genus that was last recorded on Choiseul in 1904.

The San Cristóbal rail (*Edithornis silvestris*), living in the mountains of the island whose name it bears, is known only from a single specimen and may be extinct.

It is a pleasure to note that Rennell Island, isolated south of the Solomons, is an exception to our sad catalog. It miraculously

seems to have been more or less left unchanged by European explorers and traders. Apparently the Spaniards did not bring in any
domestic animals, and even rats are said to be lacking. Therefore,
this island still possesses a rich bird life, with more than half of
the species found nowhere else.

The *New Hebrides,* about 1,350 miles east of Australia, comprise forty volcanic islands, of which many are still covered by
dense forests. Only one species has been lost in this group. In
1774 a pigeon, the Tanna ground dove (*Gallicolumba ferruginea*),
was recorded on Tanna Island but has never been seen again and
was probably exterminated by the natives.

New Caledonia, southwest of the New Hebrides, is the largest
island in the archipelagoes of Micronesia, Melanesia, and Polynesia (the Bismarck Archipelago is here regarded as a satellite to
New Guinea). It has a variety of habitats from coastal plains to
mountain ranges. Eucalypt forests grow in the drier parts, while
moist areas produce dense tropical forests. Introduced cats, dogs,
and pigs as well as rats have heavily depleted the birds. Of New
Caledonia's unique species the New Caledonia lorikeet (*Charmo-
syna diadema*) was last seen in 1860; the New Caledonia owlet
frogmouth (*Aegotheles savesi*) has never been recorded after the
single specimen collected in 1880; and the once widely distributed
New Caledonia wood rail (*Tricholimnas lafresnayanus*) was observed for the last time in 1904. Other species are going the same
way. The most famous of southwest Pacific birds is the kagu
(*Rhynochetos jubatus*), a beautiful, heronlike species and the only
representative of its suborder. Formerly widespread in New Caledonia, it is now extremely rare and restricted to a few forests.
This decline is due to predation by exotic animals and man's trapping, shooting, and habitat destruction. Killing by dogs seems to
be the main threat at the moment. The kagu is protected by law,
but only a strict reserve will save this bird from extinction.

Other decreasing and rare birds in New Caledonia are the cloven
feathered dove (*Drepanoptila holosericea*), the giant imperial
pigeon (*Ducula goliath*), and two races of the horned parakeet,
Eunymphicus cornutus cornutus and *E. c. uvaensis.*

The *Loyalty Islands,* about sixty miles east of New Caledonia,
have lost two races of the grey-headed blackbird (*Turduc poliocephalus*), the Lifu Island subspecies, *T. p. pritzbueri,* and the
Maré Island subspecies, *T. p. mareensis.* These ground-nesting
endemic thrushes could not be found on the islands in 1939, which

means that they had become extinct. The same fate has perhaps struck other isolated races of the same species on islands in the Pacific.

The *Gilbert Islands* in northern Melanesia (or, if one prefers, southern Micronesia) are a group of atolls emerging from coral reefs. Nauru Island, the westernmost of these islands, is an isolated atoll rising to about one hundred feet and was once covered by much vegetation. It was able to support its small human population until the exploitation of its guano phosphate deposits brought a sharp increase in its population. But the phosphate deposits have now been exhausted and many natural habitats destroyed. This doubtless caused a decline in the very small population of the Nauru nightingale warbler (*Acrocephalus luscinia rehsei*), which may now face extinction.

The *Fiji Islands* in southern Melanesia consist of two major islands surrounded by an archipelago of hundreds of smaller islands, volcanic rocks, and atolls. Many of the islands are mountainous and covered by forests. The Fijis have also suffered from the European practice of introducing animals indiscriminately. Both the mongoose—released to control the rats brought to the Fijis by the Polynesians—and the sambar deer have been most harmful, the former killing ground-nesting birds, the latter destroying vegetation. At least fifteen species of birds have also been introduced and they compete with local species. From two to four species of native birds were exterminated during the short period of European domination and other birds are menaced by extinction. Apparently gone forever are the almost flightless Fiji bar-winged rail (*Nesoclopeus poecilopterus*) on Ovalau and Viti Levu, and the long-legged warbler (*Trichocichla rufa*), which vanished from Viti Levu during the nineteenth century (about 1890). The Fiji petrel (*Pterodroma macgillivrayi*) is known only from a single fledgling male collected in 1855 on Ngau Island. The masked parakeet (*Prosopeia personata*), which is peculiar to Viti Levu, is restricted to indigenous forests and therefore endangered. Finally, the pink-billed parrot finch (*Erythrura kleinschmidti*), also endemic on Viti Levu, is extremely rare and may be endangered.

The *Tonga Islands,* about 150 islands in southeasternmost Melanesia, are like Samoa a transition zone to Polynesia. An endemic bird having a population of about a thousand pairs is Pritchard's megapode (*Megapodius pritchardii*), which is found only on Niuafoou Island.

POLYNESIA

The Polynesians probably moved out to the Pacific Islands about two thousand years ago. They were and still are remarkable navigators and conquered a great part of Oceania. One of the creatures that accompanied man to most islands of the tropical Pacific was the Polynesian rat (*Rattus exulans*), and this rodent may have had fatal consequences for several ground-nesting birds prior to the arrival of Europeans. Polynesians also brought pigs and dogs to the islands, but the most disastrous newcomers to Polynesia, the brown and black rats (*R. norvegicus* and *R. rattus*), came by European ships, as did the cat, another destroyer of defenseless birds. During the last two hundred years at least eight species of birds have been exterminated in Polynesia.

The *Samoa Islands,* which may be included in either Melanesia or Polynesia, lie about five hundred miles northeast of the Fijis. In addition to rats, domestic predators have ravaged the Samoas. Cats are thought to have exterminated the Samoa wood rail (*Pareudiastes pacificus*), an almost flightless bird localized to Savaii Island and not observed since 1873. Another victim of persecution by exotic predators is the tooth-billed pigeon (*Didunculus strigirostris*). Very common on Savaii and Upolu when discovered about one hundred years ago, this pigeon was near extinction fifty years later. It has recovered to some degree, but its situation is still precarious.

The *Line Islands,* named from their location on the equator, are a chain of atolls about 960 miles south of Hawaii. Polynesians landed on these islands but did not settle there, so it is entirely white whalers and traders that have changed the face of the islands by digging for guano, drying copra, and merciless hunting. They exterminated, in or shortly after 1874, the Washington Island gadwall (*Anas strepera couesi*), a duck that lived in a freshwater lake on an atoll. It was of great interest that a species so widely distributed throughout the Northern Hemisphere should have adapted to this small midocean lake and evolved a subspecies there.

The *Society Islands* including Tahiti have suffered the extermination of more animals during the European epoch than any other island group of the South Seas except Hawaii. Paradoxically, this sorry record seems to be partly explained by the unusual friendliness toward Europeans of the Polynesians on the islands. As a result, European explorers, whalers, and traders frequented Tahiti much more than other islands. At each visit, rats went ashore and eventually exterminated the following birds: Tahiti red-billed rail (*Rallus ecaudatus*), said to have survived to 1925; Tahiti sandpiper (*Prosobonia leucoptera*), extinct since about 1777; Tahiti parakeet (*Cyanoramphus zealandicus*), extinct since about 1844; Raiatea parakeet (*C. ulietanus*), extinct since about 1774; Raiatea thrush (*Turdus ulietensis*), vanished between 1774 and 1850; Tongatabu Tahiti flycatcher (*Pomarea nigra tabuensis*), extinct after 1773; mysterious starling (*Aplonis mavornata*), known only from the type specimen supposedly collected during James Cook's visit to the Society Islands in 1774.

Three species, localized to the Society Islands, are threatened by extinction: Tahiti blue lory (*Vini peruviana*), extinct on Tahiti and Moorea but still found in small numbers on Maupiti; Tuamotu, and Cook Islands; Tahiti flycatcher (*Pomarea nigra nigra*), found only on Tahiti, where it is very rare; Maupiti Island flycatcher (*P. n. pomarea*), found only on Maupiti Island.

The *Marquesas Islands* on the northeastern periphery of Polynesia, have until recently been little affected by European contact. Apparently no species has been exterminated but two very rare species are now endangered by habitat destruction, shooting, and trapping. The Marquesas ground dove (*Gallicolumba rubescens*) formerly had a wider range but is now found only on two islands. The ultramarine lory (*Vini ultramarina*) has recently been reported to be seriously menaced.

Henderson Island belongs to the Paumotous and lies in easternmost Polynesia. Its endemic rail, the Henderson Island rail (*Nesophylax ater*), still numbers almost two thousand birds, but the vulnerability of rails to habitat destruction and predators endangers the species.

HAWAII

From the depths of the Pacific Ocean rise the Hawaiian Islands, an archipelago surrounded by thousands of miles of open sea. On the map and from an airplane they look like mere specks, but this impression is rapidly modified as the plane descends and one sees peaks that rise to more than thirteen thousand feet. Actually, the

Hawaiian Islands are the tops of what is perhaps the world's mightiest mountain chain, built up by millions of years of volcanic activity. The depths aroun·l these islands are very impressive, the average being around eighteen thousand feet. Mauna Kea, a volcano on Hawaii, 13,825 feet high, is probably the highest mountain in the world if it is measured from its base at the bottom of the sea.

The Hawaiian Islands are geologically rather young and there have been many volcanic eruptions that several times probably exterminated all the plants and animals that had reached the islands. Gradually, beginning in the northwest, volcanic activity died down; thus Oahu, on which Honolulu is located, has probably not had a volcanic eruption since the Polynesians discovered the islands around A.D. 500. But Hawaii, the youngest island in the group, has volcanoes such as Mauna Loa, 13,675 feet high and the largest living volcano in the world, that are very active. These islands are also interesting because their flora and fauna are unique. Long isolation has created species found nowhere else. As an illustration of the process of the creation of species, the Hawaiian Islands are as important as the Galápagos Islands. It is therefore tragic to have to report that a large number of unique species have been exterminated there and that many others are disappearing.

What remains of the nature of Hawaii is among the most magnificent and most interesting an oceanic world of islands has to offer. The great volcanoes on Maui and Hawaii rise from a humid, tropical area to a cold, dry alpine zone. These desertlike heights are, biologically, alpine nunataks rising above the clouds in exactly the same way as the mountains of Greenland thrust up above the surface of ice fields. It is a mystery how the alpine plants reached the islands. Moreover, the late Professor Carl Skottsberg found that none of the alpine plants on the volcanoes of Hawaii exist elsewhere and that their relations to other alpine species are so distant that their origin cannot be traced with certainty. About 90 percent of all the native plants on the Hawaiian Islands are endemic.

Many birds in Hawaii are also not found anywhere else. One of the most beautiful examples of the evolution of species and the colonization of hitherto unoccupied environments is provided by the Hawaiian honey creepers. Twenty-two species are known, all probably descended from one species, perhaps even only one pair, that once upon a time reached Hawaii from America.

Before man arrived, the only vertebrates that had reached
Hawaii were birds and a bat. Nearly all the immigrants came from
America, except three, two of which can be traced to Australia
and Polynesia, while the origin of the third, a rail, is unknown.
Unfortunately, this unique fauna has suffered shockingly during
the past 150 years; twenty-four forms of birds have been exterminated and thirty are on the verge of extermination. Cultivation, the destruction of forests, and the introduction of a large
number of exotic animals and plants was a catastrophe for the
native fauna.

In the nearly two hundred years since the Hawaiian Islands
were visited by James Cook, more plants and animals have become extinct or brought to the brink of extinction in Hawaii than
in North America, except for the Caribbean. Eighty percent of
the native Hawaiian land birds have become extinct in recent
times.

Introduced domestic mammals like goats, sheep, cattle, pigs,
cats, and dogs as well as rats have seriously damaged vegetation
and preyed directly on native birds. In addition, Europeans
brought the mongoose (*Herpestes auropunctatus*) to Hawaii in
1883, making the same terrible mistake as they had made elsewhere in the world. Rabbits, axis deer, and mouflons were also
introduced, the latter as late as 1954. The mongoose occurs on all
major islands except Kauai, Lanai, and Niihau, the axis deer on
Molokai, Oahu, and Lanai, and the mouflon on Lanai alone.
However, feral goats are abundant on most islands and destroy
much vegetation. Likewise, feral pigs constitute a threat to
ground-nesting birds. Possibly several species of the Hawaiian
honey creepers have been exterminated or reduced in numbers by
introduced bird diseases, transmitted from introduced birds by
introduced mosquitoes.

The birds exterminated in Hawaii are as follows:

Laysan Island rail (*Porzanula palmeri*). Confined to Midway
and Laysan islands. Extirpated by rats. Last seen in 1943.

Hawaii Island rail (*Pennula sandwichensis*). Apparently confined to Hawaii Island. Last seen in 1884 and possibly in 1893.

Hawaii brown rail (*P. millsi*). Extinct about 1864.

Lansi thrush (*Phaecornis obscurus lanaiensis*). Confined to
Lanai. Extinct since 1931.

Oahu thrush (*P. o. oahensis*). Confined to Oahu. Extinct
since 1825.

Laysan miller bird (*Acrocephatus familiaris familiaris*). Habitat destruction by rabbits contributed to its extermination. Extinct before 1923.

Molokai oo (*Moho bishopi*). Became extinct in 1915 as a result of commercial exploration for the bird's beautiful plumage, decimation by rats, and destruction of forests. The Hawaii oo (*M. nobilis*) became extinct in 1934 and the Oahu oo (*M. apicalis*) in 1837 for the same reasons.

Kioea (*Chaetoptila angustipluma*). Confined to Hawaii Island. Last seen in 1859.

Great amakihi (*Loxops sagittirostris*). This honey creeper, which became extinct in 1900, and all of the fifteen forms listed below belong to the *Drepaniidae,* a family peculiar to Hawaii. Many factors contributed to their extermination: habitat destruction, introduced mammalian predators, competition with introduced birds, spread of disease brought to the islands. Each of the following forms was found on only one island and became extinct on the date given: Lanai alauwahio (*Loxops maculata montana*), 1937; Oahu akepa (*L. coccinea rufa*), about 1900; Hawaii akialoa (*Hemignathus obscurus obscurus*), 1895; Oahu akialoa (*H. o. ellisianus*), 1837; Lanai akialoa (*H. o. lanaiensis*), 1894; Oahu nukupuu (*H. lucidus lucidus*), 1860; Laysan apapane (*Himatione sanguinea freethi*), 1923; hopue (*Psittirostra palmeri*), 1896; Lesser koa finch (*P. flaviceps*), 1891; Kona finch (*P. kona*), 1894; ula-ai-hawane (*Ciridops anna*), 1892; mamo (*Drepanis pacifica*), 1898; black mamo (*D. funerea*), 1907.

In addition to these vanished species the following thirty birds are approaching extinction:

Hawaiian dark-rumped petrel (*Pterodroma phaeopygia sandwichensis*). On the official United States list of endangered species. Probably not more than two hundred birds on Maui and very few on Hawaii.

Newell's shearwater (*Puffinus puffinus newelli*). Formerly more widespread. Seems to breed on Maui but is also reported from Kauai, Niihau, Oahu, Molokai, and Hawaii. Recent investigations indicate that the bird still occurs in thousands.

Hawaiian duck or koloa (*Anas platyrhynchos wyvilliana*). Formerly on most of the Hawaiian Islands. At present only on Kauai and Niihau. Total population in 1965, about five hundred birds.

Laysan duck (*Anas laysanensis*). Confined to Laysan Island. In 1923 there were about twenty birds and in 1950 about thirty-three, but in 1958, after rabbits had been eliminated, there were about two hundred and in 1964 almost five hundred.

Hawaiian goose or nene (*Branta sandvicensis*). Confined to Hawaii Island and Maui. From a population of about 25,000 birds in the late nineteenth century, the Hawaiian goose was reduced almost to extinction by hunting and habitat destruction. Less than fifty geese remained when a restoration program was initiated about fifteen years ago. Especially helpful was Peter Scott's success in rearing these geese at the Wildfowl Trust in Slimbridge, England. Between 1960 and 1966 a total of 260 geese, raised in Hawaii, the United States, and England, was reintroduced on Hawaii and Maui islands. This procedure continues. More than three hundred Hawaiian geese now exist in the wild on the Hawaii Island volcanoes. On Maui fifty-four nenes were observed in the Haleakala crater in September, 1966. There are more than two hundred birds in captivity and two sanctuaries have been set aside for the nene. The conservation efforts to save this goose are a good example of how much can be done to save an endangered species.

Hawaiian hawk (*Buteo solitarius*). A useful species formerly common on Hawaii Island but now down to fewer than two hundred birds as a result of wanton shooting. Unfortunately, no protective measures seem to have been given this buzzard, but it is, of course, totally protected within the Hawaii Volcanoes National Park, where I observed it in both 1964 and 1966.

Hawaiian gallinule (*Gallinula chloropus sandvicensis*). Formerly on many islands, it now breeds only on Oahu, Kauai, and Molokai. In 1962 there were one hundred to 150 birds on Kauai and fifty to a hundred on Oahu, but in 1965 the latter totals had decreased to between twenty-five and fifty birds. Preservation of pond habitats seems to be the only way to save this gallinule.

Hawaiian stilt (*Himantopus himantopus knudseni*). About two thousand birds occur on six islands. The bird's existence is threatened by the building boom in the lowlands.

Hawaiian crow (*Corvus tropicus*). Confined to Mount Hualalai on Hawaii Island, where it was still common in 1891. In 1961 the population, now protected, was estimated to be between twenty-five and fifty birds. In 1971 perhaps fewer than twenty-four birds survived.

Hawaii thrush (*Phaeornis obscurus obscurus*). Formerly common on Hawaii Island, but now rare although not immediately in danger.

Molokai thrush (*P. o. rutha*). Confined to Molokai. Consid-

ered extinct since 1936, but on 1968 found to still exist in an
unaltered forest, where it is very rare.

Kauai thrush (*P. o. myadestina*). Confined to Kauai, where
an extremely small population seems to be localized in one forest reserve.

Small Kauai thrush (*P. palmeri*). Confined to Kauai, where
the population in 1964 was estimated at about thirty birds.

Nihoa miller bird (*Acrocephatus kingi*). Confined to Nihoa
Island, where about five or six hundred birds are restricted to
one small area in a refuge.

Kauai oo (*Moho braccatus*). Confined to Kauai, where it
was common in 1891 but is now reduced to perhaps less than
a dozen birds. It is the last survivor of a genus containing four
species.

Kauai akialoa (*Hemignathus procerus*). Confined to Kauai,
where it was widespread at the beginning of the present century. It now occurs only in one area, where two birds were seen
in 1960 and only one in 1965.

Hawaii nukupuu (*H. wilsoni*). Formerly common on Hawaii
Island but today very rare and localized in mountain forests of
Mauna Kea and Mauna Loa.

Maui nukupuu (*H. lucidus affinis*). Confined to the Kipahulu
valley on Maui. Considered extinct since 1896, but rediscovered
with three or four individuals in 1967.

Kauai nukupuu (*H. l. hanapepe*). Limited to one area of
Kauai. Only two or three birds observed from 1960 to 1964.
Again reported in 1971.

Maui alauwahio (*Loxops maculata newtoni*). Confined to
Maui. Still common in 1928 but rare in 1936 and now again a
bit more numerous.

Molokai alauwahio (*L. m. flammea*). Restricted to Molokai,
where it was considered to be extinct since 1949, but rediscovered in 1961. Small numbers seen 1962–63.

Oahu alauwahio (*L. m. maculata*). Confined to Oahu. Widespread in the 1890's, but now close to extinction.

Kauai alauwahio (*L. m. bairdi*). Formerly abundant on
Kauai but now rare.

Maui akepa (*L. coccinea ochrarea*). May still exist on Haleakala, Maui.

Maui parrotbill (*Pseudonestor xanthophrys*). Confined to a
small forested area on Haleakala on Maui.

Ou (*Psittirostra psittacea*). Confined to Kauai and Hawaii
Island. Widespread on all islands except Oahu until the 1890's.
Between 1960 and 1965 only two or three birds were recorded
on Kauai. Apparently very near extinction.

Laysan finch-bill (*P. cantans cantans*). Confined to Laysan Island, where it was reduced to about a thousand birds. At that point the rabbits destroying the vegetation were eliminated. The number of birds then increased to about ten thousand individuals by 1958. But it is still on the official United States list of endangered species.

Nihoa finch-bill (*P. c. ultima*). Confined to Nihoa Island. This subspecies increased from about one thousand birds in 1961 to about four thousand in 1964, but since the entire population is restricted to a 156-acre island, it is still in danger.

Palila (*P. bailleui*). Formerly widespread on Hawaii Island, but at present reduced to perhaps one hundred birds in the forests on Mauna Kea and Mauna Loa.

Crested honey creeper (*Palmeria dolei*). Exterminated on Molokai after 1907 and now confined to the slopes of Haleakala on Maui, where it is extremely rare.

The number of Hawaiian birds that have become extinct or are endangered is thus tragically high, particularly since almost all of them represented various stages of evolution and scientifically made the Hawaiian Islands a living museum.

Mammals, especially seals, have also suffered in Oceania. The Hawaiian monk seal (*Monachus schauinslandi*) was ruthlessly slaughtered by white sealers, whalers, plumage hunters, and guano diggers in the latter half of the nineteenth century and was nearly extinct. Complete protection since 1909 has saved this seal. Now it breeds again on a few atolls: Kure, Midway, Pearl, and Hermes reefs, Lisianski Island, Laysan Island, and French Frigate Shoals, which correspond to the entire original range. The population is at present about fifteen hundred.

BALANCE FOR OCEANIA

During the two centuries that Europeans have been exploring, trading, whaling, and settling in the island world of the South Seas, fifty-one birds have become extinct in this region. In addition, three birds are probably extinct and fifty-eight others are threatened. A mammal is also endangered. Considering the small land area these islands represent, the figures are frightening. Of the fifty-one extinct birds, no fewer than twenty-four lived on Hawaii. Of the 58 endangered birds, thirty are Hawaiian. These sad figures indicate how far the environmental destruction has gone in Hawaii.

In fact, no other comparable area of the world shows such a negative faunal balance as Hawaii.

Of the twenty-seven extinct birds in the islands of the southern Pacific, eight lived in Micronesia, ten in Melanesia, and nine in Polynesia. Of the twenty-eight birds now endangered in the Pacific archipelagoes (except Hawaii), ten are from Micronesia, eleven from Melanesia, and seven from Polynesia. It appears that the rate of avian extinctions in the southern Pacific is about equally divided on the three main island groups. All extinction during historic time has taken place in Micronesia since 1828, Melanesia and Polynesia since 1774, and Hawaii since 1825.

Species and subspecies of vertebrates extinct during historic time, probably extinct, and at present endangered by extinction. (Figures within brackets show extinctions after 1700 or, to be exact, after 1774 in the Pacific archipelagoes [Micronesia, Melanesia, and Polynesia] and after 1825 in Hawaii.) At present there are no probably extinct vertebrates in Hawaii, and only 3 species of birds that are probably extinct in the other Pacific Islands.

	EXTINCT			ENDANGERED		
CLASS	PACIFIC ISLANDS	HAWAII	TOTAL	PACIFIC ISLANDS	HAWAII	TOTAL
Mammals	–	–	–	–	1	1
Birds	27 (27)	24 (24)	51 (51)	28	30	58
Reptiles	–	–	–	–	–	–
Amphibians	–	–	–	–	–	–
Fish	–	–	–	–	–	–
Total	27 (27)	24 (24)	51 (51)	28	31	59

CHAPTER EIGHT

Isolated Islands in the Oceans

Isolated islands, whether large or small, often produce animal species that differ from those on the continents, as well as from those on the satellites of continents or large archipelagoes that we have dealt with in previous chapters.

Isolated islands are often scientifically significant because they show more clearly than other areas the mechanism of evolution working undisturbed through millenniums, the building up of bio-communities, and the rate of colonization of recently arrived organisms. Unfortunately, few such islands have been left unviolated by man. As a result of a long isolation and the absence of predators most vertebrates on remote islands had acquired characteristics that made them an easy prey of man and the mammals he brought with him.

Though isolated islands often produce species, such islands may also function as traps eliminating one species after another even without habitat alterations. In an evolutionary sense, island populations have apparently in many cases become extinct after they had reached a distinct subspecific or specific level, but most of them before they had evolved to these stages.

ISLANDS IN THE PACIFIC OCEAN

To modern man no island in the vast Pacific Ocean is remote. The isolated island's only defense against advancing civilization is its topographical inaccessibility and lack of comforts. However, these do not discourage introduced animals. Once released, they disperse quickly, destroy habitats, and exterminate species.

Cocos Island

Cocos Island, about 625 miles west of Panama, is densely covered by luxuriant forests, bushes, tree ferns, coastal palms, and mangroves. The Cocos mangrove cuckoo (*Coccyzus minor ferrugineum*) is found in the latter but it is very rare. The Cocos Island flycatcher (*Nesotriccus ridgwayi*), the Cocos yellow warbler (*Dendroica petechia aureola*), and the Cocos Island finch (*Pinaroloxias inornata*) are also threatened.

The Galápagos Islands

In the history of science the Galápagos Islands are famous. In his voyage on the *Beagle* in 1835 Charles Darwin had rounded South America and been impressed by the biological wealth of the tropics and the adaptation of animals to conditions in the Andes. He was already convinced that evolution had taken place but he did not understand how it worked. Gálapagos gave him the key to the enigma, because there he found many examples of small evolutionary changes in species due to adaptation from island to island.

The volcanic Galápagos Islands are situated on the equator about six hundred miles from the South American mainland. They were discovered by the Spaniards in 1535 and consist of five larger and ten smaller islands and a large number of islets and skerries. Their total area is about 2,870 square miles. Several islands rise to altitudes of from two thousand to 5,500 feet. The climate is dry, particularly at lower elevations. On the higher islands such as Albemarle (or Isabela, the largest isle of the group), Indefatigable (Santa Cruz), Narborough (Fernandina), James (Santiago or San Salvador), and Chatham (San Cristóbal), there is a lowland arid belt of cacti and mesquite thickets. Above this, dwarf-leafed acacias cover some sections, while others have a junglelike association of larger trees. Higher slopes may be covered by forests, sometimes of an almost luxuriant type rich in mosses and ferns. Farther up is a belt of shrubs dominated by *Miconia* mixed with fern. The summits are in general grassy.

Prominent almost everywhere is the evidence of volcanic origin. Bare basalt rocks, crater holes and fissures, thousands of lava blocks, often grotesquely shaped, are surrounded by undecomposed lava that plants have not yet been able to colonize. To the aridity of this landscape is added the burning equatorial sun. At present only Albermarle and James islands show volcanic activity.

This group of islands is still the best living laboratory of evolution of the world. It is therefore a pity that so much of it has been destroyed. In the seventeenth century buccaneers used the islands as a hideout and in the nineteenth century came the whalers. The latter loaded their ships with living tortoises as a way of storing fresh meat. The capture of Galápagos tortoises almost became an industry, not only for food but also for oil extracted from the fat. One estimate is that about fifteen thousand tortoises were taken between 1811 and 1844 and another is that American whalers captured at least thirteen thousand tortoises between 1831 and 1867. It is believed that since the discovery of the islands as many as ten million tortoises have been slaughtered. This has led to the extinction of several tortoises and is a threat to nearly all subspecies, which are different on almost each island.

Goats released on the islands spread all over them and grazed and browsed down the vegetation. They are still there threatening the existence of many native species by the destruction of vegetation. Cattle, horses, and asses were also released. Plants important as food for tortoises and land iguanas vanished or became scarce. Moreover, pigs, dogs, cats, and rats preyed directly on the defenseless native mammals, birds, and reptiles and on their eggs. Four species of mammals, and four subspecies of tortoises became extinct.

The dark prospects for the Galápagos Islands were highlighted during 1958, when the scientific world celebrated the centenary of Darwin and Wallace's public presentation of their theory on the evolution of species through natural selection. During the International Zoological Congress in London that year a small group of devoted conservationists established the Charles Darwin Foundation for the Galápagos Isles, and soon after a research station with a seagoing vessel, on Indefatigable (Santa Cruz) Island. The government of Ecuador, which rules the Galápagos, gives full support to the foundation and its conservation program. But the task of repairing several centuries of damage is extremely difficult. There are already almost five thousand human inhabitants on the Galápagos. The population has actually tripled in the years between 1961 and 1971. As this population grows, exploitation pressure will increase and inevitably endanger the native plants and animals. This trend is alarming and may jeopardize the future of the Galápagos Isles as a tourist asset and research area. A continuous development for tourism and increased scientific research are the only feasible human activities on Galápagos which are not adverse to the unique environment of the islands. Therefore they also favour the inhabitants. However, it is of great importance to restrict the spread of population. The potential of tourism and research on Galápagos is shown by the facts that more tourists have visited Galápagos in the past two years than in the whole of the first half of this century and the numbers of scientific expeditions have increased from six in 1965 to seventeen in 1971.

Though a large majority of the species of mammals, birds, and reptiles (there are no amphibians and only one freshwater fish) of the Galápagos Islands are endemic and there are some endemic genera, no family has reached the endemic level of evolution. The Galápagos finches, generally considered a subfamily (*Geospizinae*), however, are near that level. Of the only native terrestrial mammals in the Galápagos are seven endemic rodents, of which probably four have become extinct in recent time, probably owing to predation by introduced brown and black rats.

Definitely gone is the Chatham Island rice rat (*Oryzomys galapagoensis*), found by Darwin on this island in 1835. It was then abundant, but in 1898–99 an expedition searched for it in vain. On James Island another rice rat (*O. swarthi*) was discovered in 1906 but it was not observed again until 1965, when a fresh skull was found. Two other species seem also to have disappeared: *O. indefessus* and *O. darwini,* both from Indefatigable Island. The former also occurred on Seymour. On Indefatigable a new species of rodent, *Megalomys curioi,* was found as a subfossil and appears to have become extinct only recently.

The Galápagos fur seal (*Arctocephalus australis galapagoensis*) was seriously depleted through centuries of slaughter by whalers and sealers. In 1816 one ship harvested eight thousand seals, and in 1823 five thousand seals were killed by another ship. But by 1882 the total catch was down to eight hundred and in 1897–99 one schooner could collect only 224 skins. At that time the last strongholds of the Galápagos fur seal were on Narborough, Albemarle, and Wenman (Wolf) islands. There were no further reports of it until one was collected in 1906. When William Beebe worked on the Galápagos Islands in 1923 he found the fur seal to be very rare, though Ruth Rose reported a colony of sixty to seventy animals from the Guy Fawkes Islands. In 1933–35 the Galápagos fur seal only occurred on Tower (Genovesa) Island, but in the 1950's a large colony was found on James Island. In 1961 this seal was found on Narborough, Albemarle, Abingdon (Pinta), James, Jervis (Rabida), Bindloe (Marchena), Indefatigable, Baltra, Seymour, and Tower islands, and in 1962 sixty fur seals were observed on James and later about five hundred on Albemarle—an impressive recovery from a very precarious state. In 1969 several colonies were well-established.

Of birds, there are several species that have become very rare owing to man's activities. The Galápagos penguin (*Spheniscus mendiculus*) was once widespread in the group, but killing it and collecting its eggs for food have reduced its numbers sharply. It now breeds only on Narborough and Albemarle, where the population was estimated in 1971 at about two to three thousand birds. The waved albatross (*Diomedea irrorata*) has colonies only on Hood (Española) Island, where in 1962 there were from six to seven thousand birds and in 1970 probably more than 7,500. The simple fact that it is so localized to one island makes its future uncertain. The Galápagos flightless cormorant (*Nannopterum harrisi*), restricted to Albemarle, has declined from about four thousand in 1962 to about one thousand in 1965. In 1970 there were one thousand to 1,500 birds, in 1971 about 1,600. Because this species is flightless it is extremely vulnerable, but it and its eggs are still hunted for food. The dark-rumped petrel (*Pterodroma phaeopygia phaeopygia*) is breeding on several islands, but is everywhere rare, declining, and endangered owing to habitat destruction and exotic mammals.

The Galápagos hawk (*Buteo galapagoensis*) was once widespread throughout the islands and was still common in 1924. Its extraordinary tameness has made it particularly vulnerable to hunters. It has already been exterminated on several islands and survives on only seven islands. In 1962 the population did not exceed two hundred birds, in 1970 estimated at 250 to three hundred birds. The species does not have any legal protection, which is shameful.

Another rarity in the Galápagos is the Charles (Floreana) Island mockingbird (*Nesomimus trifasciatus trifasciatus*), now exterminated on the island whose name it bears, but still found on one or two small islets nearby. The population is believed to be between fifty and sixty pairs.

The famous Galápagos finches served as Darwin's main example of how a species, adapted to various ecological niches, gradually evolved forms suitable to each. Fortunately, none of these birds have become extinct. The Charles Island large ground finch (*Geospiza magnirostris magnirostris*) is, however, very rare, having been collected by Darwin in 1835 and not seen again until 1957.

The mangrove finch (*Cactospiza heliobates*) is confined to two islands where the populations number one to two hundred birds.

Fifteen forms of giant land tortoises are known from the Galápagos Islands (to which the tortoises gave their Spanish name), but because the evolutionary process is still going on there is disagreement as to whether they are species or only subspecies. If these surviving tortoises are not species today, they will be tomorrow. We will here consider all these tortoises as one species (*Testudo elephantopus*) divided into fifteen subspecies.

In the seventeenth century the Galápagos giant tortoises were incredibly numerous. Darwin observed them in large numbers on Chatham Island. But slaughter by man, the competition of goats, cattle, and donkeys for fodder, predation by rats, dogs, and cats, and the trampling of water holes by domestic animals have all taken their toll. Large numbers of young tortoises are captured and sold as tourist souvenirs. Wanton killing has also occurred. The result is that almost all forms of these tortoises are threatened by extinction.

By 1906 they were extinct on Barrington (Santa Fé) and Charles islands. In fact, the subspecies of the latter island, *T. e. galapagoensis,* has been extinct for more than a century. During the present century other local subspecies have vanished or become very rare: *T. e. hoodensis* from Hood and *T. e. wallacei* from Jervis. On Hood only two males and ten females were found in 1970–71. Some of them were taken to the research station on Indefatigable, where in 1971 twenty eggs hatched. *T. e. abingdoni* was thought to be extinct on Abingdon but was rediscovered in 1972 with two or four animals. *T. e. chathamensis* from Chatham was thought to be extinct, but in 1966 four males were found on the island. Later on further tortoises were found and females have also been seen. By 1969, 112 tortoises had been marked on the island. On Duncan (Pinzón) only three specimens of *T. e. ephippium* were recorded in 1966; and only two of *T. e. darwini* were seen on James in 1962, but there is a larger population in the interior. Fifteen were observed in 1966 and 350 had been marked by the end of 1970. Of the Duncan tortoise, over a hundred juveniles were hatched artificially for reintroduction during 1966–70, of which twenty were released on Duncan, and ninety-two were marked there in 1966. One hundred and forty were recorded on Duncan in 1970. Apparently the populations on Narborough (*T. e. phantastica*) and that of *T. e. abingdoni* on Abingdon are very small. On the former uninhabited island only one individual of *T. e. phantastica* had been found in 1966 and droppings were reported in 1964. On Albemarle, five other subspecies (*T. e. becki, T. e. microphyes, T. e. güntheri, T. e. vicina,* and *T. e. vandenburghi*) occur in various areas. The high number of races occurring on one single island such as Albemarle is unique in the Galápagos and may be explained by the fact that Albemarle probably became a single island from great lava masses that flowed together from the five volcanoes on the island. These volcanoes are still the home of the five races of this tortoise. However, except for the last-mentioned subspecies, which exists with 2,500 to four thousand individuals on Albemarle, the present main population of the Galápagos giant tortoise, about three thousand animals, is found on Indefatigable (*T. e. porteri*). On all the inhabited islands the tortoise's habitats have been declared reserves.

In 1971 the following population estimates were made in the Galápagos by the Charles Darwin Research Station:

SUBSPECIES	ISLAND(S)	POPULATION
porteri (nigrita)	Indefatigable (Santa Cruz)	3,000
darwini	James (Santiago or San Salvador)	400–500
ephippium	Duncan (Pinzón)	150
hoodensis	Hood (Española)	10
vicina	Albemarle (Isabela)	250–300
güntheri	" "	200–300
vandenburghi	" "	2,500–4,000
microphyes	" "	500 (?)
becki	" "	500 (?)
chathamensis	Chatham (San Cristóbal)	300
abingdoni	Abingdon (Pinta)	2–4 animals observed in 1972.
phantastica	Narborough (Fernandina)	1 in 1966. None seen since then.
galapagoensis	Charles (Floreana)	Extinct
wallacei	Jervis (Rabida)	"
elephantopus	Barrington (Santa Fé)	"

Because the fleshy tail of the land iguana was frequently used
as food, these lizards have also been killed in large numbers. Two
species of land iguanas, *Conolophus subcristatus* and *C. pallidus,*
are threatened by extinction in the Galápagos. The former species
inhabited seven islands but became extinct on Baltra in 1942. Its
status is critical on the other six islands. On James the species is
nearly extinct, while there are a few animals left on Seymour and
Indefatigable. Very little is known of the population on Narborough, an island free from exotic animals. On South Plaza, a small
islet off Indefatigable, the goats have been killed, which had an
immediate positive effect on the vegetation and this may have
favoured the lizards, whose population there was about fifty to
one hundred in 1963. It is believed that the largest population is
on Indefatigable. The other species, *C. pallidus,* is found only on
Barrington, with about three hundred animals remaining.

The American herpetologist H. G. Dowling believes that the
main enemy of these lizards are the goats, which have cleared the
brushy undergrowth and eaten down bushes, trees, and even cacti.
This has deprived the iguanas of food and destroyed their cover,
leaving the younger animals vulnerable to predation by the Galápagos hawk. Ironically, this buzzard has also become extremely
rare.

Juan Fernández Islands

About 415 miles west of Chile lie the Juan Fernández Islands.
They once possessed a seal, the Juan Fernández fur seal (*Arctocephalus philippii philippii*), that was probably unique and occurred there in almost unbelievable numbers. In 1683 there were
between two and three million seals; according to the buccaneer
Dampier, there was "not a bay or rock that one can get ashore on
that is not full of them." In 1792 one ship took 38,000 skins, and
in 1798 another harvested 100,000 seals. Only nine years later
seal hunting on Juan Fernández was scarcely worthwhile. It has
been calculated that two or three million fur seals were killed on
the island by 1824. At the end of the 1880's the species was gone,
but one seal was killed on Más a Tierra in 1917; since then there
had been no known record of this seal until 1968, when at least
thirty seals were rediscovered at Más a Tierra. Fishermen claim
that there is a larger population on Más Afuera.

ISLANDS IN THE ATLANTIC OCEAN

The islands of the Atlantic Ocean lie in various climatic zones. The Azores and Bermuda are located above the tropics, whereas Ascension and St. Helena are tropical. Tristan da Cunha is temperate while the Falkland Islands are cool-temperate. The locations greatly influence the animal life, but on all of them man has destroyed vegetation and in other ways threatened several island animals that do not occur elsewhere.

The more than two hundred islands and islets of the *Falkland Islands* lie on the continental shelf about four hundred miles east of southern Patagonia. Constant gales prevent the growth of trees and larger shrubs on these islands. Tussock grass (*Poa flabellata*) covers all the plains and hills, and there are vast heaths consisting of *Empetrum rubrum,* a relative of the northern crowberries. The monotony of the landscape gives an impression of desolation and solitude.

An abundance of sheep as well as cattle and horses has greatly affected the grass vegetation. Ungrazed, tussock grass grows to five or even seven feet, but on the main islands, East Falkland, it rises only a few inches or has almost vanished from large areas.

Apparently, primitive man never reached the Falkland Islands, so when the gauchos arrived they found virgin country. Now all the islands except the very smallest are inhabited (2130 people in 1971), and not only sheep but also cattle, horses, pigs, hares, rabbits, rats, and mice are found almost everywhere. Before man there was only one native terrestrial mammal, the Falkland fox (*Dusicyon australis*), restricted to these islands. At the end of the eighteenth century, after the islands came under British rule, the Falkland fox was very numerous and very tame. Gauchos attracted them by holding out a piece of meat and stabbing the fox when it came within reach. Charles Darwin, who visited the Falkland Islands in 1833, foresaw the extinction of the fox because of its lack of fear. But it was the fur trade that doomed it. By 1863 it was exterminated in the eastern parts of East Falkland. Large-scale sheep raising led to poisoning campaigns. The last individual was killed on West Falkland Island in 1876.

Unrestricted grazing by livestock—particularly sheep, which by 1899 were more than 750,000—has caused a tremendous change of vegetation. The coastal belt of tussock grass has almost disap-

peared or has been thinned out to such an extent that, besides
erosion, about half of the breeding bird species of the Falkland
Islands have lost their habitats. The farmers blame two species of
geese—the upland goose (*Chloephaga magellanica*) and the ruddy-
headed goose (*C. rubiceps*)—for the overgrazing and want to
get rid of these birds by chemical means! The upland goose is
peculiar to the Falkland Islands and has been there for millenniums
prior to the arrival of man and sheep.

Bermuda is a volcanic island about six hundred miles off the
United States coast. Parts of the island are covered by cedars
(*Juniperus barbadensis*) with an undergrowth of sagebrush and
goldenrod. Pigs and rats came ashore long ago and some of the
pigs run about in a semiwild state. About four hundred years ago
the Spaniard Diego Ramirez and his sailors caught thousands of
petrels (they called it "cahow" because of the sound it made)
during a landing on Bermuda. Other crews followed their example.
When Bermuda was occupied by the British in 1609, the bird had
almost been exterminated. No scientific description of the bird
was made until 1916, when some bones were found in a cave.
They were thought to have belonged to the disappeared cahow,
which apparently was a petrel belonging to the genus *Pterodroma*.
The species was named *P. cahow*. A live cahow had been captured in 1906 but it was wrongly identified. Then in 1935 a cahow
struck a lighthouse on Bermuda. Finally, in 1961 Dr. Robert
Cushman Murphy of the American Museum of Natural History
found about one hundred birds breeding on the islets of the Castle
Harbour Island group off southeastern Bermuda. In 1965 the
population was estimated at about seventy birds, including twenty-
four breeding pairs. The breeding islets of the cahow are now a
sanctuary. No cahow has been seen on islets where rats are established.

Unfortunately, another menace is now threatening the existence
of the Bermuda petrel. Its reproduction has declined from 1959
to 1968 at the annual rate of 3.25 percent. Residues of DDT
averaging 6.44 parts per million were found in eggs and chicks of
the cahow. This bird feeds far at sea, mainly on cephalopods.
When not breeding at Bermuda it probably ranges over much of
the North Atlantic. Apparently the cahow is contaminated by its
oceanic food, although the latter is remote from applications of
DDT. Marine food chains are complex and seemingly nowhere
without residues of DDT. If the present decline of the cahow con-

tinues, reproduction will fail completely by 1978—a parallel to similar DDT catastrophes which have stricken terrestrial birds.

The *Azores,* like so many other volcanic islands, appear to rise directly from the ocean floor. On these islands, too, the Europeans have almost completely destroyed the indigenous vegetation. This has led to a serious decline in the São Miguel bullfinch (*Pyrrhula pyrrhula murina*), which is found only in a small area of São Miguel Island, where it is near extinction. One bird was found in 1967. Also extremely rare is the Azores wood pigeon (*Columba palumbus azorica*), not observed for many years.

In a very remote part of the South Atlantic midway between South America and Africa is *Ascension Island.* Ascension is volcanic and surrounded by deep water. The island's summit rises to about 2,600 feet and there are numerous lower hills. The most developed natural vegetation is found on the cap of the mountain. Introduced plants and trees cover most of the slopes. Rats probably came ashore soon after the island's discovery in 1501 and cats were introduced after 1815. Ascension was the home of a flightless rail that was exterminated even before it had been scientifically described. It was called the Ascension flightless crake, and on the basis of drawings made in 1656 (when it was last seen) it was placed in the genus *Crecopsis.* Ascension is also ornithologically interesting because it is associated with sea birds, such as the Ascension frigate bird (*Fregata aquila*), that have a very limited distribution. The frigate bird was once very numerous and bred on Ascension itself, but the breeding population has now declined to about nine thousand birds and is restricted to an islet east of Ascension.

The island is also a breeding site for a population of green sea turtles (*Chelonia mydas*), which feed on "turtle grass" along the coast of Brazil, from which they swim more than a thousand miles to lay their eggs on the tiny nub of land in the middle of the Atlantic Ocean (cf. page 343).

St. Helena, about 1,200 miles off the African coast, is another volcanic island rising from the submarine ridge of the South Atlantic; its maximum altitude is 2,678 feet. When St. Helena was discovered in 1502 it was entirely forested, with even the tremendous cliffs overhanging the sea colonized by trees. Today nothing of these forests remains. Goats had been introduced by 1513 and in 1588 a visitor reported there were flocks a mile long. Fire also destroyed large forests. Moreover, man introduced a great number of exotic plants and these now outnumber the native ones about ten to one. Many of the native flowering plants have vanished and much of the island is barren. The native birds have also suffered. One species, the St. Helena blue dove, was described by an observer in 1775, but it has never been seen again and still has no scientific name.

Tristan da Cunha, an island with an active volcano rising to 6,760 feet, and its satellite islands lie in the South Atlantic nearly two thousand miles from the tip of South Africa. The vegetation has suffered from the heavy gales that sweep the island and, of course, from man. In sheltered places the growth is luxuriant but mostly it is stunted. The only woody tree is a buckthorn (*Phylica arborea*), and reedlike tussock grass (*Spartina arundinacea*) dominates the vegetation.

Several of the introduced domestic animals, such as pigs, goats, rabbits, and cats, are now living there in a wild state. On Inaccessible Island a whole colony of penguins was wiped out by feral pigs. This island and Nightingale seem to be still free from rats; should the rats come, the ground-nesting flightless rail (*Atlantisia rogersi*) breeding on Inaccessible would be seriously endangered.

The island hen (*Porphyriornis nesiotis nesiotis*) was a flightless moor hen confined to the main island of Tristan da Cunha, where it was wiped out about 1872, presumably by rats and pigs. Three other species are threatened. One is the Tristan starchy (*Nesocichla eremita*), an endemic thrush that occurs in three races, each confined to a single island: *N. e. eremita* on Tristan da Cunha itself, *N. e. gordoni* on Inaccessible, and *N. e. procax* on Nightingale. The Tristan bunting (*Neospiza acunhae acunhae*) became extinct on Tristan Island in 1910—another ground-nesting bird that was probably wiped out by rats and cats. About one hundred of these birds still survive on Inaccessible. Another race, *N. a questi,* still persists on Nightingale. One subspecies of Wilkin's bunting (*N. wilkinsi wilkinsi*) is restricted to Nightingale, where it occurs with seventy to 120 birds, and another, *N. w. dunnei,* has a small population on Inaccessible of forty to ninety individuals.

ISLANDS OF THE INDIAN OCEAN

Several groups of islands in the Indian Ocean have been the scene of an unbelievably wanton destruction of animal life. Among the worst examples are the Mascarenes and the Seychelles.

The *Seychelles Islands* comprise four islands and hundreds of islets about six hundred miles northeast of Madagascar. Mahé, the largest island, has peaks up to 2,390 feet with the remains of rain forests on the higher slopes. The natural forest has been destroyed on a tremendous scale on the larger Seychelles, resulting in a steppelike vegetation, serious erosion, and a sinking water table. This together with introduced cats and dogs and uninvited rats has become a great threat to many native birds. The Seychelles alexandrine parakeet (*Psittacula eupatria wardi*) was last seen in 1870. The Seychelles chestnut-flanked white-eye (*Zosterops mayottensis semiflava*) was restricted to Marianne, where it became extinct in 1888. A number of other endemic birds are very near the same end. The Seychelles kestrel (*Falco araea*), a small, quite tame falcon, has been declining sharply since 1940, when it occurred on almost all islands of the group. In 1959 it was found only on Mahé, where there were less than thirty birds in 1964–65. The Seychelles turtledove (*Streptopelia picturata rostrata*) is an endemic race, formerly distributed all over the islands, but another race, introduced from Madagascar, absorbed the local race; pure populations of the Seychelles turtledove survive only on Cousin and Cousine islands. The Seychelles Vasa parrot (*Coracopsis nigra barklyi*) lives only on the eastern part of Praslin Island, apparently in patches of palm forests. Less than fifty parrots were estimated there in 1965. Another species on the retreat is the Seychelles owl (*Otus insularis*), which exists only on Mahé. It was observed there in 1960 and 1964–65. The Seychelles magpie-robin (*Copsychus seychellarum*), which once ranged throughout the islands, has disappeared except for nine specimens reported from Frigate Island in 1967. The Seychelles warbler (*Bebrornis sechellensis*) was reduced to about fifty birds on Cousin Island in 1965. The Seychelles black paradise flycatcher (*Terpsiphone corvina*), formerly found on several islands, survives only on La Digue, where it is rare, with a maximum of twenty-eight birds in 1965 and fifty pairs in 1972. Another scarce survivor is the Seychelles fody (*Foudia sechellarum*), with only four to five hundred birds left on the islands of Frigate, Cousin, and Cousine. Also, the white-bellied white-eye (*Zosterops modestus*) and Seychelles blue pigeon (*Alectroenas pulcherrima*) are in some degree of danger. The tragic fact is that none of these endangered birds are found anywhere else in the world than on the Seychelles, a fact which emphasizes their vulnerability.

Madagascar, Aldabra, and the Mascarene Islands as well as the Seychelles had a giant tortoise, *Testudo gigantea,* that was even larger than the Galápagos species. Once it was abundant on the Seychelles (*T. g. gigantea*), but the only possible survivors are a few individuals living in captivity on Seychelles among congeners imported from Aldabra. On the latter island, a coral atoll about 230 miles northwest of Madagascar, a relatively large population is living (cf. page 335).

Since the settlement of the *Mascarene Islands,* comprising Réunion, Mauritius, and Rodriguez, in the seventeenth and eighteenth centuries, no less than thirty-eight endemic species of birds out of forty-three have become extinct. Several of these birds had, living unmolested, evolved to flightlessness and were doomed when man and his mammals ravaged these islands. Hunting, habitat destruction, rats, monkeys (the crab-eating macaque, *Macaca irus,* was released on Mauritius during the sixteenth century), sambar deer (introduced in Mauritius during the seventeenth century), mongooses (released on Mauritius in 1900), and cats as well as the competition of introduced birds were the main factors in this extermination. The explosion in human population, partly explained by labour imported from India after 1848, has also been fatal to wildlife: on Réunion, for example, there were twelve inhabitants in 1665, 1,200 in 1713, 106,000 in 1848, 370,000 in 1960, and 436,000 in 1969. Cultivation spread up the volcanic slopes, destroying vegetation and leading to the most serious erosion.

Réunion (formerly Bourbon) is the westernmost and largest of the Mascarene Islands (2,512 square kilometers), lying 708 kilometers from Madagascar. It is of volcanic origin and has a still active volcano and a maximum elevation of 3,040 meters. Although the evergreen forests which originally covered Réunion have been destroyed and altered by man, the island has more undisturbed vegetation than the other Mascarene Islands.

On Réunion eight birds have become extinct and five are threatened by the same fate. They are:

Réunion purple gallinule (*Porphyrio porphyrio caerulescens*). Extinct after 1669.
Bourbon pink pigeon (*Columba duboisi*). Last observed in 1669.
Solitaire (*Raphus solitarius*). A flightless bird, closely related to the pigeons, and along with two extinct species from

Mauritius and Rodriguez, the only representative of a now extinct family. Exterminated in 1746.

Mascarene parrot (*Mascarinus mascarinus*). A unique species with no near relatives. Known only from two specimens, the last dying in Vienna in 1834.

Bourbon parakeet (*Necropsittacus borbonicus*). Extinct after 1669.

Réunion ring-necked parakeet (*Psittacula krameri eques*). Extinct since about 1700.

Bourbon crested starling (*Fregilupus varius*). Extinct since 1862.

Réunion Island fody (*Foudia bruante*). Extinct since 1776.

Réunion petrel (*Pterodroma aterrima*). Bred on the island before 1890. It was not seen there in recent decades and it was thought to be extinct, but in 1970 one bird was obtained on Réunion.

Réunion harrier (*Circus spilonotus maillardi*). Common in 1951 but rare by 1964.

Réunion cuckoo shrike (*Coracina newtoni*). Near extinction. Probably not more than ten birds still alive in 1965. One pair observed in 1971.

Réunion olivaceous bulbul (*Hypsipetes borbonicus borbonicus*). Limited to forests. Decreasing, owing to habitat destruction.

Mascarene flycatcher (*Terpsiphone bourbonniensis bourbonniensis*). The species occurs also in Mauritius. In danger on both islands owing to destruction of indigenous forest.

It should be added here that, besides birds, the giant tortoise was exterminated on Réunion at the beginning of the nineteenth century. It belonged to the same species as that of the Seychelles and Aldabra. The subspecific identity of the Réunion giant tortoise is not quite clear, but it is believed that there were two forms, *Testudo gigantea indica* and *T. g. commersoni.* A lizard also, *Gongylomorphus bojerii borbonica,* is certainly now extinct. It was observed and collected many times during the nineteenth century but has not been recorded since then.

When the uninhabited, volcanic island *Mauritius* (1,865 square kilometers) was visited by early navigators in the sixteenth century, dense evergreen forests descended from the mountain peaks (rising to 826 meters) to the sea, and in drier areas there were palm savannas. Its position today is best described by mentioning that the population density is the highest in Africa with 402 inhabitants per square kilometer, and that "natural forests" occupy only 1 percent of Mauritius' total acreage and savannas 2.7 percent. Moreover, the remaining forests are at present nowhere entirely natural, because exotic, introduced plants are invading the native vegetation. This process threatens not only the indigenous flora but also the animals, of which Mauritius has already lost eleven species of endemic birds and three reptile species. At present six endemic birds of the still existing nine are threatened and so are five reptiles. The sad list of extinctions of the past and tomorrow looks as follows:

Dwarf darter (*Anhinga nana*). Known only from subfossil bones. Probably extinct before the arrival of man.

Mauritius heron (*Butorides mauritianus*). Known only from subfossil bones. Extinct.

Theodore's duck (*Anas theodori*). Known only from bones. Apparently extinct before the arrival of man.

Van den Broeckes' red rail (*Aphanapteryx bonasia*). When man arrived there were rails and coots on the island, but within 150 years they had been exterminated. This species is known only from bones and has probably been extinct since 1675.

Mauritius coot (*Fulica newtoni*). Known only from bones. Extinct before 1700.

Mauritius yellow rail (*Kuina mundyi*). Extinct about 1638.

Mauritius blue pigeon (*Alectroenas nitidissima*). Extinct since 1830.

Dodo (*Raphus cucullatus*). This famous bird, an excellent food resource, has become a symbol for the meaningless and shortsighted extermination of useful animals by man. The dodo was a flightless, heavy pigeon, weighing about fifty pounds. Extinct in 1681.

Mauritius broad-billed parrot (*Lophopsittacus mauritianus*). Seen alive about 1638. Known only from a 1638 sketch and subfossil bones. Extinct before 1681. It was probably flightless.

Mauritius owl (*Strix sauzieri*). Known only from bones. Probably survived until the eighteenth century.

Mauritius scops owl (*Otus commersoni*). The generic identification, based on a drawing, is uncertain. Extinct since 1837.

Mauritius kestrel (*Falco punctatus*). Formerly widespread but by 1963 reduced to fewer than ten pairs. One individual observed in 1971.

Mauritius pink pigeon (*Columba mayeri*). Once thought to be extinct, but it still exists in small numbers. I observed it in 1971.

Mauritius ring-necked parakeet (*Psittacula echo*). Formerly widespread. Now near extinction. Not reported since 1911. However, in 1971 I observed it in a forest reserve and learned that it had been recorded there several times during the last decade. Another threat besides the alteration of habitats is competition with the ring-necked parakeet (*P. krameri*), introduced in 1886, which has now colonized the remaining indigenous forests.

Mauritius cuckoo shrike (*Coracina typica*). A rare endemic species.

Mauritius olivaceous bulbul (*Hypsipetes borbonicus olivaceus*). Population dangerously small. I observed the bird in 1971.

Mauritius flycatcher (*Terpsiphone bourbonniensis desolata*). Threatened owing to disappearing forests, but seems to adapt to plantations.

Mauritius olive white-eye (*Zosterops chloronothos*). Very few birds remain of this endemic species, endangered by habitat destruction.

Mauritius fody (*Foudia rubra*). Endangered endemic species. Observed nesting in 1971.

Mauritius has also lost all its giant land tortoises. Not less than five species (*Testudo triserrata, T. inepta, T. leptoclemis, T. sauzieri,* and *T. gadowi,* the latter extinct before the island was discovered) have been described from the island, but if there were so many as five species or even subspecies is questionable. The taxonomic situation has also been confused by introductions of giant tortoises from the Seychelles which probably interbred with the natives ones. If there was only one form of Mauritius, its name should probably be *Testudo gigantea soumeirei.* At the beginning of the eighteenth century ships on their way to and from India captured thousands of these tortoises for food and export, particularly to hospitals. Between 1865 and 1877 most of them were gone, and they have been extinct since 1893. A few tortoises introduced from the Seychelles in 1766 lived in a semiwild state until the last one was killed in 1918.

Thirteen other endemic reptiles are connected with Mauritius. One of them is extinct and five are threatened by extermination. The extinct species is a large (at least 50 centimeters) lizard, *Didosaurus mauritianus,* of which today only subfossil bones remain.

Round Island, off the northeastern coast of Mauritius, is the last refuge of a remarkable reptilian fauna. Several of these endemic reptiles are primitive forms that have managed to survive on this little island. Round Island has never been inhabited and is almost inaccessible, rising steeply out of the sea. It was probably connected with Mauritius during the last glacial period. Only about a hundred years ago Round Island was covered by a forest, but because of a monumental stupidity goats and rabbits were introduced there about 1850. The result is that there is nowadays no trace of this forest. In August, 1971, I visited Round Island by flying over it at low altitude. There was very little vegetation with only some small groups of palms but a terrific erosion. These drastic habitat changes upset the ecology of the island. Insect life disappears and the endemic lizards which feed on insects vanish, too, as do the snakes that prey on the lizards. Therefore, the following reptiles of Round Island are probably doomed:

Telfair's skink (*Leiolopisma telfairii*). Last observed in 1969.

Serpent Isle gecko (*Cyrtodactylus serpensinsula*). Exists also on the very small Serpent Island close to Round Island. Last observed in 1969.

Guenther's gecko (*Phelsuma guentheri*). In 1968 the population was estimated at 150 to three hundred individuals.

Round Island boa (*Bolyeria multicarinata*). Last observed in 1969.

Plate Island boa (*Casarea dussumieri*). Extinct on Serpent Island. Last observed on Round Island in 1969.

Rodriguez, the smallest of the Mascarene Islands (109 square kilometers), is also of volcanic origin. In 1691, when man settled here, it was covered with forests, of which only patches remain on the reef. There is hardly any native vegetation left at all on Rodriguez. A large proportion of the island's vertebrates have vanished, including the following:

Flightless night heron (*Nycticorax megacephalus*). Known only from bones. Extinct before 1730.

Flightless blue rail (*Aphanapteryx leguati*). Known only from bones and descriptions by travellers. Extinct since about 1730.

Rodriguez pigeon (*Alectroenas rodericana*). Known from bones. Extinct about 1693.

Rodriguez solitaire (*Pezophaps solitaria*). A flightless relative of the dodo, known only from bones and accounts of travellers. Probably extinct since 1791.

Rodriguez parrot (*Necropsittacus rodericanus*). Last seen about 1760 and now known only from bones.

Rodriguez ring-necked parakeet (*Psittacula exsul*). Extinct since about 1875.

Rodriguez little owl (*Athene murivora*). Known only from bones. Extinct about 1730.

Leguat's owl (*Bubo leguati*). Known only from bones. Extinct after 1691–93.

Leguat's starling (*Fregilupus rodericanus*). Extinct since about 1832.

Rodriguez warbler (*Bebrornis rodericana*). Probably only ten to twenty individuals remain. They seem to adapt to the exotic vegetation, in which two pairs nested in 1971.

Rodriguez fody (*Foudia flavicans*). Less than a hundred pairs. Decreasing rapidly owing to deforestation, but seems to adapt to plantations.

Rodriguez once had huge numbers of a giant land tortoise (*Testudo gigantea vosmaeri*) and probably also a second race (*T. g. peltastes*). When the French traveller F. Leguat visited there in 1691, he reported "such a plenty of land turtles in this isle that sometimes you see two or three thousand of them in a flock, so that you may go above a hundred paces on their backs." In 1759 one ship alone slaughtered six thousand tortoises and within eighteen months thirty thousand tortoises were captured. In 1786 they were extinct.

Another reptile, the day gecko (*Phelsuma newtoni*), has survived in a few numbers until recent time. It was probably extinct on Rodriguez before 1874 but subsisted on Ile aux Frégates at least until 1917. In 1963 no individuals were found there in spite of an intensive search.

The giant gecko (*P. gigas*) was common on Rodriguez in 1691–93 but seems then to have disappeared rapidly. It attained a length of about 50 centimeters. In any case it was gone before 1874.

The remote *Aldabra Islands* in the Indian Ocean are still the home of one of the world's few surviving populations of giant tortoises. For many centuries these large reptiles were heavily exploited, but some early established reserves on these islands saved two subspecies of the Aldabra giant tortoise from extinction: *Testudo gigantea daudinii* and *T. g. elephantina*. In 1968 there were not less than about eighty thousand giant tortoises on Aldabra. If the atoll habitats had been transformed into a military airbase, which was long a threatening project during the 1960's, it would probably have been the end of Aldabra as an animal refuge; and the tortoises would have been doomed. These islands are the only natural breeding ground in the Old World for the giant tortoise and the major breeding sites in the Indian Ocean for the green turtle (*Chelonia mydas*), of which fewer than a thousand nest on Aldabra every year. In 1967 the plan of building an airbase was temporarily cancelled after having been strongly opposed by conservationists.

The Aldabra brush warbler (*Nesillas aldabranus*) was discovered only in 1967. Its population must be extremely small and owing to its low numbers the species is vulnerable. Also, the Aldabra kestrel (*Falco newtoni aldabranus*) is regarded as an endangered bird.

On *Assumption Island* the endemic white-throated rail (*Dryolimnas cuvieri abbotti*) became extinct about 1894.

BALANCE FOR THE ISLANDS OF THE OCEANS

Altogether, on the isolated islands in the Pacific, Atlantic, and Indian oceans fifty-three species and subspecies of vertebrates have been exterminated and four are probably extinct, while sixty-nine are endangered. The figures for the Pacific Ocean are seven, one, and twenty-eight; for the Atlantic three, two, and nine; and for the Indian Ocean forty-three, one, and thirty-two. Of the latter figures from the Indian Ocean, the Mascarene Islands alone have thirty-eight extinct, one probably extinct, and seventeen endangered animals. In the Pacific it is the Galápagos Isles which dominate the figures. In fact, all extinctions have occurred there, and of the twenty-eight endangered vertebrates on isolated islands of the Pacific no fewer than twenty-three occur on Galápagos. Divided according to animal classes, four mammals have been exterminated and three are endangered; thirty-four birds are extinct and forty-eight endangered; and finally, fifteen reptiles are extinct and eighteen endangered.

Species and subspecies of vertebrates extinct during historic time, probably extinct, and at present endangered by extinction. (Figures within parentheses show extinctions after 1700.)

CLASS	EXTINCT				PROBABLY EXTINCT				ENDANGERED			
	PACIFIC	ATLANTIC	INDIAN OCEAN	TOTAL	PACIFIC	ATLANTIC	INDIAN OCEAN	TOTAL	PACIFIC	ATLANTIC	INDIAN OCEAN	TOTAL
Mammals	4 (4)	–	–	4 (4)	–	–	–	–	3	–	–	3
Birds	–	3 (2)	31 (18)	34 (20)	–	2	–	2	12	9	27	48
Reptiles	3 (3)	–	12 (11)	15 (14)	1	–	1	2	13	–	5	18
Amphibians	–	–	–	–	–	–	–	–	–	–	–	–
Fish	–	–	–	–	–	–	–	–	–	–	–	–
Total	7 (7)	3 (2)	43 (29)	53 (38)	1	2	1	4	28	9	32	69

CHAPTER NINE

The Antarctic

The southernmost areas of the world—South America (including Tierra del Fuego), Australia, and New Zealand—show many geographic, climatic, and biologic features in common. The striking biologic parallels have long constituted a central problem in biogeography. Many scientists have thought that Antarctica has played an essential role in the dispersal of certain groups of plants and animals in these scattered areas.

The climate of Antarctica has for long periods been temperate, allowing forests of deciduous and coniferous trees to grow along certain coasts, for instance, on the Antarctic peninsula, and presumably also in the interior. Coal, formed by an ancient flora as well as fossil leaves and needles from a period when Antarctica was in its present location, has been found about three degrees from the South Pole.

On the basis of geographic, climatic, biologic, and paleomagnetic data several scientists have theorized that the southern continents were in the ancient past close together or perhaps even united, and lay farther to the south. According to the zoogeographer Philip J. Darlington, Jr., these continents, except Antarctica, drifted northward. This theory might explain the similarities in their flora and fauna. In 1968 a fossilized Lower Triassic amphibian (a labyrinthodont), about 200 million years old, was found by a U. S. expedition in Antarctica. This animal was probably a freshwater creature like most past and present amphibians, which points to the assumption that Antarctica was part of a supercontinent. Since then Antarctic beds rich in fossil amphibians and reptiles have been found in Antarctica showing a fauna almost identical with a corresponding one of South Africa for the same period.

Today the Ice Age still prevails in Antarctica and most of it looks like an ice desert. The continent is a large island or perhaps two; parts of it may even consist of vast archipelagoes hidden under one immense ice sheet. Several island groups surround the continent. Antarctica has a greater average elevation than other continents, the central mass rising to 13,400 feet. It is difficult to say how much of this is ice and how much is rock. Ice-free areas are mostly bare rock and are located chiefly along the low coasts and offshore islands. The sparse vegetation is chiefly lichens, mosses, and algae. The floral poverty of Antarctica—it has only three small flowering plants—is in striking contrast to the richness of plants in arctic areas. The vertebrates, all marine and all taking their food from the sea, comprise six seals and a small number of birds, notably penguins and petrels. However, the bird species are often tremendously numerous. Some of the largest bird colonies in the world are found on the subantarctic islands off Antarctica. Though several species are restricted to Antarctica, no entire family is peculiar to the continent.

Antarctica is the only great landmass that has had no human settlement until the present century. Man is now there throughout the year but only in research stations. This explains why man has not yet had any profound effect on animal life there. But this situation seems now to have ended: for instance, a few years ago marine organisms off Antarctica were found to have been contaminated by DDT compounds. In 1956 man occupied the McMurdo Sound area and there is now much icebreaker, transport ship, and aircraft traffic there. Each year between one and three thousand men are brought to McMurdo Sound to stay for various periods. They travel about by tractor and helicopter, inevitably disturbing the animals there. One can trace the effect in the decline in the colony of Adelie penguins (*Pygoscelis adeliae*) at Cape Royds on Ross Island. Four years after this colony was discovered by the explorers Robert F. Scott and Edward Wilson in 1904, there were between 1,500 and two thousand pairs breeding in it. Despite much robbing of eggs by crews there were still about two thousand pairs in this colony in 1956, when the permanent McMurdo bases were established. The penguin colony thereupon decreased to about 1,700 pairs in 1958, about 1,250 in 1961, and fewer than 1,100 in 1963.

The rarest species of seal in Antarctica and the only one restricted to the South Pole region is the Ross seal (*Ommatophoca rossi*). It is found on the edge of pack ice and off some islands,

but there is apparently no congregation for breeding purposes.
The bulk of these seals seem to live off western Antarctica from
the Weddell Sea to the Ross Sea, but they are everywhere local.
A rough guess puts the population of this seal between twenty
thousand and fifty thousand. There is some indication that the
number is decreasing.

Of other Antarctic seals the most common, the crabeater seal
(*Lobodon carcinophagus*), is also the most vulnerable, because it
congregates seasonally in large numbers. The crew of a single ship
was able to kill between four and five thousand of them in a few
years. During the nineteenth century the southern elephant seal
(*Mirounga leonina*) and the South American fur seal (*Arctocephalus australis australis*) were nearly exterminated by man but have
recovered. The scarcity of suitable breeding sites in Antarctica for
large populations of animals that feed in the open sea makes these
species very vulnerable to human interference on islands and in
coastal areas.

Because the Antarctic ecosystem is rather simple and therefore
very sensitive to disturbance, it is fortunate that its vegetation and
fauna is protected by a conservation agreement signed in 1964 by
twelve nations (Argentina, Australia, Belgium, Chile, France,
Great Britain, Japan, New Zealand, Norway, South Africa, the
United States, and the U.S.S.R.) engaged in research in Antarctica. The agreement covers harmful interference, the introduction of non-indigenous species, parasites and diseases, and so forth.
Antarctica is thus the first continent in the world where man has
tried by treaty to prevent disastrous interference with animal
populations. Antarctica is also the only continental area where not
a single animal species has been wiped out since man arrived there.

In February 1972 a Convention for the Conservation of Antarctic Seals was initialled by the twelve Antarctic Treaty States. It
applies to the high seas and floating ice south of 60° S., and affords total protection to the Ross seal, the southern elephant seal,
and fur seals of the genus *Arctocephalus*. It imposes catch limits
on the crabeater seal, the leopard seal (*Hydrurga leptonyx*) and
the Weddell seal (*Leptonychotes Weddelli*).

We do not need to give a formal balance for the Antarctic.
Of the seven species mentioned in this section, three are or have
been endangered, but all seem now to be recovering.

CHAPTER TEN

The Oceans

The oceans, in which life began and which cover 71 percent of the globe, are richer in animal species than is land. No terrestrial organisms occur in such tremendous number as do those of the ocean. The food chains in the sea are complex and support large populations of various animals from plankton to whales. However, it is not so everywhere: Some sea areas are much more productive than others.

Although man exploits fish populations on a tremendous scale and there are many local signs of overfishing and decreasing populations owing to the too efficient techniques of modern fisheries, no marine fish, so far as we know, is threatened by extermination. Unfortunately, one cannot say this about other marine vertebrates. Marine reptiles such as turtles, and mammals such as whales, have been plundered to such an extent that several species have vanished and others are very near extinction.

Although sea water looks very similar everywhere, it varies from place to place. Salinity, dissolved organic matter, temperature, solar radiation, light intensity, currents, and tides all create differences in marine habitats. Other elements such as the structure of the bottom, mangrove roots, submarine vegetation, and coral reefs also influence these habitats. In fact, such habitats are as diverse as those on land, and this is particularly true of the shallow waters along the continental shelves.

One of the ever-increasing sources of pollution of the seas is the discharge of oil from ships. Since many of the chemicals in these oils are persistent, their long-term effect on the marine organisms may be considerable, particularly on plankton, which ascend to the surface water at night. However, our understanding of the effect of floating "oil fields" in the open sea is still very inadequate.

There are many other sources of marine pollution besides ships. Industrial and urban wastes as well as contaminated soil particles are carried by water to the oceans or are dumped directly in the sea. The rivers transport vast quantities of sediments caused by man-made erosion along riverbanks, and deposit huge volumes of silt inside coral reefs, a process threatening the existence of these productive ecosystems so important for marine life. Atmospheric movement of DDT residues contaminates the ocean surface, increasing the high levels of pesticide washout to the sea through the rivers. DDT residues have for several years been found in practically all marine organisms all over the world from the Arctic Ocean to the Antarctic Ocean.

FISHES

Man has not yet exterminated any marine fishes only because fishes are so abundant, widespread, and, in general, prolific. But we should not assume that they will always be so. Obviously, too, fish populations will be depleted if pursued with increasingly efficient equipment. Bottom fishes are particularly vulnerable; pelagic species are probably more resistant.

The local extermination of certain species has been reported from some fishing banks, and since spearfishing by skin divers has become popular, it has been claimed that certain species and even whole populations have disappeared from some Mediterranean coasts and from certain coral reefs in the Caribbean Sea and in the Indian Ocean. This may be true locally but cannot yet have endangered any species.

MARINE TURTLES

Like the seals the marine turtles must go ashore to reproduce, and this is the vulnerable stage in their existence. However, unlike most seals the marine turtles have a cosmopolitan distribution. They occur in almost all tropical and subtropical seas and breed in both the Western and Eastern Hemispheres. They make no contact with land except when they deposit their eggs. They return year after year, after having travelled maybe more than a thousand miles, to the same beaches to nest, often within half a mile or less of previous nesting sites. This is, of course, a dangerous traditionalism.

Actually, few vertebrate groups are as much in danger as the marine turtles. Particularly in the Caribbean Sea, which was formerly a favourite area of theirs, they have been mercilessly persecuted ever since the discovery of America. The commercial importance of the fleets of sea turtles that annually migrated to the Caribbean islands to lay their eggs may be compared with the place of the North Atlantic herring fisheries in the life of North European populations. The turtle fleets have in fact greatly influenced the human history of the Caribbean. All expeditions to the New World, whether concerned with exploration, warfare, colonizing, or buccaneering, depended on the green turtle (*Chelonia mydas*). The exploitation of this resource continued after the Europeans settled in the Caribbean and along the American coasts. It still continues, not only for the meat and eggs but also for the carapaces, which have an economic value. The green turtle has also been hunted and drastically reduced in Asia, Africa, and on many tropical islands. All existing species of sea turtles are in danger. The green turtle occurs in all the warmer seas of the world, but the Atlantic green turtle (*C. m. mydas*) no longer breeds in many areas such as the beaches of Florida, the Bahamas, the Dry Tortugas, and the Cayman Islands. Its main nesting grounds in the New World are Tortuguero in Costa Rica and the uninhabited Islas Aves in the eastern Caribbean, and Ascension Island in the South Atlantic is still frequently used. Also, Trinidad and Surinam are important nesting areas. In 1968 a serious decline in Costa Rican breeding stocks of green turtles occurred, which is an alarming sign of how vulnerable marine turtles are to overexploitation. In 1970 the Tortuguero National Park was established. It gives protection to nesting turtles of three species along more than half of the twenty-two-mile shore and out to sea for a distance of three miles from the beach.

The Indo-Pacific green turtle (*C. m. japonica*) breeds on the African coast, for example, at Kenya, Mozambique, the Aldabra Islands, Europa Island (where about nine thousand females breed each year), and on Bajuu Island, the latter exporting about one thousand to fifteen hundred live turtles annually. The population in the western Indian Ocean has dwindled to a precariously low level, particularly on the Seychelles. On these islands the capture or killing of turtles below a certain size has been forbidden during recent years, followed by a total protection, but there is little enforcement of these regulations. A large population of the Indo-Pacific green turtle (*C. m. agassizi*) occurs on three islands off Sarawak, including about ten thousand females, of which two to four thousand lay eggs annually. From one to two million eggs are taken every year from the Sarawak coasts and about 600,000 from islands off Sabah. In 1971 the government of Sabah acquired three islands for conversion into a sanctuary for the green turtle and the hawksbill turtle (*Eretmochelys imbricata*). In the Philippines about a million eggs of the green turtle are collected annually. In addition, between fifteen thousand and twenty thousand live green turtles are marketed every year in North America and Europe. The most important population exists along Queensland in Australia, including the Great Barrier Reef (see taxonomic remark on page 347).

Fortunately, conservation measures have been undertaken not only in Australia but also in Costa Rica, Nicaragua, South Africa, the Seychelles, Borneo, and in Oceania, where the East Pacific green turtle (*C. m. agassizi*) ranges. Young turtles are raised in hatcheries and released into the sea. However, it is also important to protect the nesting beaches. In 1970 total protection was given to the green turtle in Costa Rica, Nicaragua, and Panama.

The Atlantic hawksbill turtle (*Eretmochelys imbricata imbricata*), exterminated in the Mediterranean, has at present a center of distribution in the Caribbean area, while the Pacific hawksbill turtle (*E. i. squamata*) ranges from Peru across the Pacific and Indian oceans to Madagascar and East Africa. The Japanese exploit the hawksbill to provide tortoise shell and stuffed young turtles. The species is decreasing rapidly owing to overexploitation both on the nesting beaches and on the reefs and banks at the sea. Sabah has recently established a sanctuary for this turtle.

The Atlantic loggerhead turtle (*Caretta caretta caretta*) and the Pacific loggerhead turtle (*C. c. gigas*) are widely distributed in the warmer oceans and also occur in the Mediterranean Sea. In Africa this species nests on the coasts of Madagascar and Mozambique, where it is seriously menaced, and on the coast of Natal, where it is fully protected, as well as in Queensland, Australia. In 1970 the female population nesting in Natal was estimated at 466. Important nesting localities are to be found along the Atlantic coast between North Carolina and Florida. The world population of the species is calculated to be between twenty-five and fifty thousand mature individuals. Man's use of beaches and egg collecting are the main threats to this species.

Of all sea turtles none is more in danger than the ridley (*Lepidochelys kempii*). Despite the fact that it was common in the Gulf of Mexico, its breeding ground remained a mystery until, after long years of searching, Professor Archie Carr of the University of Florida received information about a nesting site on the almost uninhabited coast of the State of Tamaulipas in Mexico. There the ridleys swarm ashore to lay their eggs on a ninety-mile stretch of beach, resulting, according to Carr, in "perhaps the most concentrated breeding aggregation of any vertebrate animal in the world." At the time of discovery in the 1950's, about forty thousand ridleys came up on the shore to lay their eggs. Unfortunately, soon after the discovery became known, the depredations of fishermen sharply reduced the number of ridleys. The turtles are valued not only for their eggs but for meat and a jellylike substance used in making turtle soup. Later on, very small numbers of nesting ridleys were found on Padre Island, Texas, and the coast of Vera Cruz, Mexico.

The magnificent turtle armadas of the 1950's are now but a memory. The last big *arribada* to Tamaulipas occurred in 1953. In a few years man reduced a species to a fraction of its former number. At present there is only sporadic breeding by three or four thousand turtles. The turtles come up the beach in twos or threes at various places. A few more years of slaughter and this extraordinary phenomenon will be a thing of the past. The Survival Service Commission of the IUCN has therefore urged the Mexican government to reinforce its protection with police patrols on the beaches during the crucial period from April to June. In April, 1966, an effort was started by the Mexican government to collect and hatch eggs of the ridley as a conservation measure.

The warana sea turtle (*L. olivacea*) is found in warmer parts of the Pacific, the Indian, and Atlantic oceans. Because it has an almost circumglobal range with several breeding places in the eastern Pacific, in Australia, on the coasts of Burma and Ceylon, in Mozambique, Madagascar, and in South Africa, as well as on four beaches in Surinam and the Guianas, its situation is not yet as precarious as that of its relative, the ridley. The majority of nesting waranas come ashore at Eilanti Beach in Surinam, where practically all the eggs laid had been taken by Carib Indians until 1966. Since 1967 the unwritten customary rights of the Indians were bought off for 80 percent of the eggs with the financial help of the World Wildlife Fund. The warana is all over its range the object of a very heavy exploitation by egg collecting, which if continued will exterminate this turtle.

The Atlantic leatherback turtle (*Dermochelys coriacea coriacea*) occurs in tropical and subtropical seas, but few of its breeding places are known. It nests on an island off South Carolina, it nested in Florida in 1947, and it has used a site in Costa Rica. It also breeds in French Guiana and Surinam. The Pacific leatherback turtle (*D. c. schlegelii*) breeds in Australia, along the Trengganu Beach in Malaya, and on the coasts of Burma, Ceylon, Natal, South Africa, Mozambique, Madagascar, and possibly in New Guinea. It also nests on the Mexican coast. The leatherback turtle is the largest of all sea turtles and the most specialized to life in the open sea. The two main breeding areas of the species are Oganaba in French Guiana and Trengganu in Malaysia, but owing to the enormous harvest of the eggs for human consumption, the future of the leathery turtle is very dark. The best measure to save the species is strictly to protect the rookeries.

Until recently leathery turtles have rarely been eaten by man, but they are now consumed in some areas. However, it is the collecting of their eggs for commercial purposes that has proved disastrous to this species. Moreover, dogs and other domestic animals dig up the eggs along the shores. Between 850 and 1,700 females breed in Burma, the main breeding area. In Natal seventy-seven females were estimated to be nesting in 1970. Conservation programs for the leathery turtle exist in Malaya, Ceylon, Natal, and Costa Rica. In Malaya and Ceylon turtles are hatched and later released. Natal is considering a controlled sanctuary.

In 1968 the government of Queensland in Australia took a very important legislative step by giving total protection to all species of marine turtles—the green, the hawksbill, the loggerhead, the leathery, the warana, and the flatback turtle (see below)—occurring along the coasts of this state as well as along the Great Barrier Reef. Only Aborigines may capture them. Apart from the leathery turtle, all the other species mentioned have nesting grounds in Queensland. This state's decision was the first rational measure to build up the populations of the declining sea turtles. As a result of Queensland's step other states as well as the federal authorities of Australia in 1971 gave total protection to all species of marine turtles which use Australian beaches as breeding grounds. They include, in addition to the breeding species mentioned above for Queensland, the leathery turtle, but it is uncertain whether the Australian flatback turtle breeds outside Queensland. The systematic position of the latter is uncertain and there are different views on its relationship to the green turtle. It frequents Australian waters and is regarded to be either identical with the Indo-Pacific race (*Chelonia mydas japonica*) or a close relative of it, called the flatback turtle, which in recent times is often ranked as a species, *C. depressa*. It is believed that Mon Repos on the Queensland coast is the only nesting ground in the world for the rare flatback.

Another lethal danger to marine turtles is the plastic bags and sheets that become increasingly a part of the pollution of the sea. Sea turtles apparently mistake plastic objects for food—perhaps jellyfish—and swallow them. Their digestive tract is blocked and this kills the turtles. A piece of plastic measuring no less than 3 x 3.5 meters was found inside a leatherback turtle that was washed ashore dead in South Africa. The same has happened with other sea turtles on a large scale off Florida and the Pacific coast of Costa Rica.

WHALES AND DOLPHINS

Large marine mammals such as whales include species which are extremely valuable. Unfortunately, the populations of whales are relatively small and the rate of reproduction is rather low. Such populations are vulnerable to human predation.

Baleen whales, the largest animals on earth, utilize the tiny plankton organisms of the sea with an efficiency that man has not yet been able to match. The blue whale, for example, is at birth about twenty-four feet long but in two or four years reaches a length of 74 to 77 feet. Thus, whales represent one of the most valuable living resources of the sea. Tragically, man has overexploited this resource far beyond the maximum sustained yield and the levels that the populations of larger whales could withstand. As everyone knows, he has killed whales without the slightest regard for the future of the various species. Since whales in no way compete with man or come into conflict with human interests, there is no excuse whatever for deliberately exterminating them. Apparently the whalers intend to take the very last bit of profit they can get from the few remaining whales and then simply abandon the whole business. This cynical approach by the main whaling countries, Japan, Norway, and the U.S.S.R., arises from the fact that the open sea is considered no one's responsibility. The whaling business is thus reminiscent of medieval buccaneering.

The story of man's destruction of the whale has so many shameful aspects that we can deal with only a few of them before briefly surveying the most endangered species.

In 1935 nearly thirty thousand blue whales were caught in a single season. In 1964–65 only one blue whale was caught! The blue-whale population in the Antarctic has in fifty years been reduced from 200,000 to about a thousand and the fin whale from 380,000 to about 32,400. Such figures sum up the fate of the whale.

In terms of edible oils for the manufacture of margarine, soap, and glycerin, as well as such by-products as meat for human and domestic-animal consumption and bones for fertilizers, whales represent a valuable resource for a hungry world. Dr. John A. Gulland, one of the scientists who advises the International Whaling Commission, conservatively estimates the normal annual harvest of whales in the Antarctic alone at more than half a million tons of meat and edible oils. Only three decades ago more than that was cropped from one species alone in the Antarctic Ocean.

Whales have long been exploited by man. The Basques hunted whales in the Bay of Biscay a thousand years ago, and by the fifteenth century had almost exterminated them in that area. Turning to the arctic waters, in the seventeenth century the whalers took only about a hundred years to deplete the whale populations there. Then the Greenland right whale (*Balaena mysticetus*) was hunted almost to extinction. In the late eighteenth century the whaling went to the southern parts of the Pacific, Indian, and Atlantic oceans, until these waters were depleted in the 1920's. So it went in one ocean after another, until after World War I, the whalers moved to the Antarctic Ocean, where they now take about 60 percent of the total catch. By that time, too, whaling ships developed into floating factories that are extremely effective in locating, killing, and preparing whales on an industrial scale. In the Antarctic only twenty years of whaling elapsed before it became clear that the whales were declining rapidly in numbers. It is true that whaling had begun in the Antarctic by 1904 from land-based stations at South Georgia and later at the Falkland Islands, but these operations depleted the whale populations less than the factory ships which operated uncontrolled on an industrial scale. When the blue whale (*Balaenoptera musculus*), largest of all species, was brought near extinction in the Antarctic, the whalers turned to the second in size, the fin whale (*B. physalus*). And now the number of fin whales is dwindling alarmingly. By the 1920's warnings against overexploitation in the Antarctic were expressed, but the depletion went on as it had earlier in all other oceans.

All scientific bodies interested in the preservation of the whales have for many years urged the International Whaling Commission to take immediate steps towards a rational management of whale population. But all pleas have been in vain. Short-term interests prevail. The whaling companies seem to dominate the commission and even the unanimous recommendations of the commission's own committee of three scientists have been constantly disregarded. The only way to save the whales and the whaling industry is a drastic reduction in the catches by establishing controlled quota based on scientific data. This is recognized by everyone except the three nations actively engaged in Antarctic whaling. The only argument these nations offer is that their whaling industries are already in such a poor condition that they cannot afford any curtailment of their activities. It is certain that many whales are still hunted illegally. There is evidence of deliberate catching of numbers in defiance of the regulations. In 1960–62 the humpback whales (*Megaptera novaeangliae*) suddenly disappeared from the waters in which Australian and New Zealand land stations operated. It has been assumed that about five thousand humpbacks were shot illegally during these years. Furthermore, international whaling statistics are also unreliable: Apparently when whaling expeditions catch whales under the legal minimum (38 feet) they often "stretch" the size in their reports. For example, according to E. J. Slijper (in 1965), out of 371 sperm whales (*Physeter catodon*) caught in 1962 in the Indian Ocean by certain whaling expeditions, 125 had a length of 38 feet and 104 a length of 39 feet. Similarly, in 1963, of 2,004 sperm whales caught in the same waters, 1,210 of them were described as being 38 feet long and 336 as 39 feet long.

The Commission's calculation of an allowable catch in the Antarctic has long, despite protests from scientists and conservationists, been expressed in so-called "blue-whale units." In this system two fin whales, or two and a half humpbacks, or six sei whales (*Balaenoptera borealis*) equal only one blue-whale unit. Sperm-whale catches are not included at all and therefore are without limitation. There is thus no particular quota for any one species. Hence, the system of blue-whale units disregards the fact that various species of whales may require different degrees of conservation measures. The system is a pure commercial approach.

The result is that in 1964–65, when a quota of ten thousand blue-whale units was set by the Commission, the catch of 6,984 blue-whale units was made up of one blue whale, nineteen pygmy blue whales, 7,811 fin whales, and 20,380 sei whales. The quotas are in fact so large that the whaling companies cannot catch the full quotas. This was again the case in 1965–66, when nine expeditions caught 4,091 units out of the authorized quota of 4,500 (two thousand had been recommended by scientists). Of these, 17,583 were sei whales, of which the catch in 1966–67 dropped to about 12,368; in 1967–68 to 10,357; in 1968–69 to 5,770; but in 1969–70 rose to 5,856 and in 1970–71, 6,193. Still, for the 1971–72 season the Commission set the catch limit at 2,300 blue-whale units, despite the fact that the scientists had been suggesting only two thousand since 1965. For many years the Commission has not even agreed to give the blue whale full protection eventually although it has nearly been exterminated. It has long been apparent that the Commission is doing nothing to prevent Japan, Norway, and the U.S.S.R. from exterminating the whales of the Antarctic. These countries have also for years refused to let international observers go aboard the whaling ships. If the populations of the fin whale and the blue whale were allowed to increase to their optimum level, according to J. A. Gulland's calculations, the annual yield would be about fifteen thousand to twenty thousand fin whales and seven thousand to eight thousand blue whales. It would take a long time before this full yield could be reached, but it could then be maintained permanently.

In 1968 Norway pulled out from whaling in the Antarctic but increased its activities in the northern seas. However, in 1969–70 Norway was back in the Antarctic. The U.S.S.R. and Japan, which take 80 percent of the kill annually, are at present again the only countries whaling in the Antarctic, which is the main scene for the depletion.

After more than a decade of suggestions from scientists and conservationists to abolish the blue-whale unit system, the International Whaling Commission finally agreed in 1971 that the blue-whale unit will be replaced by species quotas in the 1972–73 whaling season. However, these quotas will apparently remain unrealistically high. It is gratifying that finally and at least one country, the U. S., strongly reacts against the Commission's endless procrastination. At its meeting in Washington in 1971, the U. S. Under-Secretary of State said in the opening ceremony that in the view of the U. S. people the Commission had not acted either soon enough or forcefully enough to prevent the destruction of a valuable international resource. True words but mild. Already in 1970 the U. S. had prevented imports of products of eight endangered species of whales into the country.

The International Whaling Commission has operated since 1949. Its task is to regulate the whaling industry based on scientific facts and "to provide for the conservation, development, and optimum utilization of the whale resources." In view of the results achieved for twenty-two years, the work of the Commission has been a monumental failure. A world resource has been egoistically plundered chiefly by three nations to whom it was more important to make short-term profits until whale stocks were exhausted than to manage a global property on a sustained-yield basis. The Commission has seldom followed the advice of its committee of three scientists, appointed in 1960, nor has it considered the long series of constructive suggestions from IUCN and other conservation organizations. The Commission has been blinded by the greed of three countries and has deliberately ignored the abundant evidence of its own overexploitation of whale populations. The performance and attitude of the International Whaling Commission is a world scandal and criminal from moral points of view.

The decline of the whales in the Antarctic Ocean has in the past few years led to intensified whaling in the North Pacific, which in turn has meant the overexploitation of the whales in that area. In 1964 no less than 18,300 whales were caught, chiefly by the Japanese, in an area only a quarter of the size of the Antarctic. No effective conservation measures have been taken in this region and a number of species are threatened. The fin whale has a bicentric distribution in both the Northern and Southern Hemispheres in the Atlantic and the Pacific oceans. For a long time it was more or less bypassed by whalers, who concentrated on the larger blue whale. When the latter had almost been exterminated, it became the turn of the fin whale. The statistics of fin whaling in the Antarctic are as follows:

WHALING SEASON	FIN WHALES CAUGHT	AVERAGE POPULATION
The 1920's	—	380,000
1933–39	—	200,000
1955–56	25,289	110,400
1956–57	27,757	101,700
1957–58	27,473	89,000
1958–59	25,837	88,600
1959–60	27,575	65,700
1960–61	28,761	59,700
1961–62	26,438	45,300
1962–63	18,668	40,000
1963–64	14,422	32,400
1964–65	7,811	
1965–66	2,318	
1966–67	2,893	
1967–68	2,155	
1968–69	3,015	
1969–70	2,991	
1970–71	2,890	

In addition to the catches in the Antarctic, some hundreds have been taken in recent years in the North Atlantic, but very few remain there. The fin whale is also threatened in the North Pacific. Obviously, complete protection of the fin whale is urgently needed. The populations are well below the level required to sustain maximum yields. In the Antarctic fin whales smaller than 57 feet as well as females with calves are protected. The International Whaling Commission set the quota for 1966–67 to 3,500 blue-whale units, meaning seven thousand fin whales. This is a thousand units fewer than the previous year but it is far from satisfactory, because the ten expeditions operating in the Antarctic in 1965–66 caught only 2,318 fin whales. In 1966–67 nine expeditions took 2,893 fin whales and 12,368 sei whales. The latter figure means a decline of more than five thousand since the previous season. The quota for 1968–69 was 3,200 blue-whale units, which still meant a dangerous overexploitation. Outside the Antarctic 3,999 fin whales, 5,105 sei whales, and 131 blue whales were caught in 1966. In the Antarctic the sei-whale population has decreased from about 150,000 in the early 1960's to about 75,000 in 1971. In the North Pacific the normal populations of the fin whale and the sei whale were probably about 43,500 and 70,000 respectively. The fin whale was down to about 37,000 by 1950 and in 1971 numbers about 15,000. The sei whale has been reduced to about 46,000 animals and continues to decrease. The whaling in the North Pacific has recently been extended to other species since the fin- and sei-whale stocks have been thinned out. Thus the danger for these species is very great, particularly for the fin whale.

Yet the blue whale (*Balaenoptera musculus musculus*) is still the most threatened of all cetaceans. In 1930–31 this species formed 82 percent of the whaling catch in the Antarctic; the estimated population was 40,000. By 1959 it represented less than 5 percent of the catch. By 1961–62 the estimated population had dropped to 930 to 2,790. The catch figures from the Antarctic are as follows:

WHALING SEASON	BLUE WHALES CAUGHT	ESTIMATED POPULATION
Before 1920	—	200,000
1930–31	29,000	40,000
1945–46	9,192	—
1955–56	1,614	—
1956–57	1,512	—
1957–58	1,690	—
1958–59	1,192	—
1959–60	1,239	—
1960–61	1,744	—
1961–62	1,118	930–2,790
1962–63	947	650–1,950
1963–64	112	—
1964–65	1	—
1965–66 (protected)	1	2,000
1966–67 (protected)	4	—
1971 (protected)	—	1,000

The only area of the Antarctic where a small population of blue whales survives is the Kerguelen sector. In 1964–65 hardly a single blue whale was observed in other sectors. The species is now so scarce that it is uncertain whether the population is below the point where a normal reproduction rate can be maintained. In

1966 the ban on hunting blue whales from ships was extended to
the whole of the Antarctic, so that the largest animal that has
ever existed became protected at least in the Antarctic. But this
step may well have come too late. The regulations, moreover, did
not apply to land stations, and these have increased their catches.
For instance, off Peru alone eighty blue whales were caught in
1965. In 1967 the blue whale was reported as "not uncommon"
in the northwest Atlantic, but this does not mean more than perhaps a few hundreds. In the Pacific, where the blue whale has been
protected since 1966, the population is estimated to about a
thousand to 1,500 animals. In 1968, finally, also shore stations
stopped the killing. The next decade will show if the blue whale
can recover.

The pygmy blue whale (*B. m. brevicauda*) was described in
1961 as a race of the giant blue whale. It occurs in the southern
Indian Ocean and in part of the Antarctic Ocean. The taxonomic
status of the pygmy blue whale seems somewhat uncertain. It is
impossible to differentiate the blue whales as long as they are in
the water. Until recent times the pygmy blue whales were determined as young blue whales, which perhaps they are. However,
since one began to distinguish the pygmy blue whale as a separate
form, there are statistics available about it. The records indicate
that the number of pygmy whales declined from about four thousand in 1961 to about two or three thousand in 1963. In 1962–63
seven hundred were caught, in 1963–64 only 113, and in 1964–65
only nineteen. It was given total protection in 1966. The population was at that time estimated at about 3,200 animals.

The sperm whale has for a long time been persecuted in the
Pacific. The population of the North Pacific was initially estimated
to have been about 258,000. At the present time only about half
of that number remains. In the southern Pacific, particularly off
South America, there was such overexploitation during the 1960's
that the species declined from an original population of about
45,000 to only a fraction of this number. In the Indian Ocean
and the Antarctic the stock of sperm whales is probably between
twenty and thirty thousand, although estimates up to 49,000 have
been claimed. An annual harvest on a sustainable-yield basis of a
population of thirty thousand would be about 2,300 animals. Yet,
the catches have been far above that level which, for this species
also, indicates depletion.

During the last years the catches of sperm whales in the Antarctic have been a total of 4,583 in 1965–66; 4,960 in 1966–67;

2,682 in 1968–69; 3,090 in 1969–70; and 2,745 in 1970–71. Outside the Antarctic 21,677 sperm whales were caught in 1966.

The humpback whale, distributed from the arctic to the Antarctic but principally concentrated in the Antarctic Ocean, where its population probably did not exceed about 34,000, was not intensively hunted until the present century, but the ease with which it was caught soon led to its overexploitation. The number of humpbacks fell so drastically that the species was given protection as early as 1938. But in 1949 hunting was resumed in various areas and by 1962–63 the catch had dropped to 270. Between 1963 and 1965 the International Whaling Commission found it necessary to protect it in all seas and in 1967 and 1970 it was again given complete protection. However, land whaling stations were still operating. For example, 118 humpbacks were killed in 1965 off Peru alone. In 1968 shore-based whaling stations stopped the killing of humpbacks. The number of humpbacks was in 1971 still dangerously low.

In the 1930's the population of the humpback whale in the Antarctic Ocean was estimated at about 22,000, but between 1965 and 1969 there were only about 1,700. Originally the population west of Australia probably consisted of between fifteen and twenty thousand animals. In 1949 this stock had been reduced to ten thousand and in 1962 to a thousand. East of Australia and around New Zealand the humpback population was in 1952–59 estimated at about eleven thousand, but in 1962 it had dropped to between only six hundred and 1,300. In 1965 probably fewer than three thousand humpbacks occurred south of the equator and possibly five thousand in the North Pacific. In 1963, 2,339 humpbacks were killed in the latter area and about the same number the following year, so that by the time total protection was given to the species in 1965 in the North Pacific it was doubtful that many remained alive. However, the International Whaling Commission claimed there were about four thousand. The humpbacks are increasing in numbers in the North Atlantic, where they have been protected since 1955, and are said to be "fairly numerous" in the western North Atlantic. That can, however, hardly mean more than a few hundred.

The Greenland right whale was hunted almost to extinction by the end of the nineteenth century. It was chiefly found along the coasts of arctic lands and was therefore a particularly vulnerable species. Already in 1611 whalers had gone out for this species. Dutch vessels took almost seven thousand Greenland right whales in Davis Strait and Disko Bay between 1719 and 1788, and during another period, 1814–16, a fleet of 586 British vessels caught five thousand whales, mostly Greenland right whales, on the west coast of Greenland. Since the close of the nineteenth century the Greenland right whale has not been sought by whalers (though the Eskimos of northern Alaska certainly continue to kill those they occasionally come upon) but it has nonetheless remained extremely rare. Reports of the observation or killing of one of these whales have been few and far between. Finally, in 1929, the killing of this whale was definitely abandoned by the Norwegians, but it was not before 1937 that the species was given protection throughout the arctic. The only exception to the prohibition is local hunting by Eskimos. A report in 1940 indicated that the Chukchi Sea, off western Alaska, is the present center of distribution of the Greenland right whale. In April and June at least twenty specimens were observed every day. In 1964 it was estimated that the population in the Bering-Chukchi-Beaufort Sea area was roughly one thousand whales.

The North Atlantic right whale (*Eubalaena glacialis*) was probably the species which in other days constituted the largest part of the whale catch. It was once abundant and distributed throughout the Atlantic. The North Atlantic right whale was already being hunted in the Bay of Biscay in the eleventh century. This local catch developed almost into an industry and continued for five centuries, expanding into the northern Atlantic. In the beginning of the eighteenth century the numbers of this whale began to dwindle in the eastern North Atlantic and by the early 1800's the North Atlantic right whale was believed to be extinct. A hundred years have now elapsed but the numbers of this whale are still only negligible—additional evidence of the extreme slowness with which these large mammals recover after they have been brought to the verge of extinction. North Atlantic right whales are now being observed more frequently in North American waters and around Bermuda, which may indicate a slow increase and some prospect of survival. However, possibly only a few hundred persist. Since 1937 the species has been protected from commercial hunting.

The North Pacific right whale (*E. sieboldii*) was formerly abundant in the waters around Japan, the Kuril Islands, Kamchatka, the Aleutians, and in the Gulf of Alaska southward to warm temperate waters. The same overexploitation that reduced other whales has made it rare. Between 1846 and 1851 more than three hundred ships were engaged in hunting this species off Kodiak Island alone, a concentration that soon led it to the verge of extinction in this area and shortly afterward in the whole of the eastern North Pacific. By 1910 it had become only a negligible part of the Japanese whale catch. In 1937 the species was given protection, apparently at the last moment, when it was reduced to a few hundred. Since 1941 there has been a slight tendency for it to increase.

The southern right whale (*E. australis*) originally occurred in large numbers over a vast area of the southern oceans. It is still found in this area but only in small numbers. It is difficult to follow its decline because statistics concerning it are mixed with those of other baleen whales. We do know that at least 157 were caught of Chile between 1908 and 1934, but only nine between 1934 and 1963. Since 1937 there has been a complete ban on the killing of this right whale. During the 1950's and 1960's it reappeared in some areas where it had not been recorded for many years, for example, around Tristan da Cunha and South Georgia. In 1955 a female with calf was observed west of Australia, in 1963 five were sighted close to New Zealand, and in 1964 a female with young was seen near Cartagena in Spain, an exceptional northern record. The present population in the whole Southern Hemisphere is estimated at between nine hundred and 1,500 animals.

The grey whale (*Rhachianectes glaucus*) has a very limited distribution in shallow coastal waters of the North Pacific and the adjacent Arctic Ocean and is therefore extremely vulnerable to exploitation. Twice during the last century it has been nearly exterminated, and more than three decades of complete protection off North America and twenty-five years of protection off the U.S.S.R., Japan, and Korea have been required to permit the gray whale to increase substantially in its eastern range. This species breeds only in certain lagoons on the west coast of Mexico and possibly still off Korea, where the presently virtually extinct population of the western Pacific used to breed. In 1969–70 the total population was estimated at about eleven thousand gray whales. The largest breeding population is found in Scammon's Lagoon off Mexico, an area that is now jeopardized by proposed commercial developments. It has been suggested to the government of Mexico by the American Society of Mammalogists that it establish the Scammon's Lagoon as a breeding sanctuary for the grey whale. This was done in 1972.

Although the number of other species of whales has not yet

reached a critically low level, all are being reduced. With the disappearance of the blue, fin, and humpback whales as well as the right whales the hunt has turned to the sei and sperm whales, and the sharp increase in the killing of sei whales in the last few seasons indicates that this species is the next to be threatened with extermination. In 1964–65, 20,380 sei whales were taken in the Antarctic alone. Since then the catch has dropped to only one-fourth of that. The total catch of sperm whales during the same period was 26,581 animals, also an overkill. Norwegian whalers are apparently also continuing the overexploitation of the lesser rorqual (*Balaenoptera acutorostrata*). Recently, also, a new "sport" has been introduced in Canada: killing white whales (*Delphinapterus leucas*) in Hudson Bay. The whale hunts are being promoted by the Canadian National Railways and supported by the Tourist Development Branch of Manitoba; according to a press release from the railroad, any sportsman who has 350 dollars can kill a white whale. The limit is one beluga a day and two per season. Native guides supply a motorboat, harpoon, and a high-powered rifle. The belugas, averaging about fourteen feet in length and weighing up to 1,300 pounds, are run down and harpooned at low tide in the Churchill River estuary and then shot.

Whales have had the misfortune of attracting ruthless exploiters. Only an aroused public opinion and effective international control, preferably by the United Nations, which so far has paid no attention to the plundering of a global resource, can save the whales of the world.

The first serious attempt to cope with the disastrous situation for whales came in 1970 from the U. S., which has banned imports of all products made from whales by placing these animals as endangered species. In 1971 the U. S. took another step in the same direction by ending commercial whaling. This means that no whaling ships based in the U. S. will be operating any longer. One proposed bill (in 1971) would have completely barred the killing of any sea mammals in the U. S. waters.

Unfortunately, porpoises are also inadvertently killed in large numbers by commercial fishing in the Pacific. A disastrously heavy strain on common dolphins (*Delphinus delphis*), long-beaked dolphins (*Stenella longirostris*), and Graffman's dolphin (*S. graffmani*) is placed by the U. S. yellowfin-tuna fleets operating out of West Coast ports. They catch about 45,000 tons of tuna, worth 13.5 million dollars, every year, using modern nylon nets and

power winches. Since the three species of Pacific porpoises travel
the ocean currents with the yellowfin tunas, or vice versa, as many
as 250,000 of these mammals drown every year inside the nets. It
is still unknown how many more porpoises drown in the nets of
tuna boats from other countries, but the figures may well surpass
those of the U. S. kill. In the eastern Pacific alone, Mexican,
Peruvian, Japanese, Spanish, and French tuna boats are engaged
in the same kind of fishing operations.

It is not known why porpoises and tunas occur together, but
their association benefits the fishermen, because the porpoises indicate to the fishing vessels where the shoals of tuna are. The
threat to the Pacific porpoises may also jeopardize the tuna fisheries. Will the fishermen be able to find the fast travelling tuna
shoals so easily if the porpoises vanish from the sea?

Porpoises are also of direct value. They are used in large numbers for human consumption in South America, Japan, New
Guinea, the Solomon Islands, and in the Black Sea by Turkey
and the U.S.S.R. The last-named country caught annually about
3,500 tons of the common dolphin in the Black Sea until 1966,
when the population collapsed from overfishing. The catches declined from about four thousand tons in 1938 to about two hundred in 1966. In the good years adult males made up 40 to 60
percent of the catch in the Black Sea, but in the early 1960's, just
before the collapse, the adult male percentage fell to 20–25 percent. In Graffman's dolphin the proportion of adult males was in
1968 down to 15.7 percent in the samples collected from tuna
purse-seine hauls in the Pacific (Perrin in 1970). This low figure
is a warning parallel to the dolphin catastrophe in the Black Sea.

Balance for the Oceans

The vertebrate life forms in the oceans are immensely rich.
These organisms are numerically dominated by fishes, the marine
vertebrates comprising only a relatively few species of reptiles and
mammals. All marine turtles, that is, eleven or perhaps twelve
species and subspecies, are threatened by extermination by man.
In the same way, fourteen forms of whales have already been
brought to the verge of extinction, and many others are approaching it and seem doomed unless international conservation measures
are agreed upon.

CHAPTER ELEVEN

World Faunal Balance

The previous chapters have given an account of the situation for vertebrate animals on various continents and oceans of the world. It is a grim chronicle of exterminations of animals and an almost unbelievable human misuse of living natural resources, in the past due to ignorance, in modern times due to deliberate desire for short-term profit without any regard whatsoever for the future and without any responsibility to mankind and to future generations.

The gruesome picture, expressed in naked figures of extinct vertebrates and of animals brought near extinction during the last five hundred years, appears on page 361.

The extermination of animals throughout the world reflects the destruction of vegetation and habitats, e.g., of living nature in general. It is striking to find that the areas of the world where the destruction of nature and animal life is the worst are those parts of the earth where the white man has been present during a relatively short time, only a few centuries. This situation may, at first glance, give the impression of speaking in favour of the Europeans. Unfortunately for the image of European civilization, it is just the contrary, because the immense nature destruction that has struck the world has been carried through during the very short period which has elapsed since the Europeans spread out over lands and oceanic islands. Australia, South America (including the Caribbean), and the isolated islands of the oceans are frightful examples of unwise nature exploitation.

Extinction is, of course, a natural phenomenon which has gone on for millions of years as a part of evolution. However, natural extinctions are usually, perhaps always, followed by ecological replacement. When man operates on the scene exterminating animals, there is no replacement.

Species and subspecies of mammals, birds, reptiles, amphibians, and fishes of the world extinct, probably extinct, or endangered by extinction during historic time. (Figures within parentheses show extinction after 1700).

AREAS	EXTINCT	PROBABLY EXTINCT	ENDANGERED
Africa	21 (13)	9	155
Europe	5 (4) (+ 2 listed under Asia)	—	21 (+ 4 listed under Asia)
Asia	40 (39)	8	216 (+ 2 listed under North America)
North America	32 (32)	7	164 (+ 3 listed under Asia)
South America	61 (35)	6	153
Australasia	48 (45)	12	119
Oceania	51 (51)	3	59
Isolated islands in the oceans	53 (38)	4	69
Antarctica	0	0	0
The oceans	0	0	26
Total	311 (257)	49	982

CLASS	EXTINCT	PROBABLY EXTINCT	ENDANGERED
Mammals	102 (69)	13	401
Birds	173 (155)	19	388
Reptiles	17 (14)	6	81
Amphibians	—	1	17
Fish	19 (19)	10	95
Total	311 (257)	49	982

All animal extinctions in historic time have been by man, either by habitat destruction, chiefly for agriculture, or by slaughter for profit beyond the needs of personal sustenance. Usually it is a combination of these two factors which leads to animal extinctions, but the ultimate course is, in general, the hunting pressure for profit or for fun. This process of extinction continues.

For about two million years—that is, 99 percent of his existence —man has subsisted on the plants he could collect and the animals he could gather or hunt. Man is still dependent on the environment, but he seems to have forgotten it.

CHAPTER TWELVE

The Future

A world without wild animals would be a paradise lost, or, more accurately, a paradise willfully destroyed. There is a quality in wild animals that is irreplaceable and that has always inspired and enchanted men. It is a quality that he misses more and more as his life becomes increasingly urbanized, regimented, and standardized. Therefore for man's well-being, wild animals must have a place on this globe of ours. Most important for the conservation of animal populations is the preservation of habitats. This is also vital to man himself. In fact, an appreciation of ecological principles is a necessity for human survival.

But saving animals can scarcely be achieved while men are multiplying so rapidly that they are literally destroying the means of their own survival—a kind of global suicide. It is therefore absolutely necessary that human population be controlled before nature eliminates the excess, just as it does when excesses occur among other mammals. It would be a crime if man, most powerful and highly developed of living creatures, refused to recognize the essentials of his own existence.

The present process of destroying nature must, for the sake of man's future, be stopped immediately. The consequences of such thoughtless destruction are incalculable, because we never know in advance what material value various species of plants and animals will represent in the future. Who, for example, foresaw the importance of fruit flies in genetic research? Nature and animal life very often have a definite economic value and are components of an environment, of which man is just a part.

It is too often argued that the destiny of wild animals is of little concern to man because they are of little practical use. Besides the fact that we simply do not know what value animals may possess and that many animals are, or have been, important sources of food or other raw materials, this attitude is also frequently materialistic. What is the usefulness of paintings, sculptures, fountains, poems, or music? The answer, of course, is that it is the pleasure, inspiration, recreation that these give man that make them "useful." Flora and fauna are the music, poetry, and painting created by nature.

But they are also much more. They are a living part of the environment, a guarantee for continuity of life on the earth. Without plants there would be no more air to breathe, the water economy of many countries would collapse, the soil would be eroded, and there would be no animals, no man. Without animals the vegetation would be poorer and more uniform, the productivity of waters and lands would sink to a fraction of its normal wealth, the prairies and forests would become a silent, almost lifeless world.

All these factors are becoming growingly meaningful to human beings living in countries which have material wealth and where great amounts of leisure time are a normal part of life. But in most parts of the world human populations have not reached such a cultural level and few individuals there can afford to think of recreation, leisure, or intellectual interests. Instead, they have to struggle to feed their families. In coping with this daily problem of existence the concept of wildlife conservation has no place, despite the fact that the environmental destruction leads to increasing difficulties for the human individuals concerned.

Therefore, the conservation concept as applied by educated conservationists is not understood by most parts of humanity. To starving illiterates conservation of natural resources appears as a nonfunctional luxury. They cannot understand their own ecology.

On the other hand, modern conservationists working for the conservation, management, and wise utilization of animal resources in underdeveloped parts of the world must include sociological and economic factors in their ecological considerations of local or regional conservation problems.

The basic problem is the human overpopulation, which is the main reason for the tragic environmental destruction and animal exterminations which characterize our world.

For almost every extinct or endangered species or subspecies of animals mentioned in previous chapters of this book, the two main causes of the decline and ultimate extinction during the last centuries are destruction of habitats and excessive cropping by man either for his own survival or simply for greediness. While habitat destruction is affecting animal species drastically and may lead to extinction, overexploitation by man has in recent centuries been the primary cause of the decline of all wild populations of any economic importance. Connected with this depletion is often the lack of knowledge about the essential needs of a species for survival, its dependence on the habitat, and its reproductive capacity.

The uncontrolled depletion of useful animal populations is clear from the data available to the Survival Service Commission of IUCN. It has, therefore, been agreed by IUCN to adopt a policy that all wild plant and animal populations of economic value should only be exploited on sustainable yield principles.

For that purpose IUCN will establish an information center of wildlife population and trade statistics that provide basic data for management purposes.

NATIONAL PARKS AND NATURE RESERVES

Today few people deny that living plants and animals are important to mankind for a variety of reasons that transcend usefulness. It is therefore our duty to preserve as much as we can, not only for ourselves but also for future generations. One means of doing this is to set aside national parks and nature reserves representing the major habitats of the world.

First of all, at a time when human activities are altering the face of the earth in so many ways, such areas must be set aside for scientific investigation. They will enable scientists to follow the evolution of ecosystems not used by man compared with those exploited by man and thereby to determine the best use of land. National parks also give us significant data on the productivity of natural areas, which often is much higher than that of cultivated areas, especially in the tropics. It was the flourishing condition of some national parks in tropical Africa that opened the eyes of scientists to the fact that these areas can support extremely dense populations of wild ungulates of different species without any deterioration of the environment, while similar areas used by cattle and goats are rapidly destroyed.

National parks also serve as storehouses and gene pools for plant and animal species that prove important for human welfare. There are already too many examples of industrial or agricultural enterprises that have failed economically and ruined a landscape that was formerly a flourishing, highly productive natural area. Such schemes have often proved disastrous because biologists were not consulted or because their advice was ignored. In such a situation biological and ecological factors are at least as important as purely economic and social ones. In fact, ecology here becomes a synonym for conservation of nature, and conservation may be interpreted as applied ecology or human bioeconomy. To be able to give sound advice in such matters, biologists need national parks which help them to understand the functioning of biocommunities. Man still knows far too little of natural environments.

The management of natural resources, so essential for the well-being of man, must be based on a wise, long-term utilization of nature's renewable resources—air, water, soil, flora, and fauna. The goal must be to reach a biological balance between man's demands and nature's capacity to maintain its productivity. Reaching such an ideal bioeconomic equilibrium is not a simple task. There is no one approach that can be applied to all areas. Every habitat differs from every other one. In addition the biotope of an area is never stable. To investigate such matters, scientists need large untouched areas in which to do their research. And the results obtained from such studies should be published not only in scientific journals but also in a popular form, so that people may realize that national parks are valuable not only for nature preservation, education, recreation, and enjoyment but for economic reasons as well. The fact that scientific research in national parks serves important purposes, essential for the social and economic development plans of a country, must be generally recognized.

If national parks and equivalent areas are to function as a smooth instrument for the understanding of conservation of nature, it is essential that the same national parks are not considered by different groups of people as antagonistic to national interests. Unfortunately, such opinions are often expressed. Mostly they are based on biased views, which neglect what habitats of different types can teach us.

For the same reasons certain zones within national parks or nature reserves should be completely restricted, free from tourists and even from human activities in surrounding areas. Such areas would serve as a kind of living archive containing stored material for future research. Here the study of evolution and speciation could be pursued under the most favourable conditions. Such zones could be achieved if industrial tourism were limited to, let us say, about ten percent of a national park's area.

As ecology becomes more and more important as a school study, especially in universities, national parks will play an increasingly important role also in education.

INTERNATIONAL CONSERVATION OF NATURE

Several international conservation organizations and societies are working desperately to save the world's endangered animals. They were briefly mentioned in the Foreword (pages x–xi). In the front line are the International Union for Conservation of Nature and Natural Resources (IUCN), the World Wildlife Fund (WWF), the International Council for Bird Preservation (ICBP), and the International Waterfowl Research Bureau (IWRB). In the United States the Conservation Foundation, intimately connected with the New York Zoological Society, is very active in international conservation work. Also, the Smithsonian Institution in Washington turns more and more to active conservation. The Fauna Preservation Society in London has long made effective contributions to the work of saving threatened animals. Also, specialized UN agencies like UNESCO and the FAO are active in the field of conservation. UNESCO particularly has since its establishment been active in conservation and ecology. Through various projects, UNESCO works for the promotion of ecology and ecological research as a basis for conservation of ecosystems, habitats, and species. In particular, the recently launched program "Man and the Biosphere" (MAB) is bringing these aspects into focus. It is a long-term intergovernmental program which is gradually taking over from the International Biological Program (IBP). UNESCO played an important role in the creation of IUCN in 1948 and ever since there has been a close co-operation between these two organizations.

The IUCN is organized in commissions, the most important for the preservation of wildlife being the Survival Service Commission and the International Commission on National Parks. The former specializes in saving threatened animals by research, negotiations with governments, various action treatments, and so forth. The latter works for the establishment of national parks and reserves and deals with management problems. The WWF contributes financially to IUCN, ICBP, and IWRB, but is also active directly, sponsoring and financing various conservation operations all over the world. The total financial contribution from the WWF to conservation in the form of projects was, as of November 15, 1971, $6,373,216.

All these organizations are run by devoted men who do their utmost to save habitats from destruction and animal species all over the world from extinction. In most cases it is a hard and bitter fight, an almost superhuman task to overcome all difficulties. So many human factors—social, economic, political, and religious— are involved in problems concerning endangered animals in different parts of the world that the modern conservationist must be more than a trained ecologist to be successful when he goes out on missions in various corners of the world. He has to know the country and the psychology of its people well. In fact, in conservation work it is easier to work with animals than men.

Partly as a result of the work of conservation organizations, governments and people have become more and more aware of the importance of preserving wildlife. An example of this growing conscience and international concern is the African Convention on Conservation of Nature and Natural Resources, signed by the African heads of state in 1968 and in force since 1969. Ecologically it is a far-reaching treaty reflecting modern concepts of conservation on a continental scale. It gives particular attention to the values represented by wild animals. Another example is the Convention on Wetlands of International Importance especially as Waterfowl Habitat, covering Africa, Asia, and Europe and adopted in 1971. A third example is a convention on export and import of threatened animal species regulating the international trade in wild animals and their products; an international conference is convened for 1972 to conclude a treaty on the subject. IUCN has been involved in the preparatory work of all three conventions and took the initiative in two of them. UNESCO, ICBP, and IWRB have also contributed to these conventions.

It is a hopeful sign that the future of the world's wildlife is of increasing concern to more and more human beings. However, it is a battle with time. Will people and governments be aware of the necessity of preserving wild animals and their habitats before too many and too much of them have been destroyed forever?

Bibliography

It would be impractical to list all the publications, reports, and papers that have been consulted in the preparation of this book. The few references given below have been of particular value because, at the time of writing this book, they contained important information or detailed data about various natural regions, a complex of species, or a single species.

Allen, G. M., *Extinct and Vanishing Mammals of the Western Hemisphere.* New York: American Committee for International Wildlife Protection, 1943.

Allen, R. P., *The Roseate Spoonbill.* Research Report No. 2 of the National Audubon Society. New York, 1942.

————— *The Whooping Crane.* Research Report No. 3 of the National Audubon Society. New York, 1952.

————— *The Flamingos: Their Life History and Survival.* Research Report No. 5 of the National Audubon Society. New York, 1956.

A Review of the Natural Resources of the African Continent. Paris: UNESCO, 1963.

Aubréville, A., *Climats, forêts et désertification de l'Afrique tropicale.* Paris, 1947.

Bourlière, F., and Verschuren, J., *Introduction à l'écologie des ongulés du Parc National Albert.* 1–2. Exploration du Parc National Albert. Mission F. Bourlière et J. Verschuren. Brussels, 1960.

Brown, Leslie, *Africa: A Natural History.* New York: Random House, 1965; London: Hamish Hamilton, 1965.

————— *Eagles.* London: Michael Joseph, 1955.

Conservation of Nature and Natural Resources in Modern African States. IUCN Publications. New series. 1:1–368 (1963).

Craighead, J. J. and F. C., *Hawks, Owls, and Wildlife.* Harrisburg: Wildlife Management Institute, 1956.

Curry-Lindahl, K., *Contribution à l'étude des vertébrés terrestres en Afrique tropicale.* 1. Exploration du Parc National Albert et du Parc National de la Kagera. Mission K. Curry-Lindahl (1951–1952, 1958–1959). Brussels, 1961.

————— *Europe: A Natural History.* New York: Random House, 1964; London: Hamish Hamilton, 1964.

Darling, F. F., *Wild Life in an African Territory*. London: Oxford University Press, 1960.

Darlington, P. J., *Biogeography of the Southern End of the World*. Cambridge, Massachusetts: Harvard University Press, 1965; London: Oxford University Press, 1965.

—— *Zoogeography: The Geographical Distribution of Animals*. New York: Wiley, 1957; London: Chapman, 1957.

Dasmann, R. F., *African Game Ranching*. Oxford, England: Pergamon Press, 1963.

—— *The Last Horizon*. New York: Macmillan, 1963.

de Vos, A., Manville, R. H., and van Gelder, R. G., "Introduced Mammals and Their Influence on Native Biota." *Zoologica:* 41:163–194 (1956).

Dorst, J., *Avant que nature meure*. Neuchâtel, 1965.

Errington, P. L., *Of Men and Marshes*. New York: Macmillan, 1957.

Fisher, J., and Peterson, R. T., *The World of Birds*. New York: Doubleday, 1964; London: Macdonald, 1964.

Glover, P. E., *A Review of Recent Knowledge on the Relationship Between the Tsetse Fly and Its Vertebrate Hosts*. IUCN Publications. New series. 6:1–84 (1965).

Greenway, J. C., Jr., *Extinct and Vanishing Birds of the World* (2nd rev. ed.). New York: Dover, 1968.

Grossman, M. L., and Hamlet, J., *Birds of Prey of the World*. New York: Potter, 1964; London: Cassell, 1965.

Grzimek, B., *Auch Nashörner gehören allen Menschen*. West Berlin, 1962.

—— *Kein Platz für wilde Tiere*. Munich, 1954.

Grzimek, B. and M., "A Study of the Game of the Serengeti Plains." *Zeitschrift für Säugetierkinde*. 25:1–61 (1960).

—— *Serengeti Shall Not Die*. London: Hamilton, 1960; New York: Dutton, 1961.

Harper, F., *Extinct and Vanishing Mammals of the World*. New York, 1945.

Harrison, B., *Orang-utan*. London: Collins, 1962.

Heim, R., and others, ed., *Derniers Refuges*. Brussels, 1956.

Howard, W. E., *The Rabbit Problem in New Zealand*. New Zealand Department of Scientific Industrial Research. Information Series. 16:1–47 (1958).

Huxley, J., *The Conservation of Wild Life and Natural Habitats in Central and East Africa*. Paris: UNESCO, 1961.

Keast, A., Crocker, R. L., and Christian, C. S., ed., *Biogeography and Ecology of Australia*. The Hague, 1959.

Koford, C. B., *The California Condor*. Research Report No. 4 of the National Audubon Society. New York, 1953.

Mackintosh, N. A., *The Stocks of Whales*. London: Heighway, 1965.

Marshall, A. J., *The Great Extermination*. Melbourne: Heinemann, 1966.

Mohr, E., *Das Urwildpferd*. Wittenberg-Lutherstadt, 1959.

Moorehead, A., *No Room in the Ark*. New York: Harper, 1959; London: Hamilton, 1959.

Osborn, F., *The Limits of the Earth*. Boston: Little, Brown, 1953.

—— *Our Plundered Planet*. Boston: Little, Brown, 1948.

Pedersen, A., *Der Eisbär (Thalarchos maritimus Phipps)*. Copenhagen, 1945.

Petrides, G. A., *Big Game Densities and Range Carrying Capacities in East Africa*. Transactions of the 21st North American Wildlife Conferences. 21:525–537 (1956).

Phillips, J., *Agriculture and Ecology in Africa*. London: Faber & Faber, 1959.

Rudd, R. L., *Pesticides and the Living Landscape*. Madison: University of Wisconsin Press, 1964.

Russell, E. W., ed., *The Natural Resources of East Africa*. Nairobi: D. A. Hawkins, 1962.

Sanderson, I. T., *The Continent We Live On*. New York: Random House, 1961.

Schaller, G. B., *The Mountain Gorilla*. Chicago: University of Chicago Press, 1963.

Schantz, H. L., and Turner, B. L., *Photographic Documentation of Vegetational Changes in Africa Over a Third of a Century*. Tucson, 1958.

Scott, P., ed., *The Launching of a New Ark*. London: The World Wildlife Fund, 1965.

Sidney, J., *The Past and Present Distribution of Some African Ungulates*. Transactions of the Zoological Society of London. 30:1–397 (1965).

Simon, N., *Red Data Book*. 1. Mammalia. IUCN. Lausanne, 1966.

Slijper, E. J., *A Hundred Years of Modern Whaling*. Nederlandsche Commissie voor Internationale Natuurbescherming. Mededelingen. 19:29–61 (1965).

——— *Whales*. London: Hutchinson, 1962.

Talbot, L. M., *A Look at Threatened Species*. London, 1959.

Tanner, J. T., *The Ivory-billed Woodpecker*. Research Report No. 1 of the National Audubon Society. New York, 1942.

The Ecology of Man in the Tropical Environment. IUCN Publications. New Series. 4:1–356 (1964).

Thomas, W. L., ed., *Man's Role in Changing the Face of the Earth*. Chicago, 1956.

Troughton, E., *Furred Animals of Australia*, 7th ed. Sydney, 1962.

van Mieghem, J., and van Oye, P., *Biogeography and Ecology in Antarctica*. The Hague, 1965.

Verschuren, J., *Écologie et biologie des grands mammifères*. Exploration du Parc National de la Garamba. Mission H. De Saeger. Brussels, 1958.

Vincent, J., *Red Data Book*. 2. Aves. IUCN. Lausanne, 1966.

Willgohs, J. F., *The White-tailed Eagle Haliaëtus albicilla albicilla (Linné) in Norway*. Acta Universitatis Bergensis. 12:1–212 (1961).

Wood, Alan, *The Groundnut Affair*. London: Lane, 1950.

Working Conference on Birds of Prey and Owls. Caen, 10–12 April 1964, International Council for Bird Preservation (1964).

Young, S. P., and Goldman, E. A., *The Wolves of North America*. Washington, D.C.: American Wildlife Institute, 1944.

Zeuner, F. E., *A History of Domesticated Animals*. London: Hutchinson, 1963; New York: Harper, 1964.

Zisweiler, V., *Bedrohte und ausgerottete Tiere*. Berlin, 1965.

Index